HUMAN ANATOMY

and

NELLIE D. MILLARD, R.N., M.A.

Science Instructor, Cook County School of Nursing, Chicago; Formerly Instructor in Anatomy and Physiology, Wesley Memorial Hospital School of Nursing and Michael Reese Hospital School of Nursing, Chicago

BARRY G. KING, Ph.D.

Medical Division, Aviation Safety, Civil Aeronautics Administration; Associate Professor of Physiology, Ohio State University School of Medicine; Lecturer in Physiology, University of Maryland

MARY JANE SHOWERS, R.N., M.S.

Formerly Director of Educational Program, Instructor in Biological Sciences, the Christ Hospital School of Nursing, Cincinnati

W. B. SAUNDERS COMPANY

PHYSIOLOGY

Fourth Edition

315 Illustrations with 55 in Color

225 BY LUCILLE CASSELL INNES

Philadelphia and London

PREFACE

THE CAREFUL reviews and constructive criticism of many of the instructors who are using this text, both in professional courses in schools of nursing and in undergraduate courses in colleges and universities, have been most helpful in preparation of the fourth edition. In the comments, there appeared to be general agreement on a need to change the order of presentation of the material so that the nervous system would appear in the early part of the text. We also believe that there is an advantage in considering how the nervous system acts as an integrating mechanism by which the many activities of the body are adjusted in response to stimuli from the external and internal environments, before taking up the other body systems in which the particular nervous control is discussed. Thus we have been able to comply with this constructive suggestion and have, at the same time, retained the over-all plan with the material organized into the five functional units: Unit 1, The Body as an Integrated Whole; Unit 2, Integration and Control of the Body by the Nervous System; Unit 3, The Erect and Moving Body; Unit 4, Maintaining the Metabolism of the Body; and Unit 5, Reproduction of the Human Being. As before, a general introduction is given in each unit to define the scope of the functional area treated. Some additional introductory material is presented to orient and guide the student as he takes up the more detailed study of a system or of a special topic. Anatomic systems serve as a basis for elaboration of physiologic principles. Structure is presented from the standpoint of architectural designs which are frequently repeated in the body. Physiologic principles are developed to afford an understanding of the mechanisms by which various parts of the body function.

Careful attention has been given to developing presentations to illustrate experimental methods of observation and to encouraging the spirit of scientific inquiry, the use of precise terminology and adherence to logical thinking on the part of the student.

In considering each unit, material based upon new developments and new knowledge has been included, emphasis has been shifted when such change was considered necessary or desirable, and correction, clarification, and modification of the presentation have been made where warranted. We have constantly kept in mind the need for maintaining the text at the same instructional level and at approximately the same length. Discussions of earlier concepts or views have been deleted in almost all instances where new material is used. This material, although new, is not more difficult for the undergraduate student, since he is not required to reconcile it with previously learned concepts as is the advanced science student for whom the details of development of successive theories and reconciliation of apparently conflicting views constitute an important aspect of training.

Particular attention has been given to the physicochemical processes of exchange since these are basic to an understanding of physiology. This, with new material on cell permeability, water metabolism and electrolyte balance, provides the students with a background which has become essential in studying current basic medical science. Calculations of osmolar and milliequivalent solutions have been introduced as an optional exercise and for reference.

The account of the initiation and propagation of the nerve impulse has been rewritten in accordance with current concepts. Special senses are discussed following the anatomy of the brain and cranial nerves as a concept of functional association to parallel the somesthetic sensations, spinal cord and spinal nerves.

The example of the structure of long bone has been used to introduce the organs of the skeletal system. The articulations have been reclassified in terms of structure and ultimate movement at the joint axes. The description of the ankle, foot and toes has been rewritten relating structure and function; the arches of the foot are discussed.

The presentation of the histology of muscle has been revised. The section on the chemistry of muscular contraction has been rewritten. The material supplements the new material on carbohydrate metabolism. Revisions have been made in the discussion of tonus.

New material has been added to the section on blood. Descriptions of the process of blood coagulation and the antianemic factor have been brought up to date; a brief discussion of blood typing and the Rh factor has been added. Various aspects of blood pressure are included in treating blood pressure determination.

The anatomy of the lung has been elaborated; typical mechanisms of nervous control of respiration in normal man are presented with comment on nervous control in animals under experimental conditions.

The discussion of the metabolism of carbohydrates, fats and proteins has been rewritten. The significance of water balance in the body is presented and serves to relate specifically to metabolism, the material on exchange, hydrostatic and osmotic pressure relations and electrolyte balance that appears in separate sections of the text.

The treatment of the endocrine system has been considerably revised and expanded. It includes known hormone and parahormone effects upon the body tissues; there are new drawings of the hypophysis, pancreas and adrenal glands.

The discussion of the reproductive system precedes that of the prenatal development of the body. Placental hormones are introduced to correlate the presentation of endocrine controls of the reproductive system.

Lucille Cassell Innes has continued to improve the illustration of the text by the addition of twelve new drawings as well as by correcting and clarifying a number of the illustrations previously employed.

The questions at the ends of the chapters were formulated to encourage students to understand, relate and apply all the information acquired as their instruction progresses. The format of the questions is constructed so that there is no one "correct" answer. Thus discussions can be adjusted to provide for a continuous integration of the concepts presented throughout the book.

We gratefully acknowledge the friendly encouragement and assistance of our associates using this text in their courses, who have given time and thought in developing and forwarding their comments and suggestions; special acknowledgment is due Dr. Charles A. Hoffman and Dr. Edwin B. Steen for their detailed, comprehensive review of the previous edition. Again we wish to thank Dr. George F. Piltz for the excellent critical comment and the worthwhile suggestions which he has made during this as well as during previous revisions. Further, we are sincerely grateful to our publishers, W. B. Saunders Company, for their whole-hearted cooperation, sound advice and effective assistance in the preparation of the revised edition.

NELLIE D. MILLARD
BARRY GRIFFITH KING
MARY JANE C. SHOWERS

CONTENTS

Unit One.   The Body as an Integrated Whole

Unit Two.   Integration and Control of the Body by the Nervous System

Unit Three. The Erect and Moving Body

Unit Four. Maintaining the Metabolism of the Body

Unit Five.   Reproduction of the Human Being

Unit
1

THE BODY AS AN INTEGRATED WHOLE

UNIT ONE introduces the sciences of anatomy and physiology. It is intended to provide a general, if somewhat elementary, over-all account of the structure and functions of the body. This is necessary because the interrelations of the parts and systems of the body are so close that understanding of any one function or system requires some knowledge of all systems. The introductory material is presented to provide this knowledge so that, in the discussion of a single part or system, the necessary references to other functions or systems will have meaning.

Since the body as a whole is an aggregation of cells, the structure of the cell, its chemical composition, its physical nature and its method of division or reproduction are described in detail.

The physicochemical processes — filtration, diffusion and osmosis — explain how materials enter and leave cells. A knowledge of these processes is an important step toward an understanding of cell physiology.

The epithelial and connective tissues are discussed in this unit because they are widely distributed throughout the body and form important building materials in all parts.

Chapter

1

The Body as a Whole

ANATOMY AND PHYSIOLOGY—DEFINITIONS AND SUBDIVISIONS

IN CONTRAST with art, which implies *doing,* science implies *understanding.* The science of Anatomy teaches an understanding of the architecture of the body as a whole and the structure and relations of its parts. Physiology teaches an understanding of the mechanisms by which the body performs its various functions or, more simply, how it works. These sciences have various subdivisions, or branches; those which will be considered in this introduction to anatomy and physiology are:

Gross or macroscopic anatomy—the study of structures which can be distinguished with the unaided eye;

Microscopic anatomy or *histology*—the study of the minute structure of tissues and organs requiring the use of the microscope;

Developmental anatomy—which deals with the growth and development of an individual throughout his life;

Embryology—a branch of developmental anatomy, which treats of that part of development from origin to birth; and

Human physiology—a specialized part of mammalian physiology concerned with a study of the mechanisms of man.

2

Actually, we begin our observations in these two sciences at an early age and with little training. As children we learn the names of the parts of our bodies. When we observe the way in which we move, eat and breathe, we are making elementary physiologic observations. Anatomy and physiology as studied in the medical arts and sciences are continuations of such observations in a systematic and far more detailed manner. The more advanced observations require special training and technics. The medical sciences have advanced because of the insatiable curiosity of men and women throughout the ages who continued to ask *how* various activities of the body are carried out and *how* various parts are formed. With every increase in knowledge new questions arise, so that the search continues for more detailed knowledge and for further understanding of the underlying mechanisms.

In an introduction to anatomy and physiology we carry on from the knowledge common to intelligent but untrained students.

It is an advantage to have had preliminary courses in zoology, comparative anatomy and elementary physics and chemistry. When this training is lacking, it is necessary to acquire at least a superficial acquaintance with the body as a whole—its architectural plan and the organization of its functional units. This is because there is such a close relationship between structure and function, and such a close dependence of one function on another, that it is necessary to refer to many activities and parts of the body when discussing a single structure or function.

PLAN OF THE HUMAN BODY

Man belongs to the group of animals known as vertebrates. This group is characterized by possession of a backbone or vertebral column. His body shows bilateral symmetry; that is, one side of the body is like the other side.

In describing the body precise terms are used to denote position and describe the location of parts. These are shown in Figures 1 and 2. Some of the more important descriptive terms are listed in Table 1. In defining the terms it is assumed in the case of man that he is in the *anatomic position,* that is, standing erect, with the arms at the sides and the palms of the hands turned forward.

Cavities.   Internal body structure in the vertebrate is characterized by two body cavities (Fig. 3):

The *dorsal* cavity, which contains the brain and spinal cord, is divided into the *cranial* cavity, formed by the bones of the skull, and the *vertebral* cavity, formed by the vertebrae.

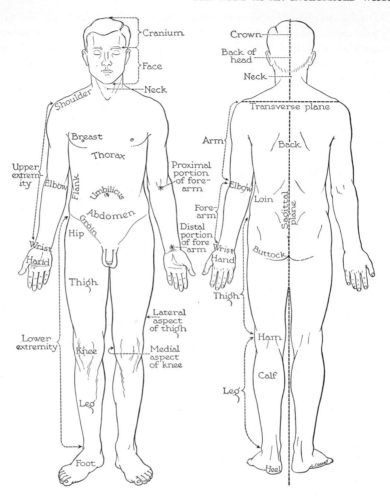

Fig. 1. Human figure in anatomical position; planes of reference; parts of the body.

The *ventral* cavity of man is divided into the thoracic and abdomi-nopelvic cavities by the diaphragm (Figs. 3, 4). The *thoracic* cavity is subdivided into the pericardial cavity, which contains the heart, and the pleural cavities, which contain the lungs. Trachea, bronchi, esoph-agus, thymus gland, blood and lymph vessels lie between these sub-divisions in the thoracic cavity. The *abdominopelvic* cavity has two portions which are continuous—an upper abdominal part, and a lower pelvic portion. The abdominal portion contains the liver, gallbladder, stomach, spleen, pancreas and small and large intestines. The pelvic portion contains the bladder, rectum and sigmoid colon. In the female the pelvic portion has, in addition, the ovaries, uterine tubes and uterus; in the male, the prostate gland, seminal vesicles and a part of the ductus deferens. The organs contained in any of the three great body cavities are called *viscera*.

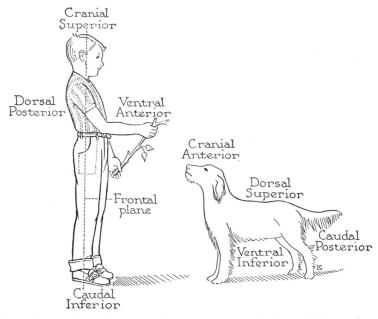

Fig. 2. Terminology of quadruped and man compared. Frontal plane is shown.

Organization of the Body. The cell is both the structural and the functional unit of the body. In spite of great variations in appearance and consistency, all parts of the body are aggregates of many of these units. During the early stages of the development of the embryo the cells look alike. They are known as undifferentiated or embryonal cells. Soon, however, they begin to show changes in structure; this process is called differentiation. As the structural changes occur, groups of cells become specialized in function; that is, they perform chiefly one type of physiological activity. Such differentiation and specialization of groups of cells results in the formation of the tissues of the body.

A *tissue* may be defined as an organization of like cells, bound together with intercellular substance and performing a special bodily function. There are four primary tissues. *Epithelial* tissue forms the covering

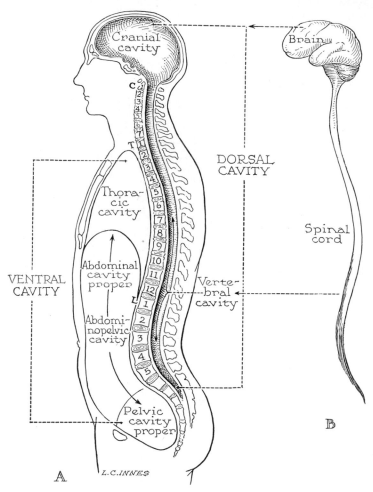

Fig. 3. Body cavities as seen in a midsagittal section of head and trunk. *A*, Diagram of midsagittal section of head and trunk, showing vertebral column and body cavities. *B*, Organs of the dorsal cavity.

of the body, the lining of its parts and the secreting portions of glands. *Connective* tissue forms the supporting framework of the body and binds the parts together; vascular and lymphatic tissue, which arises

Table 1

Descriptive Terms Used in Anatomy

TERMS	NAME	EXPLANATION		
Plane or section	Sagittal	Vertical plane or section, dividing body into right and left portions		
	Midsagittal	Vertical at midline; dividing body into right and left halves		
	Frontal or Coronal	Vertical, but at right angles to sagittal sections, dividing body into anterior (front) and posterior (back) portions		
	Transverse	Horizontal, hence at right angles to both sagittal and frontal sections, dividing body into upper and lower portions		
Surface or relative position	Anterior or Ventral	*Man* Front of body, hence on or nearest abdominal surface	*Quadrupeds* Anterior—head end Ventral—abdominal or lower surface	
	Posterior or Dorsal	Back of body	Posterior—tail end Dorsal—back	
	Superior	Upper or higher		
	Inferior	Lower		
Relative position or direction	Cranial (Craniad) or Cephalic (Cephalad)	Nearest or toward the head		
	Caudal (Caudad)	Away from the head		
	Medial (Mesad)	Middle or nearest the midsagittal plane		
	Lateral (Laterally)	Side or farthest from midsagittal plane		
	Proximal (Proximally)	Near the source or attachment		
	Distal (Distally)	Away from source or attachment		
	Afferent	In relation to nerves or blood vessels—conducting toward structure or organ		
	Efferent	Conducting away from structure or organ		

from the same more primitive parent material as connective tissue, performs the functions of transporting substances throughout the body and providing the immediate environment of the cell. *Muscular* tissue is specialized for the performance of work by its ability to shorten or contract. *Nervous* tissue, because of its specialized properties of irritability and conductivity, may carry impulses to all parts of the body, thus coordinating its functions.

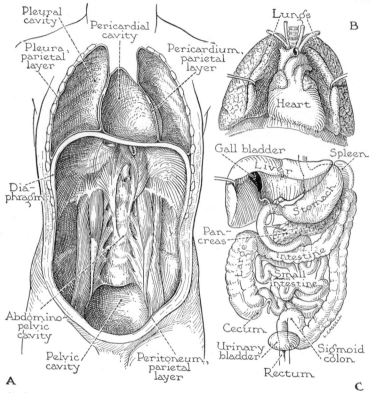

Fig. 4. *A*, Front view of the trunk, showing subdivisions of the ventral cavity. *B*, Organs of the thoracic cavity. *C*, Organs of the abdominopelvic cavity.

Two or more tissues grouped together, which perform a highly specialized function, form an organ. The stomach, the heart and the lungs are organs. On examining the stomach, for example, we find that it is made up of all the types of tissues; it is covered and lined with epithelial tissue; connective and muscular tissues form the stomach walls; and nervous tissue is distributed throughout its structure. The stomach carries out early stages of digestion by secretion of digestive juices and by muscular activity which mixes the food and passes it along to the small intestine. Thus the organ, a combination of tissues, performs specialized functions not accomplished by the separate tissues.

Groups of organs which act together to perform a highly complex but specialized function are called systems. Thus the entire process of digestion is carried out through the coordinated activity of the organs of the digestive system. Nine body systems are commonly recognized: the skeletal, muscular, circulatory, respiratory, digestive, excretory, endocrine, reproductive, and nervous systems. A brief description of each follows. In succeeding chapters we shall study the cell, the tissues and then again in detail the different systems in which each organ will be considered.

SOME CHARACTERISTICS OF THE BODY SYSTEMS

The Nervous System.   The brain, spinal cord, nerves and ganglia constitute the nervous system. The nervous system in the process of its formation develops from a tube. Knowledge of this factor in development is of importance in visualizing the architecture of the brain and spinal cord as enclosing a continuous cavity. In the brain the parts of this cavity are called ventricles; in the spinal cord, where it is relatively small, the cavity is called the central canal.

The brain and the spinal cord—that is, the structures contained in the dorsal body cavity (Fig. 3)—constitute the *central* nervous system. Those parts of the nervous system lying outside the dorsal body cavity constitute the *peripheral* nervous system.

The brain is made up of the *cerebral hemispheres* (the forebrain), the *midbrain,* and the *cerebellum,* the *pons* and the *medulla oblongata* (which comprise the hindbrain). The cerebral hemispheres contain the higher centers, including those concerned with sensations, associative memory and other forms of consciousness. Other parts of the forebrain mediate complex reflexes or activities which are not directly concerned with consciousness. The midbrain contains principally the tracts, or nerve pathways between the forebrain and parts of the hindbrain and the spinal cord. The cerebellum is an elaborate integrating system, especially for muscular activity. The pons, or bridge, is chiefly made up of pathways between the halves of the cerebellum. The medulla oblongata contains all the nerve pathways which connect the spinal cord to the higher parts of the nervous system; it includes important nerve centers, such as the "center" for breathing.

The function of the nervous system is to coordinate activities of the body. It provides for the mechanism through which the body responds to the outside world in avoiding injury, obtaining food and performing many more complex acts. Some of these acts do not depend on conscious activity and may be controlled at various levels of the brain and spinal cord.

SENSE ORGANS. Man receives his information concerning the outside world through his sense organs, which are specialized endings of the sensory division of the peripheral nerves. The eyes, the ears and the membranes of the nose contain such specialized endings. They give information concerning objects in the outside world which are at a distance from the body. The skin contains receptors for touch, temperature and pain which give information about objects in contact with the body.

The sensory receptors respond to a variety of conditions, but the basic factor in all the conditions is a sudden change in the environment. This sudden change, which constitutes a *stimulus,* excites the sensory receptors. If a piece of ice is suddenly placed against the skin, it causes a sudden change in environment of the body and the sensation of cold results. If an object passes in front of the eyes, the changes in the intensity of the light stimulate the nerve endings in the eye. Blows or electric shocks may constitute stimuli.

In addition to the receptors which give information as to the outside world, there are receptors which give information as to conditions or activity within the body. We are aware of the position of an arm or a leg without looking at it. This information is supplied by the *proprioceptors,* which are nerve endings that register muscle tension and sense of position. The proprioceptors in the muscles not only supply information as to the condition of the muscles, but through numerous connections aid in controlling the energy and extent of muscular activity. Proprioceptors in the inner ear aid in maintenance of balance.

The body acts upon a great part of the information received by the receptors. Stimulation of a sensory nerve may bring about activity of muscles or glands, since there are physiologic connections between the sensory nerves and motor nerves (the nerves capable of causing movement or activity).

A response to a stimulus may be either voluntary or reflex. Most harmful stimuli, unless they are expected, cause reflex responses. The harmful stimuli, which are so intense that they may cause injury, bring about a rapid reaction because they travel over a direct and relatively uncomplicated pathway. In the reflex (involuntary) response the nerve impulse resulting from the stimulus travels over a series of connecting nerves from a receiving structure (receptor), into the central nervous system and out to a responding structure (effector). This pathway, which forms the physical basis of the reflex, is called a *reflex arc.*

THE AUTONOMIC NERVOUS SYSTEM. Though skeletal muscle is under control of the central nervous system and its peripheral nerves, all other functions of body tissues are controlled by the autonomic nervous system. We are not generally conscious of such activities as the heart beat, the contraction of the smooth muscles of the blood vessels and digestive tract and the secretion of glands, all of which are under autonomic control. These activities are regulated for the most part by two sets of nerves to a single structure, one set causing increased activity, the other causing decreased activity (inhibition). The performance of the structure is a result of the combined effect of these two influences.

The Skeletal System. The skeletal system is composed of bones held together by ligaments. It serves as the bony framework for the attachment of voluntary muscles and for support and protection of the more delicate organs.

The Muscular System. There are three types of muscle: the quick-acting *voluntary* or *skeletal muscles,* the more slowly acting *smooth muscle* of the blood vessels and the viscera, and the *cardiac* or *heart muscle.*

The *skeletal muscle* tissue forms the organs of the muscular system. These muscles are, with few exceptions, attached to two or more bones. They are capable of various degrees of shortening or contraction. Contractions of the muscles attached to the bones of the thigh and leg act across the knee joint. When several of these muscle groups shorten just enough to cause tension—that is, *muscle tone*—they keep the knee in a fixed position and aid in maintaining a standing posture. When the muscle groups which act to bend the leg and those which act to straighten the leg contract alternately, and shorten to a greater extent than when merely maintaining posture, they cause movement of the body.

The skeletal muscles are under voluntary control. This does not mean that all the coordinated activities of the muscle groups used in making a movement must be consciously directed. It is more probable that, once the voluntary movement is started, the degree of the contractions and finely coordinated activity of the many muscles involved is controlled to a large extent through nerve endings in the key muscles.

Muscle groups that cause opposite effects when acting across a joint are said to act antagonistically. Thus the muscles which shorten when bending the arm are *antagonistic* to those which shorten when straightening the arm. Muscles which contract together to carry out a certain movement are said to be *synergistic.*

The architecture of a skeletal muscle is such that some of the fibers making up a single muscle may contract while other fibers are at rest. This results in an economy of energy for contractions just sufficiently strong to maintain posture.

Smooth muscle tissue forms parts of other systems, such as the digestive and circulatory systems. The smooth muscle in the walls of the blood vessels is important in altering the size of the vessel. In the viscera the extent of the contraction of the muscle alters the capacity of the organ. Thus the muscles of the stomach, by relaxing, may increase its capacity to accommodate the food taken at a meal. Contraction of the muscles diminishes its size and empties the stomach during digestion.

Heart muscle tissue forms an organ; together with smooth muscle it makes up a major part of the circulatory system. Heart muscle is responsible for pumping blood through the blood vessels. The architecture of cardiac muscle is such that all fibers act together in contrast to the fibers of skeletal muscle, which may act either out of step or in unison.

The Circulatory System. The circulatory system includes the heart, the blood vessels and the lymphatics.

The heart pumps blood through an elastic system of blood vessels. The blood vessels form a continuous closed system made up of three main divisions. The *arterial* system carries blood away from the heart to a vast network of minute vessels, the *capillaries*. From the capillaries the blood is collected and returned to the heart by the *venous* system.

The blood in the arteries carries oxygen from the lungs to all the tissues of the body. Nutrient material is also distributed throughout the body by the circulation. Waste products are collected from all the bodily tissues and carried to the excretory organs.

There is, however, a "middleman" in any exchange between the blood stream and the tissues. Some of the fluid portion of the blood, the plasma, passes through the capillary walls to form the *tissue fluids*. Oxygen, nutrient and other materials pass through the thin-walled capillary system into the tissue fluid which bathes all the cells of the body. These substances pass from the tissue fluid into the cells, while waste products pass in the opposite direction. A circulation of the fluid is achieved as it is returned to the blood stream through a system of lymphatic vessels.

Great variations in the blood supply in any part of the body may be brought about by the nervous system and other systems of the body acting upon the heart and blood vessels. The heart beat can be increased to pump more blood, or the same amount of blood at a higher pressure. The blood supply to any part of the body may be altered by an increase or decrease in the size of the blood vessels in that area. Changes in the caliber of the vessels are brought about by the action of the nervous system and by chemical means.

The Respiratory System. This system comprises the nose, pharynx, larynx, trachea, bronchi and lungs. The first five structures form the air passages connecting the lungs with the outside air. The muscles of respiration, chiefly the diaphragm, enlarge the chest cavity by their contractions so that fresh air flows into the air spaces of the lungs. Oxygen then passes through the air sacs or alveoli of the lungs into the capillary blood vessels of the lungs. At the same time carbon dioxide passes from the capillaries into the air spaces. Relaxation of the respiratory muscles diminishes the size of the chest and the air is expired.

Respiration, a characteristic of all living material, is a term used to describe all the physiologic activities concerned with the consumption of oxygen and the release of carbon dioxide. Accessory functions of the respiratory system are talking, sneezing and coughing.

The Digestive System. The digestive system is composed of the mouth, pharynx, esophagus, stomach and the small and large intestines. Accessory structures are the teeth, hard and soft palates and the salivary glands associated with the mouth. Three pairs of salivary glands pour their secretions through ducts into the mouth. The liver, gallbladder and pancreas are accessory structures associated with the small intestine.

A second characteristic of living tissue is that it grows by the process of intussusception, that is, through deposition of new particles of formative material in a tissue. Thus, through digestion, substances from outside of the body may be incorporated in the tissues. In this respect intussusception, or *growth* in living things, is different from the growth by accretion of nonliving material. Accretion is growth by addition, as in the increase in size of a snowball when it is rolled down a snow-covered hill.

Food entering the body is acted upon mechanically and chemically in the digestive system in such a way that it is reduced to a state in which the body may draw upon it for energy and for material for growth and repair of the tissues.

The stomach acts primarily as a storage reservoir for food. The early stages of digestion are brought about by chemical and mechanical action in the stomach. By far the greater part of absorption takes place in the small intestine. The mechanical movements not only aid in the division of the food, but control the rate at which food passes through the digestive tract. If the passage occurs too rapidly, there is not sufficient time for absorption of the foodstuffs.

The Urinary System. The kidneys, ureters, bladder and urethra constitute the urinary system, which rids the body of liquid and soluble waste products.

The kidney filters the fluid portion of the blood into a system of small tubes. The waste products and products foreign to the body, which are dissolved in water, are carried to the bladder and excreted

as urine. Many substances, important to the body economy, are reabsorbed through the tubules together with sufficient water to maintain
the concentration of the body fluids at a relatively constant level.

Additional excretory functions are carried out by organs in other
systems. Water is lost from the lungs and skin. Carbon dioxide is
excreted through the lungs. Bacteria, cast-off cells from the lining of
the digestive tract, some secretions, and indigestible parts of the diet
are eliminated through the intestines as feces.

The Endocrine System. The endocrine system is composed of the
glands of internal secretion. These are the hypophysis, the thyroid,
the parathyroids, and the suprarenals, together with the islet cells of
the pancreas and parts of the stomach, duodenum, ovaries and testes
(Fig. 293, p. 501). The secretions of the endocrine or ductless glands
are taken up directly by the blood stream, in contrast to the exocrine
glands, which empty their secretions into ducts.

The endocrine system and the nervous system share in the control
of all the activities of the body tissues. For the most part the nervous
system controls the more rapid responses of the body to changes in
the outside world or external environment which require immediate
response if the organism is to survive. The endocrine system, on the
other hand, more frequently controls the slower changes or adaptations of the body to its environment.

The Reproductive System. The reproductive system in the female
is composed of the ovaries, uterine tubes, uterus, vagina and the external genitalia. In the male the organs are the testis, epididymis, ductus
deferens, seminal vesicle, ejaculatory duct, and prostate gland, penis
and urethra.

It has already been said that respiration and growth by intussusception are properties that distingish living from nonliving matter. A
third such characteristic is that of *reproduction*. Living organisms are
capable of reproducing their kind, thus assuring continuation of the
species. Reproduction has another meaning, namely, the increase in
the number of units or cells which allows for growth and repair
of the body.

This superficial account of the organization and systems of the body
raises innumerable questions as to architecture and function. Some
of these questions will be answered in the following chapters.

SUMMARY

Anatomy is the science which describes the architecture of the body.
Its subdivisions are gross, microscopic and developmental anatomy.

Physiology is the study of the mechanism by which the body performs its various functions. Human physiology is the study of the mechanisms of the body of man.

Certain terms are used for precise descriptions when referring to the body: the planes of reference (sagittal, midsagittal, transverse and frontal); the surfaces (anterior, posterior, superior and inferior); and the directions and relative positions (cranial, caudal, medial, lateral, proximal, distal, afferent and efferent).

The internal body structure in the vertebrate is characterized by two body cavities, the dorsal and the ventral. The dorsal cavity consists of two portions, the cranial and the spinal. The ventral cavity is divided by the diaphragm into thoracic and abdominopelvic portions.

The various animal forms are built of structural units, the cells. The cells, during embryonic development, differentiate into tissues, and the tissues are grouped together to form organs. Organs which work together in performing a common function comprise a system.

The systems of the human body are skeletal, muscular, circulatory, respiratory, digestive, urinary, endocrine, reproductive and nervous.

The skeletal system is composed of bones held together by ligaments. It affords attachment for voluntary muscles, gives support and protects the more delicate organs.

The muscular system is composed of the skeletal muscles. Smooth muscle tissue of the viscera, and cardiac or heart muscle form parts of other systems.

The circulatory system includes the heart, the blood vessels and the lymphatics.

The respiratory system comprises the nose, pharynx, larynx, trachea, bronchi and lungs.

The digestive system is composed of the mouth, pharynx, esophagus, stomach, small and large intestines and certain accessory structures.

The urinary system consists of the kidneys, ureters, bladder and urethra. These, together with skin, lungs and intestines, perform excretory functions.

The endocrine system is composed of the following glands: hypophysis, thyroid, parathyroids and suprarenals, together with the islet cells of the pancreas and parts of the stomach, duodenum, ovaries and testes.

The reproductive system in the female comprises the ovaries, uterine tubes, uterus and external genitalia. In the male the organs are the paired testis, epididymis, ductus deferens, seminal vesicle, ejaculatory duct and the prostate gland, penis and urethra.

The nervous system includes the brain, spinal cord, ganglia and nerves.

QUESTIONS FOR DISCUSSION

1. Examine Figure 2. Which terms are applicable to both man and the quadruped? Do these terms depend upon position?

2. Which branch of anatomy developed first, macroscopic or microscopic? Explain.

3. What are the contents of the various body cavities? Relate these structures to the different systems.

4. Explain how nutrient materials, respiratory gases and waste products are exchanged in the body.

Chapter 2

The Whole Body and Its Component Parts

CELLULAR STRUCTURE AND FUNCTION

The Cell Theory. Huxley* speaks of the "wonderful unity of plan in the thousands and thousands of diverse living constructions, and the modifications of similar apparatuses to serve diverse ends." This unity of plan, which is difficult to appreciate upon observing the widely differing external forms of living things, becomes evident when we realize that all living things are made up of the same units—the cells.

In 1838 Schleiden and Schwann, German scientists, postulated the Cell Theory. They worked separately, but came to the same conclusions, publishing the results of their studies in the same year. Cells had been observed much earlier than this by Leeuwenhoek, Robert Hooke, Malpighi and others, in both animal and plant forms. The contribution to science made by Schleiden and Schwann was the theory that all living forms, both plants and animals, are made up of similar units called cells. This generalization brought order out of chaos. No matter how different plants and animals seemed on superficial inspection, they were alike in the sense that they were made up of groups of similar units. This explains why all living things have fundamentally the same characteristics.

* Thomas Henry Huxley, English biologist (1825–1895).

17

The Protoplasm Doctrine. With the improvement of the microscope a more extensive study of the cell became possible. As the name implies, the cell was thought at first to be a compartment, or an empty framework. Later it was learned that the cell contents provide the vital part of the cell. To this cell substance the name *protoplasm* (meaning "first molded thing") was given. In 1861 the work of Max Schultze firmly established the Protoplasm Doctrine, which affirms that the architectural units are masses of protoplasm and that this substance is similar in all living organisms. The word "protoplasm" has come to mean the material out of which the whole cell is made. It is the living jelly defined by Huxley as "the physical basis of life."

Chemical Composition of Protoplasm. Since protoplasm is living matter, it seems reasonable to expect that its chemical composition should differ from the nonliving substances by containing some peculiar or rare element. Still, although protoplasm has been subjected repeatedly to chemical analysis, no element peculiar to living things has been found. Every living organism contains the following elements: oxygen, carbon, hydrogen, nitrogen, calcium, phosphorus, potassium, sulfur, chlorine, sodium, magnesium and iron. Other elements present in certain forms are silicon, iodine, bromine, aluminum, manganese and copper. An analysis of the human body shows the following composition:

Table 2

Elements Composing the Human Body

ELEMENT	PER CENT
Oxygen	65.00
Carbon	18.00
Hydrogen	10.00
Nitrogen	3.00
Calcium	2.00
Phosphorus	1.00
Potassium	0.35
Sulfur	0.25
Chlorine	0.15
Sodium	0.15
Magnesium	0.05
Iron	0.004
Other elements	0.046

Examination of the table shows that 99 per cent of the body is composed of six common elements: oxygen, carbon, hydrogen, nitrogen, calcium, and phosphorus.

The compounds which make up protoplasm are both organic and inorganic. The inorganic substances are water and inorganic salts. The organic constituents are the proteins, carbohydrates and fats.

The most abundant compound found in protoplasm is water. About 60 to 90 per cent of protoplasm is composed of this familiar substance. *Water* is of first importance in all physiologic reactions because of its unusual physical and chemical properties.

Water dissolves a great many substances and allows acids, bases and salts to separate into electrically charged particles. It enters into many chemical reactions in the body. Water requires more heat per unit of weight to increase its temperature 1 degree than any other common substance. This means that it can absorb more heat per unit of weight with less change in its own temperature than any other substance in the body. As a result of these properties water plays an important part in essential biologic processes. As the principal ingredient in body fluid, it carries all materials to the tissues and makes possible the processes of exchange, excretion, absorption and secretion.

The *inorganic salts* in the body are composed chiefly of the chlorides, carbonates, phosphates and sulfates, of sodium, potassium, calcium and magnesium. Familiar examples are sodium chloride, sodium bicarbonate and calcium carbonate.

The salts do not exist in the molecular form, but rather as positive and negative ions; e.g., NaCl would be present in the body fluids as Na^+ and Cl^-. The positive ions are called *cations,* because in an electric field they travel toward the cathode or negative pole; the negatively charged ions, which are repelled by like or negative electrical charges, move toward the anode, or positive pole, and hence are called *anions.* The principal cations are H^+ and the *basic ions* Na^+, K^+, NH_4^+, Ca^{++}, and Mg^{++}. The principal anions are OH^- and the *acidic ions* Cl^-, HCO_3^-, HPO_4^{--} and SO_4^{--} and the organic acidic ion, proteinate, P^-. Although present in small amounts, usually less than 1 per cent, the inorganic salts are extremely important. They aid in the maintenance of osmotic pressure (see Fig. 10, p. 30), in the transport of oxygen and carbon dioxide, in maintaining the reaction (alkalinity) of the blood and tissue fluids, in blood clotting and in the building of bone. They also influence the irritability and contractility of tissue.

The *organic* substances—the proteins, carbohydrates, and lipids—comprise approximately 10 to 30 per cent of protoplasm. *Proteins* form the framework of protoplasm. Recognition of the presence of two of these proteins in certain structures of protoplasm has become essential in the understanding of the physiology of cells, particularly in the repair of tissues and the building of new tissues. These proteins are desoxyribonucleic acid (DNA) and ribonucleic acid (RNA). Further, proteins may be oxidized to produce energy. *Carbohydrates* provide a readily available source of energy. *Lipids,* fats and fatlike substances, aid in the formation of the structure of protoplasm, especially the cell membrane, in which position they play an important role in exchanges between cells. The lipids are also a source of energy.

Physical Nature of Protoplasm. Although we know of the chemical compounds present in the protoplasm of the cell, it has not been possible to put these compounds together in the laboratory and synthesize protoplasm. It is a uniquely organized system of substances of many types, and only because of its specific organization can the characteristic activities be carried on with such orderliness. The physical chemist tells us that protoplasm is colloidal in nature. When water is mixed with a *colloid,* a translucent but cloudy or opalescent liquid which is thick and sticky is the result. Familiar examples of colloid are egg white, glue and starch paste. A colloid may be in a liquid state known as a *sol,* or in a more solid state known as a *gel.* The particles of a colloid are small enough to pass through the pores of filter paper, but too large to pass through the pores of membranes of plant and animal cells. That the colloid protoplasm cannot pass through the cell membrane is significant, for it means that the organization and identity of the cell substance are held intact and cell individuality is preserved.

Cell Structure. The structural plan of the cell is about the same in plant and animal forms (Fig. 5). The cell is made up of cytoplasm and, in nearly all cases, a nucleus. The outermost surface film of cytoplasm, composed chiefly of proteins and lipids, is called *the cell membrane.* It is believed to be a condensation of the cytoplasm. In addition to having a cell membrane, plant cells are encased in a heavy nonliving cellulose covering or *cell wall.* The mass of the cell protoplasm or *cytoplasm* is a translucent, viscous, colorless gel or sol in which living and nonliving cell inclusions are embedded. Food and waste materials in crystals, granules and vacuoles comprise important nonliving cell inclusions. Any cavity within the cytoplasm filled with liquid may be considered a *vacuole,* but the term usually applies to cavities within the cells containing a watery solution known as cell sap. Vacuoles are rare in animal cells, but universally present in plant cells.

Centrosome and attraction sphere, Golgi apparatus, mitochondria and plastids are living cell inclusions. The tiny granule of the *centrosome* is located near the nucleus of an animal cell in a relatively clear area of cytoplasm, the *attraction sphere,* and surrounded by radiating fibrils or strands of cytoplasm. *Golgi apparatus,* which frequently

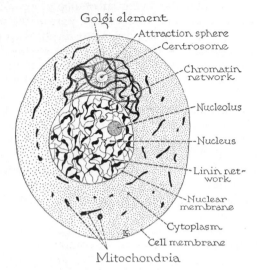

Fig. 5. Diagram of a cell.

appears as a network enveloping the centrosome and attraction sphere, is thought to be composed principally of lipids. Minute, delicate rods, granules and filaments of lipids and proteins are generously distributed throughout the cytoplasm as the *mitochondria*. RNA protein is found in the mitochondria and throughout the cytoplasm. *Plastids,* such as food-forming chloroplasts, are found in plant cells.

The *nucleus* is usually a globular or oval body lying near the center of the cell, sharply delimited from the surrounding cytoplasm by a nuclear membrane. Inside the nucleus are masses of material called *chromatin* which stain deeply with basic dyes. The chromatin material appears as granules or fibers supported on a fine network known as linin. RNA and DNA are present in the chromatin. Only RNA is found in the one or more *nucleoli* that may be present in the nucleus. The material filling the meshes of the network is a clear liquid nucleoplasm.

Characteristic Activities and Properties of Protoplasm. This living jelly, protoplasm, exhibits certain properties which we associate in our thinking as the characteristics of living material. It is difficult to separate these characteristics entirely since they appear to depend one upon the other.

Metabolism is a broad general term used to include all the physical and chemical reactions taking place in living material. The processes are complex and varied, but a simplified account will serve to give a preliminary concept of metabolism in animal cells.

Food and oxygen enter the living substance or protoplasm. In the presence of certain "activators" or *enzymes,* part of the nutrient material is more or less completely burned, or oxidized, with the liberation of energy. Other portions of the food are broken down into simpler chemical components. A part of the energy which results from complete oxidation of one portion of the food is utilized in building new elements of the living material from the chemical products of digestion of the other portions of the food. The new elements serve for the growth and repair of the cell. The remainder of the energy appears as work, that is, activity, or as heat.

The phase of metabolism concerned with the breakdown or oxidation reactions is known as *catabolism.* The building or synthetic phase of metabolism is known as *anabolism.*

Respiration is the gaseous exchange by which oxygen is taken in, the food or protoplasmic elements are oxidized with an accompanying release of energy, and carbon dioxide is given off. Carbon dioxide and water represent the final end products of combustion, i.e., oxidation of nutrient material.

Digestion is a term used to include all the metabolic processes concerned with the breakdown of food or body elements into simpler compounds which are either utilized by the body or are cast off as waste products.

Assimilation is a term used to include reactions sometimes referred to as intermediary metabolism, that is, the processes by which material derived from digestion is incorporated into the protoplasm.

Excretion includes all the processes by which waste products are discharged or removed from the living material.

Elimination is a form of excretion in which indigestible substances and accumulated waste are discharged from the body or cell (in unicellular animals) as a mass or particulate matter.

Growth is the developmental increase in the size of an organism. It is the natural result of nutritive changes occurring in constructive metabolism in which the total amount of protoplasm is increased. In the single-celled animal, growth is shown by an increase in the size of the cell; in the many-celled animals, growth is accomplished principally by an increase in the number of cells. Closely associated with growth is the ability of cells to replace damaged parts with new protoplasm or to replace worn-out cells with new ones.

Reproduction. The essential factor of reproduction is cell multiplication. A living cell can produce cells like itself by cell division. Living organisms are capable of reproducing their kind, thus assuring continuation of the species.

Irritability is the property which enables protoplasm to react to sudden changes in the environment. The reactions involve changes in the metabolism of the cell. The nature of the response depends upon the specialized function of the cell and its state of readiness to react to the exciting value of the change.

Conductivity is the property of propagating a physiologic response or excitation from one point to another within the organism.

Contractility is that power of shortening or decreasing in length by which protoplasm may respond to certain stimuli by movement.

Elasticity is the capacity to return to original length or shape after shortening or stretching.

Viscosity of protoplasm is its resistance to change in shape.

As we have already noted in the discussion of the organization of the body, differentiation and specialization of cells occur in the course of development, so that these properties of protoplasm may become either more or less highly developed in cells in the human body.

Functions of Cell Parts. The nucleus of the cell is chemically very active. Portions of the cytoplasm separated from the nucleus soon disintegrate and die. The nucleus controls normal growth as well as the repair or regeneration of injured cells, and it initiates cell division. The chromatin material is responsible for the transmission of hereditary traits from parents to children. Many theories have been advanced to explain the part played by the nucleolus, but there is still much uncertainty concerning its nature and function. The cytoplasm controls cellular absorption and excretion. Interaction of RNA and DNA in the cytoplasm is thought to result in increase in individual cell size, increases in numbers of cells and differentiation of cells into tissues. The oxidative enzymes of cytoplasm are found in the mitochondria, where most of cellular respiration occurs. Changes in Golgi apparatus of cells appear to be associated with the secretory activities of cells. Centrosome and attraction sphere are important in cell reproduction. Substances taken into the cell are synthesized into cytoplasm itself or into storage products or cell inclusions such as starch grains, fat droplets, protein particles, pigment and crystals.

Cell Division. Cell division provides for an increase in the number of cells and hence in the mass of tissue for reproduction, growth and repair of the body. The two methods of division are direct cell division, or amitosis, and indirect cell division, or mitosis.

Amitosis is accomplished by a construction and separation of the cytoplasm into two daughter cells. Cytoplasm may not divide in all cells. Amitosis is not common in multicellular organisms.

Mitosis occurs in almost all plants and animals in sex and somatic or

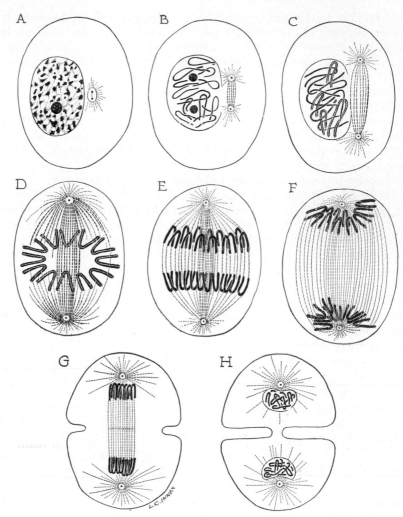

Fig. 6. Diagram showing various phases of mitosis. *A*, Resting cell. *B*, *C*, and *D*, Prophase. *E*, Metaphase. *F*, Anaphase. *G*, *H*, Telophase.

body cells. The phases of this division are shown diagrammatically in Figure 6. Prophase, metaphase, anaphase and telophase are convenient but arbitrary terms used for the description of a progressive process of cell division.

PROPHASE.   In this stage chromatin is arranged into tiny bent filamentous rods, or *chromosomes*. Nuclear membrane and nucleolus disappear and a spindle begins to form (Figure 6, *B*).

In the structure of the chromosome, two longitudinal halves or chromatids are joined at a central constriction, the centromere. Threadlike chromonemata spiral through the chromatids. Particles of DNA protein form the *chromomeres*, or enlargements on the chromonemata. Each chromomere contains one or more *genes*. The gene can be thought of as a special arrangement of enzyme molecules with the capacity to reproduce itself.

While these changes are occurring in the nucleus the centrosome has divided into centrioles, which migrate to opposite poles of the nucleus. Fibers of the attraction spheres form *asters* as their extensions grow to meet one another at the equator in the development of a *spindle*. The whole figure composed of asters and spindle is called the *amphiaster*.

METAPHASE (Fig. 6, *E*). The centromere of each chromosome becomes attached to a spindle fiber at the equatorial plane. Longitudinal chromatids are now more apparent in the structure of the chromosome.

ANAPHASE (Fig. 6, *F*, *G*). Longitudinal separation of the chromatids beginning at the centromere precedes the migration of the halves of the chromosome toward opposite centrioles. The passage of the chromatids is aided by the spindle fibers.

TELOPHASE (Fig. 6, *H*). A nuclear membrane forms about the mass of chromosomes near each pole. They, in turn, re-form chromatin as nucleoli reappear. The spindle fibers disappear, constriction of the cytoplasm occurs at the equator, and its final separation results in two new daughter cells.

The significant feature of mitosis is the formation and exact division of the chromosomes and the distribution of equivalent halves to each of the daughter cells. This *chromosome number* in any given plant or animal species is constant, the identical number appearing at each mitosis. The chromosome number for man is forty-eight. In this manner the genes, or determinants of heredity, are likewise equated in the daughter cells where they may act to produce one chemical product or a number of chemical products. The substances so produced are mediators of the effect of the gene. The expression of heredity is seen in mental and physical characteristics of the whole body, as well as the form and behavior of the individual cells.

Physiochemical Processes. The ceaseless chemical activity of the cell requires the continuous entrance and exit of materials. Though the quantities of any one substance within the cell remain remarkably constant, this does not mean that the same particles of that substance remain indefinitely in the cell. Small amounts of many substances are continually leaving the cell, while at the same time the same amounts of identical substances are entering it. Since the composition of the cell is constant, it is said to be in a state of *equilibrium;* and since this composition is maintained while particles are constantly entering and

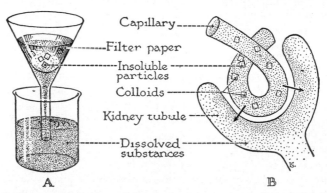

A   B

Fig. 7. Filtration. *A*, Water and dissolved substances pass through the filter paper into the beaker. *B*, Water and dissolved substances in the blood pass from the capillaries into the kidney tubule. Colloids of the blood which do not pass through the capillary wall correspond to insoluble substances in the funnel.

leaving the cell, the condition is called a *dynamic* equilibrium (an equilibrium based upon movement). The arrangement of cell constituents is such that the outermost boundary of the cytoplasm acts as a membrane. The lipid material of the cell is concentrated in the cell membrane. Physical processes are responsible for much of this molecular exchange. Filtration, diffusion and osmosis, often encountered in nonliving systems, are all involved.

Filtration is a process which depends upon mechanical pressure to produce the movement of materials across a barrier. It is essentially the same process as straining a broth or jelly. The substances which are passed through the barrier or filter depend upon the size of the particles and the fineness of the filter. Filtration may be defined as the passage of water and dissolved substances across a membrane because of differences in mechanical pressure on the two sides of the membrane. In the laboratory we separate a liquid from insoluble particles by filtration (Fig. 7, *A*). The water and substances in solution pass through the pores of the filter paper, but the solid and insoluble material is held back. Hydrostatic pressure, or the effects of gravity on the column of water, provides the mechanical force in this instance. In the body, filtration takes place through the walls of the capillaries (Fig. 7, *B*). The cells of the capillary walls form the membrane. Some of the fluid portion of the blood with dissolved substances filters through the membrane because of the blood pressure produced by the beating of the heart.

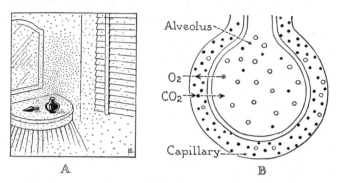

Fig. 8. Diffusion. *A*, Molecules of perfume spread throughout enclosure. *B*, Diffusion in air sac of lung. Carbon dioxide, represented as black dots, passes from capillary into alveolus. Oxygen molecules, shown as circles, pass from air sac into blood capillary.

Diffusion may be described as the tendency of substances to distribute themselves uniformly throughout a space. It depends upon the fact that the particles of substances are in constant motion. Gases diffuse rapidly from a point of higher pressure to points of lower pressure until they are uniformly distributed in the area in which they are enclosed. If a mixture of gases is concerned, each gas acts independently and becomes evenly distributed throughout the space. If a bottle of ammonia and one of perfume are opened in a room, the odors may be detected at distant points. Figure 8, *A*, shows diffusion of perfume molecules. Separating two gases by means of living membranes such as are found in the capillaries or in the air sacs of the lungs (Fig. 8, *B*) does not interfere with diffusion. The carbon dioxide diffuses from the site of high pressure, in the lung capillaries, to the point of low pressure in the air sacs. Since the oxygen pressure is greater in the air sacs than in the capillaries, the oxygen diffuses from the alveoli into the blood stream.

When a small amount of a substance is dissolved to make a weak solution, its active particles (i.e., the molecules, or if the substance is an electrolyte, the ions) exert the same pressure as they would if they were in a gaseous form at the same temperature and the same volume.*

* One gram molecule, i.e., the molecular weight in grams, of a gas occupies a volume of 22.4 liters at 0°C. and 760 mm. (sea level) pressure.

The intensity of the bombardment by the particles of dissolved substance—first of the surrounding liquid, and then of the restraining walls of the container—is dependent upon their concentration (see Fig. 8, A and B). Diffusion in liquids is, however, a much slower process than in gas because of the greater density of the medium in which the distribution of particles is taking place. For example, if a crystal of copper sulfate is placed in a glass and covered with water, it will take months before the solution attains a uniform blue color, if extreme care is taken to avoid stirring and temperature changes. Mixtures of solutes (dissolved substances) behave in the same manner as mixtures of gases; the active particles of each substance act independently and become uniformly distributed throughout the water (the solvent).

If two solutions of different strengths are separated by a membrane which will pass both water and the dissolved substance, the solute will pass from the side of higher concentration into the solution of lower concentration, while the solvent will pass in the opposite direction until the solutions are of the same concentration. If we depart momentarily from the standard custom of referring to the more concentrated solution as the one containing more of the dissolved substance, we can recognize more readily that water is behaving like a gas or solute, in that it passes from the area of *higher concentration of water molecules,* until the water molecules are uniformly distributed on the two sides of the membrane. If solutions contain both substances that will pass through a membrane and other active particles which, for example, are too large to pass through it, a modified diffusion known as *dialysis* takes place. The method of dialysis can be used to separate larger molecules to which the membrane is impermeable from diffusible salts. The process of movement of water molecules across a membrane from a weaker to a stronger solution is known as *osmosis.* Thus osmosis takes place both through membranes which permit passage of all solutes and through selectively permeable membranes which permit dialysis of diffusible solutes, but hold back other moleclues.

In osmosis, water molecules pass through membranes in both directions, but their final distribution on the two sides of a membrane when an equilibrium is established will depend upon the pressures exerted by the active particles in the two solutions (Fig. 9). A simple, though perhaps inadequate, picture of the process of the passage of water across a membrane from the weaker solution to one of greater concentration may be gained from the following illustration. Because of their constant motion, the molecules of the two solutions would be constantly hitting the membrane separating them. Now, the number of water molecules striking any given area per unit of time would

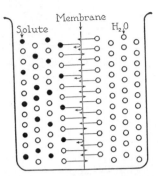

Fig. 9. Osmosis. Black dots represent molecules of dissolved substance; circles indicate the water molecules.

determine the exchange of water between the two solutions. In the stronger solution, however, particles of the dissolved substance would occupy a greater total area of the membrane in contact with the solution and would prevent molecules from striking and passing through the membrane at those points. In the weaker, more water molecules would strike and pass through the membrane in a unit of time. As a result of the differences in the number of molecules in contact with the two sides of the membrane, more water will pass from the weaker to the stronger solution (see Fig. 9). If the membrane permits the solutes to pass, the conditions on the two sides of the membrane will finally be alike, the water uniformly distributed and the rate of exchange of water in both directions across the membrane will be equal. When the membrane holds back some of the solute particles, however, the molecules which are held back continue to occupy areas of the membrane, so that water enters the stronger solution faster than it leaves it, and the volume of stronger solution increases. If the container is open, the fluid level rises and a difference in hydrostatic pressure results. At some point the hydrostatic pressure becomes sufficiently great to force the water out at the same rate it enters the solution containing the impermeable solute. The development of hydrostatic pressure demonstrates the force of the process of osmosis. Osmotic pressure will occur and be maintained only by solutes held back by a membrane which allows the water molecules to pass (Fig. 10).

Osmotic pressure may be demonstrated and measured by an *osmometer*. We can construct an osmometer by covering a thistle tube with a membrane impermeable to sugar molecules, introduce a sugar solution into the tube and immerse the membrane end of the tube in a container of pure water. If we mark the original height of the column

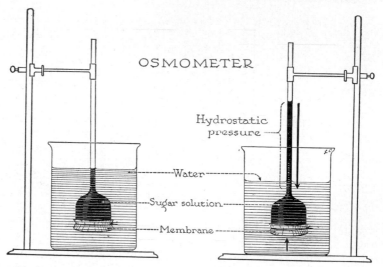

Fig. 10. Osmotic pressure. More water molecules strike and pass through the semipermeable membrane from the side in contact with pure water than from the side in contact with the sugar solution. Since more water is entering than leaving the thistle tube through the membrane, the height of the column of the sugar solution increases.

of sugar solution in the tube, we can note the rise in its level (see Fig. 10). After allowing time for a dynamic equilibrium to be established, i.e., an equal transfer rate of water in two directions across the membrane, the hydrostatic pressure, which results from the difference in the levels of the solutions inside and outside the thistle tube, closely approximates the osmotic pressure of the stronger solution.

OSMOTIC EFFECTS OF SOLUTIONS ON BODY CELLS. Red blood cells may be used to demonstrate osmosis (Fig 11). In the blood, the cells and plasma are in osmotic equilibrium. If we should separate the red blood cells from the plasma and place them in distilled water or a salt solution which is dilute as compared to plasma, the cells will swell until the osmotic pressure becomes so great that the cell bursts. This destruction of red blood cells is called *hemolysis*. Solutions and plasma in which hemolysis occurs show a red tinge which becomes deeper as greater numbers of cells are destroyed and greater amounts of hemoglobin are released. Should we alter the procedure and substitute a concentrated solution for the plasma, water will pass out of the cell and it will be shriveled or *crenated.*

The osmotic pressure of the contents of the red cell can be determined by finding the weakest solution that will cause only slight

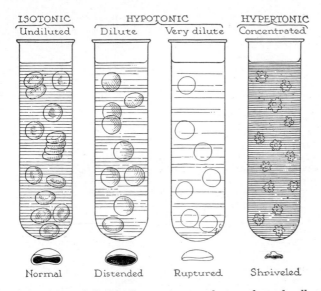

Fig. 11. Osmosis. In whole blood, or isotonic solution, the red cells are typical biconcave discs. In hypotonic solutions, or in plasma in which the salt concentration has been reduced, water enters the cells and distends them so that they appear rounded. In very dilute salt solutions (water or diluted plasma) the cell envelope ruptures and the contents escape. In concentrated salt solution (hypertonic), water passes out of the cells and they become shriveled.

hemolysis and the strongest solution at which no hemolysis occurs; the osmotic pressure midway between the two solutions will be approximately equal to that of the red blood cells. This method also tests the fragility of the cell membrane, i.e., its resistance to rupture from osmotic pressure. A more accurate measurement of the red cell osmotic pressure, then, would be to observe the effects of a graded series of solutions and determine the values at which changes in the volume of the cell occur (see Fig. 11).

All body cells are susceptible to the osmotic effects shown by the red cells. In consequence, great care is taken in the selection of solutions for medical use and for laboratory research in order to avoid subjecting body tissues to chemical insult. A solution that is in osmotic equilibrium with cells and tissues is said to be *isotonic* or *isosmotic*. Unless otherwise described, the terms isotonic and isosmotic are commonly used to mean that the solution has the same osmotic pressure as normal human blood plasma; if the solution is isosmotic for cells of a cold-blooded species such as frogs or for plant cells, this should be specifically stated. The terms hypotonic and hypertonic are used to describe solutions that are weaker or stronger than normal blood plasma.

STATEMENT OF CONCENTRATIONS OF BIOLOGICAL SOLUTIONS. Solutions are commonly described in terms of per cent, i.e., weight or volume of the solute per 100 cc. of solvent. This does not give us the biological information we require when, for example, we wish to inject the solution, use it in the artificial kidney for diffusion of waste products from the blood, bathe exposed tissues to prevent drying or for other clinical or laboratory purposes. If we are to know how these solutions will act, we must know the concentration (a) in terms of osmotic pressure, and (b) in terms of chemical combining power (gram-equivalent weights).

(a) Descriptions of concentration and osmotic pressure in terms of molarity and milliosmols:

1. *Molar Solutions.* A solution containing the molecular weight of a solute, expressed in grams, dissolved in one liter of water is known as a molar solution. To convert per cent concentration to molar concentration, multiply the number of grams per 100 cc. times 10 to obtain the number of grams per liter, and divide this value by the molecular weight. The general formula, then, is:

$$\text{molar concentration} = \frac{\text{wt. in gm. per 100 cc.} \times 10}{\text{molecular wt.}}$$

Examples:

PER CENT SOLUTION	GRAMS/L.		MOL. WT.	MOLARITY
5.4% glucose	5.4 gm. (per 100 cc.)	$\times$ 10 $\div$	180	= 0.30
0.9% NaCl	0.9 gm. (per 100 cc.)	$\times$ 10 $\div$	58.5	= 0.15

2. *Osmols and Milliosmols.* When speaking of the osmotic pressure of a solution, the concentration of osmotically active particles is given in *osmols*. Where the solute is a non-electrolyte, a one molar solution is identical with a one osmolar solution since the osmotically active particles are molecules. If the solute is an electrolyte, both ions act independently as osmotically active particles, so that a gram molecular weight of solute per liter of water makes a two osmolar solution. A smaller unit, the *milliosmol*, or $\frac{1}{1000}$ of an osmol, is customarily employed in referring to body fluids or solutions. The general formulae are:

$$\text{milliosmolar conc.} = \text{non-electrolyte molar conc.} \times 1000$$
$$\text{milliosmolar conc.} = \text{electrolyte molar conc.} \times 2 \times 1000$$

Examples:

% SOLUTION	MOLARITY		MILLIOSMOLS/L.	MILLIOSMOLAR CONC.
5.4% glucose	0.30 M. $\times$ 1000		= 300 (mOsm.)	= 300
0.9% NaCl	0.15 M. $\times$ 2 $\times$ 1000		= 300 (mOsm.)	= 300

3. *Osmotic pressure of isotonic solutions.* The purpose of describing a solution in terms of pressure is so that it can be readily related to the osmotic pressure of the body fluids. We may consider that a mol of a gas or non-electrolyte, or a half mol of an electrolyte, when contained within the volume of one liter, will exert a pressure which is 22.4 times greater than the pressure of the atmosphere (see footnote, p. 27). A milliosmol is, thus, a unit of osmotic pressure equivalent to 0.0224 atmosphere. The solutes in a liter of blood plasma exert a pressure of approximately 6.72 atmospheres. The blood plasma, then, is an approximate 300 mOsm.

solution (6.72 atmos. ÷ 0.0224 = 300 mOsm.). Reference to the examples in section 2 shows that 5.4 per cent glucose and 0.9 per cent NaCl are 300 mOsm., and hence are isotonic solutions.

In a solution containing a mixture of ions, the osmotic pressure exerted by each ion may be obtained by dividing the quantity of the ion in grams per liter by the *atomic weight* (since the ions are the active particles). Adding the result for each ion and multiplying by 1000 will give the total milliosmols per liter.

(b) Description of concentration in terms of chemical combining power:

A *gram equivalent* weight of a chemically reactive unit will react with or displace one gram of hydrogen or one equivalent of other substance. For monovalent ions, i.e., those carrying a single electrical charge, an *equivalent* is equal to its atomic weight. For example, $Na+$, $K+$, and $Cl-$ are monovalent ions; the atomic weight of $Na+$ is 23, so 23 grams is its gram equivalent weight. For divalent cations like $Ca++$ and $Mg++$, the gram equivalent weight is given by dividing the atomic weight by 2, i.e., by the valence. The divalent anions $SO_4{}^{--}$ and $HPO_4{}^{--}$ receive somewhat special treatment.* For trivalent ions the atomic weight is divided by 3. The term milliequivalent, which is one thousandth of a gram equivalent weight, is used for describing the concentration of solutes in biological solutions. To convert concentrations given in milligrams per 100 cc., i.e., milligrams per cent, to milliequivalents, multiply the weight in milligrams by 10 to obtain milligrams per liter, divide this value by the atomic weight and multiply by the valence. The general formula is:

$$\text{milliequivalents per liter (mEq./L.)} = \frac{\text{mg. per 100 cc.} \times 10}{\text{atomic wt.}} \times \text{functional valence.}$$

Examples:

(i) The $Na+$ in plasma is given as 330 mg.%. Convert this to mEq./L.
(ii) The $Ca++$ in plasma is given as 10 mg.%. Convert to mEq./L.

	CONC. MG.%			ATOMIC WT.		FUNCTIONAL VALENCE	mEq./L.
(i)	330	× 10 = 3300 ÷		23	×	1	= 143
(ii)	10	× 10 = 100 ÷		40	×	2	= 5

Thus, plasma sodium may combine with 143 equivalents or ions of chloride or other monovalent substance, while the divalent calcium of the plasma may combine with 5 equivalents or ions of Cl or replace 5 hydrogen ions.

Factors Influencing Cell Permeability.
Permeability is the resistance offered by the cell to the exchange of substances across its membrane. While the characteristics and mechanisms which determine permeability are incompletely understood, we know that the movement of substances may be influenced by molecular size, electrical charge and solubility of the substance. We know that transport in and out of a cell may be either passive or active.

* $SO_4{}^{--}$ is considered as a divalent S alone with the atomic weight of 32; $HPO_4{}^{--}$ is taken as P with the average valance (average for the two inorganic phosphates) of 1.8 and the atomic weight of 31.

FORCES INFLUENCING MOVEMENT OF IONS. The movement of ions (or molecules) through space depends on factors quite similar to those which would determine the rate of travel of a stone sinking through water. In essence, the velocity with which ions move represents a balance between accelerating (speeding up) and decelerating (slowing down) forces. Some of these forces are:

Accelerating forces:
1. Attraction between unlike electrical charges placed at opposite ends of the path.
2. Repulsion of like electrical charges existing in the same region.
3. Migration of ions due to thermal agitation.

Decelerating forces:
1. Repulsion between like charges placed at opposite ends of the path.
2. Attraction of unlike charges in the same region.
3. Viscous resistance to motion of the ions.

At any one time, and in any one cell system, all of these forces are acting to a greater or lesser extent.

Thus, it may be seen that any factor which produces a separation of ions, whether based on electrical forces or other forces, will alter the "permeability." Factors active in this way may be "passive," in which case they are influenced only by the forces listed above; or they may be "active," in that the transfer of ions proceeds in a manner that opposes the influence of the forces in this list. Let us discuss these different mechanisms separately.

PASSIVE TRANSPORT.   In passive transport, no energy is expended by the cell for transfer of material; substances move from a higher concentration or higher electrochemical potential, to a lower concentration or electrical potential. If there is sufficient time for an equilibrium to be established, substances may be distributed equally on the two sides of the membrane. If the substances are electrolytes the positive and negative charges on each side of the membrane will be equal. If, on the other hand, there are anions (such as protein) which are held back by the cell membrane, electrical forces create a situation in which the concentration of the permeable cation is greater on the same side of the membrane as the nondiffusible anion, while the concentration of the permeable anion is greater on the opposite side of the cell membrane. The electrical charge of the cations inside the cell balances both the permeable and impermeable anions; outside, the permeable cations and anions balance. This type of distribution in which the product of the permeable anions, times the cations inside the cell, equals the product of the permeable anions, times the cations outside the cell, is known as the Donnan equilibrium. This may be expressed as:

$$\left\{ \begin{array}{l} \text{Outside cell} \\ Na^+ \times Cl^- \\ \text{in protein free} \\ \text{solution} \end{array} \right\} = \left\{ \begin{array}{l} \text{Inside cell} \\ Na^+ \times Cl^- \\ \text{in solution with } P^-; \\ \text{i.e., protein ion} \end{array} \right\}$$

or by the ratios:

$$\frac{(Cl^-) \text{ protein free}}{(Cl^-) \text{ protein}} = \frac{(Na^+) \text{ protein}}{(Na^+) \text{ protein free}}.$$

The distribution by passive transport of permeable electrolyte and nonelectrolyte substances is known as *diffusion permeability;* that involving both permeable and nonpermeable substances is known as *osmotic permeability.*

We may think of a permeable or selectively permeable membrane (i.e., one which will pass some dissolved substances in addition to water) as having minute pores large enough to admit water and some of the smaller molecules. This would permit exchange by bulk flow of water and some of the contained solutes through the pores, as through the holes in a sieve. It would also permit thermal diffusion of smaller molecules through the water filling the pores of the membrane.

Electrical charges on the membrane would influence exchange by repelling ions of like charge and attracting ions of opposite charge. Still another feature of permeability is the solubility of the molecules being exchanged. Fat soluble substances would appear to be transported by first dissolving in the fatty parts of the cell membrane.

ACTIVE TRANSPORT. Some substances may not be distributed equally inside and outside the cell, even though the membrane is quite permeable to them. For example, the principal cation inside the cell is potassium while the principal cation outside the cell is sodium. Where such inequality exists there must have been movement of ions from a lesser to a greater concentration, i.e., *against* the concentration gradient. Increasing the concentration of any given constituent of a solution requires work, just as work is necessary to compress a gas so that a greater number of molecules are contained within a given volume. This transfer against concentration and electrochemical activity gradients must be carried out by active transport, in which the energy for the performance of the work is furnished by the cell. Active transport results in maintaining the characteristically low concentration of sodium inside the cell by expelling or forcing out the Na^+ which has entered the cell by transversing the cell membrane. Further, it can concentrate K^+ inside the red blood cell, and possibly other types of cells, by active transport in the opposite direction. When not exchanged by active transport, the difference in K^+ concentration is probably determined by differences in electrochemical activity inside and outside the cell.

SUMMARY

The Cell Theory was postulated by Schleiden and Schwann in 1838. As a result of their studies they came to the conclusion that all living forms, both plants and animals, are made up of similar units, the cells. This theory explained why all living things have fundamentally the same activities.

The Protoplasm Doctrine affirms that the architectural units, the cells, arc masses of protoplasm and that this substance is the same in all living organisms.

Ninety-nine per cent of the body is composed of six common elements: oxygen, carbon, hydrogen, nitrogen, phosphorus, and calcium.

Protoplasm is made up of organic and inorganic compounds associated in cells as a colloidal dispersion in sol or gel states. Water forms 60 to 90 per cent of protoplasm, and inorganic salts less than 1 per cent. The organic substances—the proteins, carbohydrates and lipids—comprise approximately 10 to 30 per cent of protoplasm.

The main parts of the cell are the cytoplasm and nucleus. The outermost surface film of the cytoplasm is the cell membrane. The nucleus is chemically very active and influences the growth, repair, and division of the cell. The cytoplasm controls cellular absorption and excretion.

The characteristic activities of protoplasm are metabolism, respiration, digestion, assimilation, excretion, elimination, reproduction and growth. Principal properties of protoplasm are irritability, contractility, conductivity and viscosity.

Cell division provides for reproduction, growth and repair of the body. The two methods of division are amitosis and mitosis.

The outermost boundary of the cell acts as a membrane through which water and dissolved substances enter and leave the cell. The physical processes—filtration, diffusion and osmosis—are responsible for transfer of substances in the body.

Some of the factors influencing movement of substances across the cell membrane are size of the molecule, electrical charge and solubility.

QUESTIONS FOR DISCUSSION

1. Explain the effects the Cell Theory and Protoplasm Doctrine had on the biologic sciences.

2. How are the characteristic properties and activities of protoplasm manifested in the individual cell?

3. Explain how a qualitative and quantitative division of chromatin is achieved in mitosis. What is the significance of such division? What type of cell division is characteristic in man?

Chapter 3

Epithelial and Connective Tissues

EPITHELIAL and connective tissues form important building materials in all parts of the body. Muscular and nervous tissue and the blood and lymph will be considered later in connection with the systems of which they form the integral parts.

EPITHELIAL TISSUES

General Characteristics. The epithelial tissues are composed of cellular elements united into continuous membranes by a small amount of intercellular material. They have no blood vessels, but are richly supplied with nerves. Epithelial tissues cover the surface of the body, line cavities and passageways, and form secreting portions and excretory ducts of all glands, and important parts of sense organs. The most convenient classification of epithelial tissues is based on the shape and arrangement of the cells. They may be squamous, cuboidal or columnar in shape. They may be arranged in a single layer or sheet of cells called a simple epithelium, or in layers forming a stratified epithelium. A variety of combinations of these shapes and arrangements is encountered in the body.

Classification. SQUAMOUS EPITHELIUM. *Simple* squamous epithelium is composed of one layer of thin scalelike cells fitting together with regularly or irregularly outlined edges and forming smooth surfaces. This epithelium is found in the alveoli of the lungs. Endothelium and mesothelium describe simple squamous epithelium found in certain

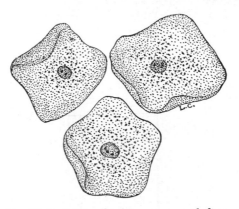

Fig. 12. Isolated cells of squamous epithelium.

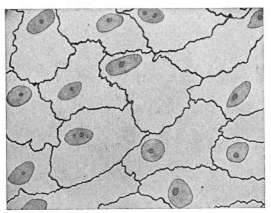

Fig. 13. Surface view of the simple squamous mesothelium of a frog's mesentery. (Maximow and Bloom.)

parts of the body. Endothelium lines the walls of the blood and lymph vessels, and the heart. Mesothelium lines the serous cavities of the body, pleural, pericardial and peritoneal (Fig. 4, p. 8). Squamous epithelial cells are shown in Figures 12 and 13.

Stratified squamous epithelium is composed of several layers, the surface cells of which are squamous in type. Beneath the surface there is a gradual transition to cells of the cuboidal or even elongated and columnar shape. The outer layers are subject to mechanical and other injuries, so that their cells degenerate continuously and are shed. Mitotic divisions in the basal layers provide for constant renewal. As the deeper layers approach the surface the cells become flattened. Stratified squamous epithelium forms the epidermis of the skin and is continued into the body as the surface portion of the lining in the oral cavity, pharynx and esophagus (Fig. 14), the epithelium of the conjunctiva, the vagina and the external auditory canal.

CUBOIDAL EPITHELIUM. Simple cuboidal epithelium differs from the simple squamous type only in that the cells are higher. They appear

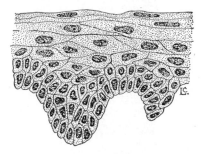

Fig. 14. Stratified squamous epithelium of the esophagus.

as short, many-sided prisms. Their outlines are as a rule regular, and in cross sections the ribbon-like sheet appears as a row of squares in which the centrally placed nuclei of the cells emphasize the precise form of the structure. Cuboid epithelium is found in the smaller and smallest bronchi of the lungs and in glands and their ducts.

COLUMNAR EPITHELIUM. *Simple* columnar epithelium is formed of a layer of cells which take the shape of tall columns or prisms. This type of epithelium lines the stomach and the small and large intestines (Fig. 15). In the uterus and uterine tubes and in the small bronchi the cells of the simple columnar epithelium have hairlike processes called cilia (Fig. 18) on their free surfaces.

Pseudostratified ciliated columnar epithelium is a highly specialized epithelium composed of a single layer of cells with cilia on the free surface. Although the cells appear to be arranged in several layers, all of them touch the underlying tissue. These cells are of an irregular, triangular or spindle shape. Some cells, while remaining in contact

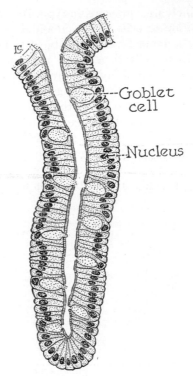

Fig. 15. Simple columnar epithelium of the intestine.

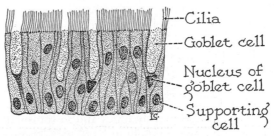

Fig. 16. Pseudostratified ciliated columnar epithelium of the trachea.

with the underlying tissue, lose their connection with the free surface. In vertical section the nuclei form several rows and give the impression of a stratified epithelium (Fig. 16). It is found in the nose, nasal pharynx, larynx, trachea and bronchi and is frequently referred to as "respiratory epithelium."

Many of the columnar cells of the intestinal canal and respiratory passages take on the function of secretion and become unicellular glands. The protoplasm elaborates mucous granules which distend the cell and are eventually extruded. These cells are called "goblet cells" because of their peculiar shape (Figs. 15, 16). After extrusion of the mucous secretion the cell collapses and may again start the formation of new granules.

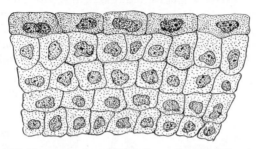

Fig. 17. Transitional epithelium from the urinary bladder.

TRANSITIONAL EPITHELIUM. This is a type which is thought to represent a transition between the stratified squamous and columnar epithelia. Transitional epithelium lines the urinary tract. When the ureters, urethra and bladder are relatively empty the epithelium appears to have many layers. Cells of deeper layers are of irregularly columnar, cuboidal or triangular shape; the surface layer is formed of large many-sided multinucleated cells with convex free surfaces (Fig. 17). Binucleated

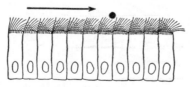

Fig. 18. Cilia moving a particle.

cells are common. However, when the urinary passages are distended the epithelium appears to consist of only two layers; the deep layer is made up of irregular cuboidal cells, while the superficial layer is composed of squamous cells.

Cilia. In describing simple and pseudostratified columnar epithelium, we spoke of the presence of cilia on the free surfaces of many of the columnar cells. These structures are fine, hairlike extensions of the cytoplasm which have the power of rapid contraction. Each cilium flips quickly in one direction and then slowly returns to its original position. The movement of the cilia is coordinated in such a way that the beat of one cilium begins slightly later than the beat of the one ahead of it in the direction of the movement (Fig. 18). This produces a wavelike appearance over the surface covered by the ciliated cells which has often been likened to the "waves" caused by wind over a wheat field. Fluids or particles coming in contact with the surface are moved along by the concerted action of the cilia. In the respiratory passages, sheets of mucus are moved toward the mouth and eliminated.

Glandular Epithelium. Glandular epithelium occurs in the unicellular glands of columnar epithelium in the gastrointestinal and respiratory tracts previously described and in multicellular glands such as the

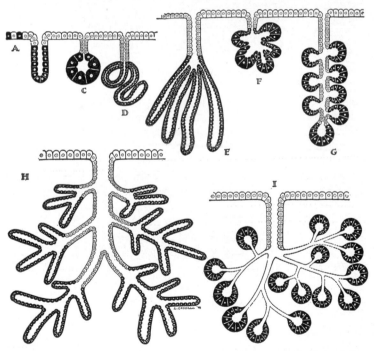

Fig. 19. Diagrams of various types of glands, shown as invaginations from the epithelial sheet. Shaded portions represent secreting cells. A, Surface cells differentiated as unicellular glands. B, Simple tubular gland. C, Simple acinus or alveolar gland, each formed from a group of glandular cells. D, Simple coiled tubular and E, Simple branched tubular glands. F and G, Simple branched alveolar glands. As complexity increases, each tubule or acinus has its own duct, and all ducts communicate with a common duct which leads to a single outlet. H, Compound tubular gland. I, Compound tubulo-alveolar gland.

salivary glands. Multicellular glands arise as invaginations of the epithelial sheet into the underlying connective tissue. The epithelium lining the sac thus formed takes on a secretory function. From this simple form all types of multicellular glands develop (Fig. 19). Subsequent invaginations arise as a result of new centers of growth in the wall of the glandular cavity which produce a complicated system of branching glandular spaces. The epithelial lining of the cavities is differentiated into secretory portions and excretory ducts. The cells of the secretory portions are usually in a single layer in the blind end of the glandular cavity, while the cells of the excretory ducts line the passages through which the secretion is eliminated. Secretory cells become highly differentiated, while the cells of the excretory ducts remain simple in structure. Usually we consider secretion as a polarized process in a cell, materials from blood and lymph being taken up at one end, and the secretion, whatever it may be, passed into cavities or ducts at the free end of the cell. From the standpoint of design glands may be classified as follows:

Tubular glands
  Simple tubular
    Straight, as intestinal glands in the small and large intestines
    Coiled, as in sweat glands
    Branched, as in the uterus
  Compound tubular in the kidneys
Alveolar or saccular glands
  Simple branched in sebaceous glands of skin
Compound tubulo-alveolar or acinus in mammary glands and the pancreas

Functions of Epithelial Tissue. In summary, epithelial tissue gives protection to the body by covering the surface; it forms smooth linings for blood vessels and heart; it provides the body cavities with smooth secreting surfaces, minimizing friction; it forms parts of sense organs, and in glands it plays an important part in the metabolism of the body through its specialized secretory activities. The adaptation of structure to function has been noted in the resistant and regenerative qualities of the stratified squamous epithelium of the skin, the secreting functions of columnar epithelium with goblet cells in the respiratory and gastrointestinal tracts, the sweeping action of the cilia of the respiratory tract, and the thinness of the simple squamous epithelium which in the alveoli of the lungs facilitates diffusion of gases, and in the capillary walls aids in diffusion and filtration of substances in solution.

CONNECTIVE TISSUES

General Characteristics. In connective tissues the quantity of intercellular material is far greater than the amount of cellular material; the cells are usually small, few in number and, on the whole, inconspicuous. The tissues are with few exceptions highly vascular. They perform many functions in the body: they constitute the supporting structures, serve to bind parts together and hold them in place, aid in the distribution of nutrient materials and provide an important defense mechanism of the body.

Origin. All connective tissues differentiate from the mesenchyme, an embryonic tissue developed from the middle germ layer, the mesoderm. The mesenchyme is composed of a spongy network of branching cells whose processes appear to be connected. Between the cells there are open spaces filled with a liquid. The mesenchyme undergoes many changes as it differentiates to form the various connective tissues.

Classification. The type of intercellular material which determines the physical characteristics of the tissue serves as the basis of classification of the connective tissues. Four main types are recognized:

1. Blood and lymph, in which the intercellular material is liquid;
2. Connective tissue proper, of which there are many types and in which the intercellular substance varies from a soft gelatinous material to a tough fibrous mass;
3. Cartilage, in which the intercellular substance has a rubbery consistency;
4. Bone, a hard, unyielding tissue, in which the intercellular material is impregnated with calcium salts.

Structural Features. Fibers and cells constitute characteristic elements of connective tissue proper.

Fibers. Collagenous or white fibers are found in connective tissue proper, cartilage and bone. As the mesenchyme differentiates, fine fibrils appear in the gelatinous ground substance. The fibrils aggregate into bundles and are held together by a cementing substance. The fibrils in the bundle or fiber are parallel, although the fibers are often wavy. Fibers may branch, but fibrils are unbranched. The fibers contain a protein substance, collagen, which on boiling yields gelatin. The origin of the fibers has been interpreted variously. Some investigators hold that the fibrils develop within the cytoplasm of the cells, but observation on living connective tissues indicates that they develop in an intercellular ground substance secreted by the cells. Most observers accept this latter view.

The elastic fibers develop later than the collagenous variety. They are homogeneous, highly refractive, yellow threads which branch and anastomose freely. Unlike the white fibers, they are not composed of smaller elements or fibrils. They are very elastic; when extended, they appear straight; when relaxed, they form bold, broad curves or spirals.

Cells. There are many types of cells in the connective tissue, all of which arise from the mesenchymal cells. Fibroblasts and histiocytes will be described at this time.

The _fibroblasts_ are the common connective tissue cells, so called because of their alleged role in the formation of the intercellular fibers. Fibroblasts are flattened cells with large oval nuclei and a large amount of cytoplasm which sends out a number of long, tapering processes.

The _histiocytes,_ known also as fixed macrophages, are almost as numerous as the fibroblasts and are similar in structure. They vary in shape from squamous or oval forms to long, spindle-shaped cells with branching processes. They are phagocytic; that is, they are able to ingest many types of particles: cell fragments, debris, bacteria and dye granules.

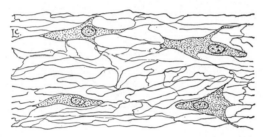

Fig. 20. Embryonic connective tissue, showing syncytial structure.

Connective Tissue Proper. The recognized varieties of connective tissue proper are:

1. Mucous	4. Elastic
2. Areolar	5. Adipose
3. White fibrous	6. Reticular

Mucous tissue is a form of loose connective tissue similar to mesenchyme. It occurs in the embryo just beneath the skin and in the jelly-like tissue of the umbilical cord. It consists of large, star-shaped fibroblasts whose processes touch to form an interlacing meshwork or syncytium (Fig. 20). The spaces between the cells are filled with a soft, gelatinous groundwork or matrix in which fine collagenous fibers can be distinguished.

Areolar tissue consists of a semifluid ground substance or matrix in which cells and a loose network of white and elastic fibers are embedded (Fig. 21). The chief cells of areolar tissue are fibroblasts and histiocytes, although all cellular elements common to connective tissue are also present. Areolar tissue is widely distributed: it forms the layer of tissue under the skin, where it is called superficial fascia; it is found under the epithelial layers of mucous and serous membranes; it fills out the spaces between organs, and penetrates with blood vessels and nerves into the interior of organs. The functions of areolar tissue are threefold: mechanical, serving as a supporting and connecting medium; nutritional, aiding in diffusion of food elements to other tissues embedded in it; and protective, forming part of the defense mechanism of the body.

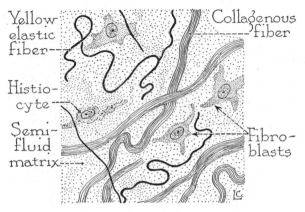

Fig. 21. Areolar tissue of the superficial fascia.

White fibrous tissue is composed of closely packed collagenous fibers accompanied by fine elastic networks and cells. The connective tissue layer of the skin, the derma, some fibrous membranes, tendons, ligaments and aponeuroses are all composed of this tissue. In the derma of the skin the collagenous bundles are irregularly arranged; white fibers run in all directions to form a dense feltwork. All types of cells found in areolar tissue are present. In tendons the arrangement of fibers is regular and precise. The collagenous fibers run parallel with rows of flattened fibroblasts between them (Fig. 22). In ligaments

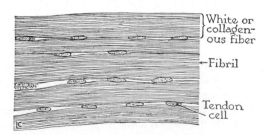

Fig. 22. White fibrous tissue from a tendon.

and aponeuroses the pattern is similar, but the arrangement of the collagenous bundles is less regular. Tendons, ligaments and aponeuroses have a white, glistening appearance. These structures are inelastic and very strong.

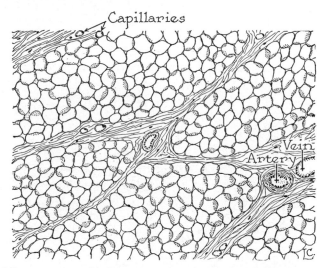

Fig. 23. Adipose tissue under low magnification. Lobules of fat cells are separated from one another by partitions of fibrous connective tissue.

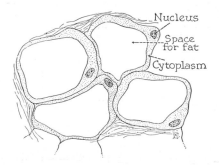

Fig. 24. Adipose tissue under high magnification; a few fat cells.

Elastic tissue is composed of yellow elastic fibers interspersed occasionally with a few white fibers. Fibroblasts are present, but are not numerous. Elastic tissue is found in the walls of the blood vessels, in the lungs and bronchi, where its elastic qualities are of special value. Elastic tissue predominates in certain ligaments of the vertebrae.

Adipose Tissue. Adipose tissue may be thought of as areolar tissue in which fat cells have displaced most of the other elements (Figs. 23, 24).

Some of the mesenchymal cells give rise to lipoblasts, which are the forerunners of the fat cells. A lipoblast deposits within its cytoplasm droplets of fat which increase in number and coalesce to form a globule. As the fat globule enlarges, it distends the cell and pushes the nucleus to a peripheral position. In this way adipose tissue stores neutral fat, which serves as a nutritional reserve. The fat deposit in the subcutaneous tissue cushions and protects parts exposed to pressure; and, as it is a poor conductor of heat, it minimizes heat loss through the

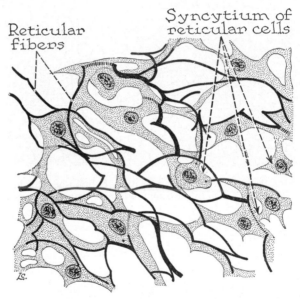

Fig. 25. Reticular tissue of a lymph gland.

skin. Organs such as the eyes and kidneys receive support and protection from the adipose tissue accumulated in relation to them.

Reticular Tissue. Similar to areolar tissue, but much more delicate, reticular tissue is thought to be more primitive in form, since it exhibits less differentiation from embryonic connective tissue. It consists of primitive reticular cells with a network of fine, nonelastic fibers. The cells are stellate or spindle-shaped and adhere closely to the fibers of the reticulum. As in the mesenchyme, the cell processes are in contact and appear to form a syncytium; that is, cell membranes delimiting one cell from another are not easily distinguished, and the cytoplasm is shared in common with the nuclei (Fig. 25). It forms the supporting framework of lymph glands, liver, spleen, bone marrow, lungs and kidneys.

Reticulo-endothelium. The term "reticulo-endothelium" is used to designate groups of cells scattered throughout the tissues of the body which have the ability to engulf and store or destroy foreign particles. These cells differ in shape and appearance, and they have accordingly been given different names in the various organs and tissues in which they are found. They include the fixed macrophages or histiocytes of the loose connective tissues, the reticular cells of the spleen, lymph glands and bone marrow, Kupffer's cells of the liver sinusoids, the lining cells of sinuses of the adrenal glands and the hypophysis. Antibody chemicals are thought to be produced in the metabolism of lymphocyte and plasma cells elaborated by reticulo-endothelial tissues.

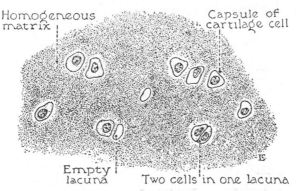

Fig. 26. Hyaline cartilage.

These antibodies aid in the neutralization and destruction of foreign protein, particularly those of bacterial origin. As a result of some stimulus, particularly an inflammatory one, histiocytes, reticular cells or any of the stationary cells may become detached and actively motile.

Cartilage. Cartilage, commonly known as "gristle," has a firm tough, resilient texture. It is composed of cells and the intercellular substance or matrix. The space in the matrix occupied by a cartilage cell is called a lacuna. The cells may be irregular in shape, but usually appear round or oval and tend to be arranged in groups of two, three, four and sometimes more cells (Fig. 26). Except on bare surfaces in joint cavities, cartilage is always covered by a sheath of dense connective tissue, the perichondrium. The fibroblasts of the perichondrium transform into young cartilage cells, deposit matrix and become mature cartilage cells.

In the parts of the embryo where cartilage will develop, the mesenchymal cells accumulate in dense masses. Closely crowded together, they soon lose their processes and become rounded; the spaces between them decrease, and compact cellular precartilage is formed. As development proceeds, matrix forms in abundance between the cells, and they become widely separated. Cartilage grows externally through the activity of the perichondrium and internally by mitotic division of cartilage cells and increase in the matrix. Cartilage contains no blood vessels, and, since the cells lie in isolated lacunae, the lymph from the blood vessels of the perichondrium must pass through the matrix to reach the cells. According to the texture of the intercellular substance, three types of cartilage are distinguished: hyaline or glassy cartilage, fibrous cartilage, and elastic cartilage.

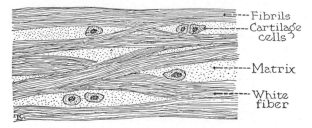

Fig. 27. White fibrous cartilage.

Hyaline cartilage (Fig. 26) is the simplest and most widespread. It has the blue-white color of skimmed milk. The matrix is homogeneous, but, when stained, the portion surrounding the cartilage cell is often more deeply stained than elsewhere and is for this reason referred to as the capsule of the cell. Hyaline cartilage covers the surfaces of bones within joints, forms the rib cartilages, the cartilage of the nose, and ring cartilages of the trachea and bronchi; in the embryo it constitutes most of the temporary skeleton.

Fibrous cartilage contains large numbers of collagenous fibers arranged in parallel rows in the matrix (Fig. 27). This type is found in the discs between the bodies of the vertebrae, between the two pubic bones in the pelvis and in the articular discs in many joints.

Yellow elastic cartilage has a network of yellow fibers through the matrix (Fig. 28). It forms the cartilages of the external ear, auditory tube, epiglottis, and some small cartilages of the larynx.

Bone. Osseous tissue, like cartilage, is a dense form of connective tissue consisting of cells distributed through the intercellular material (Fig. 29). The matrix is rendered hard by the deposition of lime salts, mainly calcium phosphate and calcium carbonate. The bone cells lie in spaces in the matrix called lacunae, as in cartilage. Fine projections of the cell body grow out into channels in the matrix. These canals are called *canaliculi*. They radiate from the lacunae and penetrate the hard matrix in all directions, connecting with canaliculi of other lacunae, thus forming a continuous system of communicating cavities.

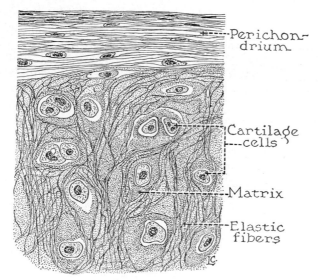

Fig. 28. Yellow elastic cartilage.

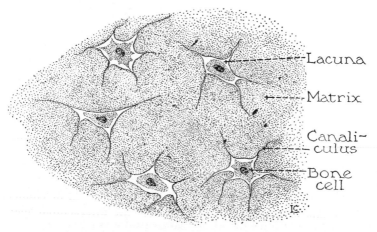

Fig. 29. Decalcified bone; connections of canaliculi are not evident.

Bone tissue is formed in layers or lamellae. A *lamella* is composed of bone cells and the matrix which these cells have deposited. Bone may be divided into two types, depending on the arrangement of the lamellae: porous or spongy, and hard or compact. In spongy or cancellated bone the lamellae are arranged to form an interlacing lattice-work with large spaces. In compact bone the lamellae are arranged in layers to form solid masses. The organization consists of a large number of Haversian systems (Fig. 30). A *Haversian system* consists of a central canal around which concentric lamellae of bone have been deposited. The canal of the Haversian systems contains blood and lymph vessels. The Haversian systems are held together by the ground or interstitial lamellae.

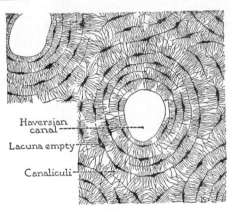

Haversian
canal
Lacuna empty
Canaliculi

Fig. 30. Compact bone as seen in thinly ground cross section.

MEMBRANES

The word "membrane" conveys the idea of a thin expanse of tissues. Membranes are composed mainly of epithelial and connective tissues.

An epithelial membrane is composed of epithelium with connective tissue beneath it. Two important types are serous and mucous membranes. A *serous membrane* is composed of a layer of squamous epithelial cells, mesothelium, beneath which is a thin layer of areolar tissue. The surface is moistened by a small amount of serous fluid. Serous membranes line the cavities of the body and cover the organs which lie in them. Pericardium, pleura and peritoneum are examples of serous membranes. A *mucous membrane* has a superficial epithelial layer and a layer of areolar connective tissue called the lamina propria. This type of membrane lines the alimentary, respiratory and genito-urinary tracts. In general, the distinction can be made that mucous membranes line parts or passageways which communicate with the exterior, while serous membranes line closed cavities.*

Fibrous membranes are composed entirely of connective tissues. They consist of bundles of collagenous fibers among which are fibroblasts and a fine network of elastic fibers. Examples of fibrous membranes are perichondrium, periosteum, synovial membranes and membranes encapsulating organs.

INTEGUMENT

The skin or integument is composed principally of epithelial and

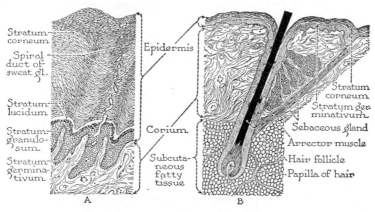

Fig. 31. *A*, Section of skin from sole of foot. *B*, Section of scalp, showing hair follicle with sebaceous gland. Semidiagrammatic.

connective tissues. It consists of two layers, an outer, the epidermis, and an inner, the derma or corium (Fig. 31).

The *epidermis* is composed of stratified squamous epithelium. The superficial portion forms the stratum corneum. Here the cells are horny in nature and devoid of nuclei, and the outermost layers are being shed constantly. The deep portion is the stratum germinativum, or germinating layer, in which mitosis of cells replaces those shed from the surface. The *corium* is composed of connective tissue and contains many blood vessels and nerve endings. In most of the skin of the body the upper surface of the corium is thrown into conelike elevations called papillae which appear as ridges on the surface of the skin, especially on the palms and the soles. The papillae contain capillary loops and, in many cases, special nerve endings for the sense

* An exception is the peritoneal cavity of the female, which connects with the exterior through the reproductive tract.

of touch. The deep surface of the corium fuses with the subcutaneous tissue so that there is no sharp boundary between them, and the fibers of one layer extend over into the other layer.

The accessory organs of the skin are the nails, hair, sebaceous glands and sweat glands.

The *nails* are modifications of the epidermis.

Hair is distributed over almost the entire body. The parts of the hair are the root, or portion below the surface, and the shaft, or portion extending above the surface. The root is embedded in a pitlike depression called the hair follicle which widens out at its lower end to enclose a small vascular papilla. This papilla is homologous with the other dermal papillae and projects upward into the roof, providing nutrition for the growth of the hair. Hair grows as a result of division of the cells of the root. The hair follicle is placed obliquely in the skin, and a small muscle, called the *arrector muscle,* fastened to the side causes it to stand up in cold or fright and gives the appearance of gooseflesh to the skin.

The *sebaceous glands* secrete sebum or oil. They are of the simple, branched alveolar type, and their ducts usually empty into hair follicles, although some open directly on the surface of the skin. The alveoli of the gland are filled with cells. The cells in the center become infiltrated with fat droplets and then degenerate to yield the oily secretion as a result of their own destruction. Sebum anoints the hair and keeps it from drying and becoming brittle. On the surface of the skin it forms a protective film which limits the absorption and evaporation of water from the surface.

The *sweat glands* are simple, coiled tubular glands. The secreting portion of the gland is coiled into a ball and lies in the deep part of the corium. A network of capillaries surrounds the coil. The cells are supplied with nerve fibers from the thoracolumbar division of the autonomic nervous system. The sweat, the product of these cells, passes upward through the duct which opens on the surface of the skin. The amount of sweat secreted varies greatly with changes in environmental temperature, exercise, emotional stress and other factors. Sweat is a weak solution of sodium chloride in water with traces of other salts and urea.

The various *functions* of the skin are described in different sections of this book. They are discussed briefly here.

1. Protection: The skin covers the body and protects the deeper tissues from injury and drying. Ordinarily, bacteria cannot penetrate the epidermis.
2. Regulation of body temperature: The skin serves a major role in maintaining a constant body temperature in warm-blooded ani-

mals. It forms a large radiating surface for heat exchange. The rate of heat exchange between the body and the environment will be influenced by the difference in their temperatures, the circulation of blood through the superficial vessels, evaporation of sweat from the body's surface, and movement of the layer of air which makes up "a private environment" immediately surrounding the skin. A more extensive discussion of this function is given in Chapter 27.

3. Excretion: The excretory function of the skin (sweat glands) is slight and is confined mainly to the elimination of water, together with some salts and small quantities of urea.

4. Absorption: The absorbing power of the skin is extremely limited; only a few substances can pass this barrier. Examples of such substances are ointments and lotions containing methyl salicylate or compounds of mercury.

5. A sense organ: The skin is an important organ of sensation because it contains the receptors for touch, pain, heat and cold. Through these receptors placed in the outermost layer of the body we receive information of changes in the immediate environment. Not only do we become aware of external conditions, but stimulation of these receptors initiates reflexes which are important in adaptation to the environment. These sensory organs in the skin and their mechanisms are discussed more fully in Chapters 4 and 6.

SUMMARY

Epithelial tissues are distinguished by their cellular elements, which are united into continuous membranes by a small amount of intercellular material. They have no blood vessels, but are richly supplied with nerves.

Epithelial tissues are classified according to the shape and arrangement of the cells. They may be squamous, cuboidal or columnar in shape. An epithelium composed of a single layer of cells is called a simple epithelium; one formed of several layers is called stratified epithelium.

The types found in the body are: simple squamous epithelium, stratified squamous epithelium, simple cuboidal epithelium, simple and pseudostratified columnar epithelium and transitional epithelium. Columnar epithelium is ciliated in some regions.

The glands of the body are formed of epithelial tissue.

The connective tissues are distinguished by a large amount of intercellular material; the cells are small and inconspicuous. Connective tissue is classified on the basis of the character of the intercellular substance. The recognized types are: the blood and lymph, connective tissue proper, cartilage, and bone.

The skin and the membranes are composed mainly of epithelial and connective tissues.

QUESTIONS FOR DISCUSSION

1. List types of epithelium found in the respiratory tract; in the digestive tract. Discuss the relationship between the types of epithelium and the function of the part.

2. Discuss how the types of connective tissues are related to the function of the part of the body to which they belong.

3. Discuss the influence of at least two of the functions of the skin on organs or systems of the body.

Unit
2

INTEGRATION AND CONTROL OF THE BODY BY THE NERVOUS SYSTEM

IT IS MAINLY through the agency of the nervous system that tissues, organs and systems of the body function as a smoothly running unit. The nervous system acts as an integrating mechanism by which activities of the body are adjusted rapidly in response to stimuli received from the internal and external environment. The high degree of specialization in the properties of irritability and conductivity make nerve tissue admirably suited for the performance of this function.

Chapter 4

Nervous Tissue

The Nervous System as a Coordinating Mechanism. The nervous system constitutes the link between the external environment and the many physiologic and psychologic mechanisms which bring about man's continuous adjustment to the outside world. Sudden environmental changes stimulate advantageously located sensory receptors of the nervous system. The impulses which result travel centrally over sensory nerves, through various connections and finally to effector organs which bring about a response. Besides providing for receiving information and for acting upon it in a coordinated manner, the central nervous system "records" and "relates" both stimulus and response, so that man builds up a background of experience which may be used in determining his future reactions. The nervous system also plays a leading role in integrating adjustments to changes in the internal environment with the result that the total response, made up of many separate responses, is coordinated rather than chaotic.

Components of the Nervous System. The nervous system consists of a *central* portion, composed of the brain and spinal cord, and a *peripheral* portion, composed of cerebrospinal nerves and the peripheral parts of the autonomic nervous system. The brain lies within the cranial cavity and is continuous through the foramen magnum with the spinal cord, which lies within the vertebral canal. The peripheral nerves of the brain are called cranial nerves; they may be either purely sensory or motor and sensory. The nerves of the cord are called spinal nerves; they contain both sensory and motor fibers. After emerging from the vertebral foramen, the spinal nerves divide into anterior and posterior branches. The sensory and motor fibers from one or more spinal nerves, together with autonomic fibers, form the mixed peripheral nerves; these are called "mixed" because of their motor and sensory components. The autonomic fibers may travel either with the spinal nerve fibers to the blood vessels, sweat glands and erector muscles of the hairs, or separately to the viscera.

Nervous Tissue. Nervous tissue consists essentially of *neurons,* or nerve cells, which are the active irritable and conducting units, and the *neuroglia cells,* which play the passive role of making up the supporting framework. The neuron is composed of a cell body and one or more processes.

THE CELL BODY OF THE NEURON. The cell body has a spherical nucleus in which there is a conspicuous nucleolus, but very little

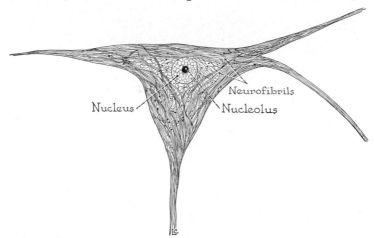

Fig. 32. Neurofibrils in a cell from the anterior gray column of the human spinal cord.

chromatin. The cytoplasm consists of a homogeneous ground substance in which fine neurofibrils and Nissl bodies are embedded. The delicate neurofibrils traverse the cytoplasm and extend into all the processes. They play some part in nerve conduction. The Nissl bodies are granular masses of ribonucleic acid (RNA) which stain brightly with basic aniline dyes (Fig. 34). They are related to the metabolism of nerve cells; these granules disintegrate upon injury to the cell body or its processes.

THE PROCESSES OF THE NEURON. Nerve cells may be classified according to the number of cytoplasmic processes which extend from the cell body as *unipolar, bipolar* and *multipolar.* Typical unipolar neurons are not found in man. The cells of the spinal ganglia, i.e., those making up the sensory or afferent components of the spinal nerve, and the ganglia cells of the cranial nerves have the appearance of unipolar cells, since they have what looks like a single process. These cells, however, are primitive bipolar cells in which eccentric growth has

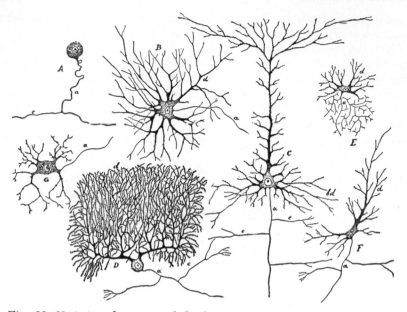

Fig. 33. Varieties of neurons of the human nervous system. A, From spinal ganglion. B, From anterior horn of spinal cord. C, Pyramidal cell from cerebral cortex. D, Purkinje cell from cerebellar cortex. E, Golgi cell, type II, from spinal cord. F, Fusiform cell from cerebral cortex. G, Autonomic ganglion cell. a, Axon; d, dendrite; c, collateral branches; bd, basal dendrites. (Morris, Human Anatomy, The Blakiston Co.)

occurred, so that what were originally two processes fuse as they emerge from the cell body. It will become apparent in the subsequent discussion that the cells of the spinal ganglia do not follow the more general architectural pattern exhibited by most other neurons in the nervous system, so that they will require special comment. Bipolar cells, in which the two processes may be seen to leave the cell separately, are found only in the ganglia of the two branches of the eighth or auditory nerve, in one layer of the retina of the eye, and in the olfactory receptors. The unipolar and bipolar cells are sensory nerve cells. The multipolar neurons, i.e., those with more than two processes, although showing considerable variation in detailed structure, furnish the general pattern for the majority of the neurons. Multipolar cells are distributed widely throughout the central nervous system and the autonomic ganglia. The motor nerve cells and the correlating or connector cells are multipolar. The connector cells, which are the *internuncial* or *associational neurons,* are located in the central nervous

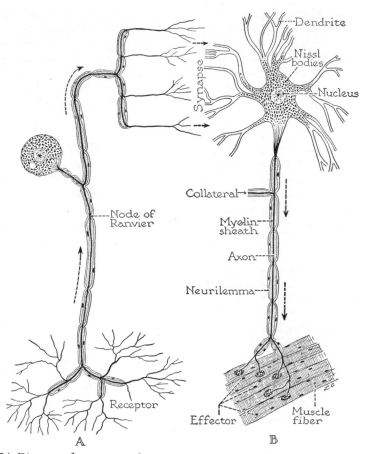

Fig. 34. Diagram of two types of neurons. *A*, Sensory or afferent neuron. *B*, Motor or efferent neuron.

system and transmit impulses from one neuron to another within the spinal cord or the brain.

All but one of the cell processes of the neuron are *dendrites*. These conduct impulses *toward the cell body*, serving in the same relation to the cell that the afferent nerve trunks serve in relation to the central part of the nervous system. Dendrites, a word derived from the Greek meaning "tree," show characteristic branches which spread out like those of a tree. Another histologic characteristic of dendrites is the presence of Nissl substance.

Both bipolar and multipolar neurons have but a single axon. The axon conducts impulses *away from the cell body.* These efferent processes have relatively few branches or collaterals. Histologically, they lack Nissl substance and usually arise from a part of the cell body, known as the *axon hillock,* which is relatively free of Nissl granules. The cytoplasm within the axon is known as *axoplasm.*

In the ganglia cells of the spinal and cranial nerves, there is no histologic difference between the peripheral process, which conducts impulses toward the cell, and the central process, which, like an axon, conducts impulses away from the cell body.

COVERING OF NERVE FIBERS. Nerve fibers are the processes of the nerve cell. Many of the processes are invested with a layer of lipid material called myelin. Such processes are called myelinated or medullated fibers, while those without the sheath are called unmyelinated or unmedullated fibers. The myelin sheath is broken at intervals into a number of separate segments. The places between the segments are called the *nodes of Ranvier.* Medullated fibers are found in great numbers in the cerebrospinal nerves and in the white matter of the brain and spinal cord. Unmedullated fibers are abundant in the autonomic nerves, and many fine afferent fibers of cerebrospinal nerves are also without the myelin sheath.

Peripheral nerve fibers have an outer covering composed of a thin nucleated membrane called the *neurilemma.* The neurilemma closely invests the myelin sheath and is continuous across the nodes of Ranvier. There is usually one nucleus for each internodal span. Unmyelinated fibers of peripheral nerves have a covering of neurilemma. The neurilemma may aid in regeneration of the nerve in case of injury. Fibers within the brain and spinal cord which have no neurilemma do not regenerate if injured. The myelin sheath appears to be concerned with conduction of the nervous impulse. Transmission is always more rapid in myelinated than in unmyelinated fibers.

THE NEURON AS A UNIT OF THE NERVOUS SYSTEM. The neuron, as a structural unit, is associated with a sensory receptor, with other neurons to provide a pathway for integration in perception and in action, or with an effector. The receptor structures associated with peripheral (dendritic) branches of the cranial or spinal ganglion cells are the end organs for touch, pressure, heat, cold and pain, and the proprioceptor nerve endings of the muscles and joints.* The connections between axons and dendrites in a chain of neurons are called *synapses.* The junction of motor nerve fibers with effector organs may be with nerve endings on muscle, connective tissue or epithelium.

---

* Each of the receptors associated with the cranial nerves will be taken up separately in a subsequent chapter because of their elaborate architectural structure and complex mechanisms.

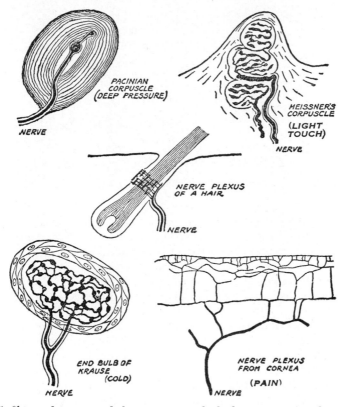

PACINIAN
CORPUSCLE
(DEEP PRESSURE)

NERVE

MEISSNER'S
CORPUSCLE
(LIGHT
TOUCH)

NERVE

NERVE PLEXUS
OF A HAIR

NERVE

END BULB OF
KRAUSE
(COLD)

NERVE

NERVE PLEXUS
FROM CORNEA
(PAIN)

NERVE

Fig. 35. Skin and organs and the sensations which they arouse. (Starling, Human
Physiology, J. & A. Churchill, Ltd.)

END ORGANS FOR TOUCH, PRESSURE, COLD, HEAT, PAIN AND MUSCLE
SENSE. Endings for touch, pressure, heat, cold and pain are widely
distributed in the skin; those for pain and pressure are located also in
other parts of the body. The architecture of the end organs shows great
variations; they may be simple or quite elaborate in design (Fig. 35).
The simplest type of receptor is called the free sensory nerve ending.
It consists of a dendritic process ending which has lost the myelin
sheath. All pain receptors and some of the receptors for touch, cold,
heat and muscle sense are of this type. Specialized organs for temperature are the *end bulbs of Krause* for cold and the *brushes of Ruffini*
for heat. For light touch and pressure, structures called corpuscles
serve as receptors. *Meissner's corpuscles* in the papillae of the corium
just beneath the epidermis are the organs for light touch. *Pacinian*

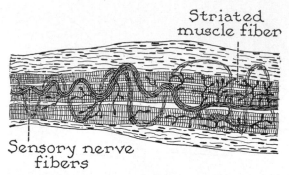

Fig. 36. Neuromuscular spindle of a human fetus. (Redrawn from Ramon-Cajal.)

corpuscles in the deep parts of the corium and in the loose connective tissue about joints receive stimuli resulting from deep pressure. Muscle sense, also called proprioceptive or kinesthetic sense, is the sense of position and movement. It is mediated by (1) specialized structures called *neuromuscular* or *neurotendinous* spindles (Fig. 36), depending upon whether they are found in muscle or in tendons, (2) the Pacinian corpuscles and (3) free nerve networks.

The receptors for changes in the internal environment are called visceral afferent receptors or *interoceptors;* in general, they show a less complex architecture than receptors acted upon by the external environment. The visceral afferent impulses do not normally reach the level of consciousness, but signal mechanical stimuli, including pressure and tension, and chemical changes occurring in the viscera.

JUNCTIONS BETWEEN NEURONS: SYNAPSES. The synapse, or junction between two neurons, is the point of functional contact between the axon of one neuron and the dendrite of another. There are a number of architectural patterns displayed by the synapses. A common arrangement is such that the *boutons terminaux,* or club-shaped swellings at the ends of the fine terminal branches of an axon, which are called *telodendria,* make contact either with the surface of the dendrite or the body of the next cell in the chain. There are many separate junctions or contacts between one axon and the succeeding cell. Furthermore, one neuron may make connections with many other neurons, so that excitation of one cell may be propagated to a number of neurons simultaneously.

JUNCTIONS BETWEEN NEURONS AND EFFECTORS. The neuro-effector junctions of the central nervous system, i.e., the somatic efferent junctions, form functional connections with the skeletal muscle fibers. They are called *motor end plates* or myoneural junctions. As the axon of the motor nerve cell reaches the muscle, it divides into numerous branches which enter the muscle and end near muscle fiber nuclei. A single motor nerve cell axon, together with the muscle fibers it innervates, is known as a motor unit. A single axon may supply a hundred or more fibers of the postural or supporting muscles, while axons which supply muscles adapted for skilled tasks, such as those in the fingers, may form connections with only a relatively few of the muscle fibers. Small motor nerves supply the muscle fibers which are in the neuromuscular spindle. Relatively little is known of the motor endings in the smooth and cardiac muscle; autonomic fibers supplying glandular tissue appear to be free, i.e., undifferentiated, naked nerve fiber endings. These are termed visceral efferent junctions.

NEUROGLIAL CELLS. These are the non-nervous interstitial cells of the nervous system. They correspond to the connective tissue in other parts of the body. The neuroglial cells have numerous processes which interlace to form a dense network between the neurons. They give mechanical support and in some instances seem to carry out nutritive functions.

SUMMARY

The nervous system functions as a coordinating mechanism.

The nervous system consists of a central portion composed of brain and spinal cord and a peripheral portion composed of cerebrospinal nerves and the autonomic nervous system.

Nervous tissue consists of conducting units called neurons or nerve cells and a supporting framework of neuroglial cells.

A neuron is composed of a cell body and its processes.

Structural features in the cytoplasm of the cell body are neurofibrils and Nissl bodies. Neurofibrils play some part in conduction, and Nissl bodies are related to the metabolism of the nerve cell.

The processes of a neuron are of two types, an axon and a number of dendrites. Dendrites carry impulses toward the cell body; the axon carries impulses away from the cell body.

Depending upon the number of processes, nerve cells may be described as unipolar, bipolar and multipolar.

Neurons are designated as afferent, efferent and internuncial, according to their function.

Nerve fibers are the processes of the nerve cell. Many fibers are invested with a layer of lipid material called myelin. Such fibers are said to be myelinated.

Peripheral nerve fibers are covered with a thin membrane, the neurilemma.

The neurilemma may aid in regeneration of the nerve in case of injury.

The myelin sheath appears to be related to the conduction of the nervous impulse.

The neuron, as a structural unit, is associated (1) with a sensory receptor, (2) with other neurons to provide a pathway, or (3) with an effector.

The various types of receptors include free sensory endings, end bulbs of Krause (for cold), the brushes of Ruffini (for heat), Meissner's corpuscles (for light touch), Pacinian corpuscles (for deep pressure), and neuromuscular and neurotendinous spindles (for muscle sense).

The junction between two neurons is the synapse. It is the point of functional contact between the axon of one neuron and the dendrites or the cell body of another.

The somatic efferent neurons are connected with skeletal muscle cells by neuro-effector junctions called motor end plates. Visceral efferent neurons form the connections with smooth muscle, cardiac muscle and glands.

The neuroglial cells are the non-nervous interstitial cells of the nervous system which correspond to the connective tissue in other parts of the body.

QUESTION FOR DISCUSSION

1. The study of nervous tissue introduces many new structural features. Make a complete, concise statement about each one of the following: neuron, axon, dendrite, Nissl bodies, neurofibrils, myelin sheath, nodes of Ranvier, neurilemma, receptor, effector, afferent neuron, efferent neuron, internuncial neuron, synapse, ganglion, motor end plates, and neuroglia.

Chapter
5

Initiation and
Propagation of the
Nerve Impulse

Artificial and Physiologic Stimulation of Nerve and Muscle. In normal man, nerve impulses are initiated by the receptors in response to changes in the internal and external environment. These changes or *stimuli* are natural, but they may be simulated by artificial means so that their characteristics can be predetermined and controlled. Artificial stimuli are employed in many kinds of physiologic experiments on nerve and muscle. Electrical stimulation is frequently used because it can be readily measured and controlled. The four other types of environmental changes which are most frequently imposed experimentally are: mechanical, resulting from stretching, pinching or a sharp blow; thermal, from sudden changes in temperature; chemical, from changes in the chemical environment of the cell; and radiant, such as changes in an artificial light or infra-red lamp.

A stimulus, to be effective in bringing about a response in excitable tissue, must have certain characteristics: (1) it must be of sufficient strength, (2) the rate of change of environmental conditions of the cell imposed by the stimulus must be sufficiently rapid, and (3) the stimulus must be applied for a certain minimum duration. For example, if you were to touch an electric wire and receive a shock of from 4 to 5 milliamperes (ma.) of either direct or alternating current you would not only feel it, but the muscles of your hand and arm would contract violently. If the intensity were reduced to below 1 ma. you would not feel it, nor would your muscles contract. Now suppose you were to start with a very low direct current and increase it very gradually. You could tolerate a much higher current, say 5 to 10 ma., without muscle contraction or sensation, provided electrical contact were good enough to avoid changes in current. You would not respond because the rate of change of electrical potential was insufficient. If, again, you were treated for a muscular pain by high frequency diathermy current, there would be no muscle response because the electrical fluctuations were so rapid that exposure to each pulse of current was less than the minimum duration required for stimulation.

When the energy of an applied stimulus is too low to bring about a reaction, such as a muscle contraction or excitation of a nerve impulse, the stimulus is said to be *subthreshold* or *subliminal;* if the energy is just sufficient to excite the tissue, the stimulus is said to be *threshold* or *liminal.* Stimuli above threshold level of such intensity as to bring about full response of groups of fibers may be referred to as *maximal* or *supramaximal.*

The imposed changes or stimuli may occur once or may be applied in rapid succession. Under certain conditions, where the intervals between stimuli are sufficiently brief, the energies of sublimal stimuli may be additive, and may bring about a response.

When we use the term "threshold" stimuli, we are referring to the energy which is just sufficient to elicit a response *when the tissue is normally excitable.* Just after a tissue responds, it loses its excitability to such a degree that no stimulus, regardless of intensity, can excite it. The tissue is then said to be in a refractory state, and the duration of this interval is called the *refractory period.* For a short time after this, when the tissue has partially recovered its excitability, it is said to be in the *relative refractory period.* At this time, stimuli of an intensity greater than that at normal threshold level are required to bring about a response.

It should be borne in mind that, in most instances, the value of an artificial stimulus lies in the fact that it mimics natural changes which take place in intensity, duration and rate of change.

In our present social environment, even electrical potential differences in domestic and industrial installations, and chemical substances —not encountered in a more primitive society—form part of our environment and may act as harmful stimuli when accidental contact is made with them directly. Nervous activity may also be initiated in the higher centers of the central nervous system and result in responses which appear to be quite unrelated to changes occurring in the environment at the time.

We will first concern ourselves primarily with the physiologic mechanisms of the responses of the receptor and of the nerve impulses which result. Discussion of the consequences of the stimulation, i.e., motor response, inhibition and sensation, will be taken up in the following chapters.

Methods of Study. Special methods are used in studying excitation and discharge of the receptors and conduction of the nerve impulse, since direct observation or reports of subjective reactions are totally inadequate for revealing the detailed mechanisms involved. Activity of nerve tissue results in the active area becoming electrically negative to the resting or inactive areas. The electrical disturbances which accompany the nerve impulse may be recorded by cathode ray oscillographs or other suitable types of galvanometers, connected to the nerve by special electrodes. This affords a means of studying not only the nature of the discharge from the receptors, but also conduction of the impulse within the peripheral process of the afferent nerve and in the other peripheral neurons which may be affected; special methods of electrical recording also serve to provide us with some information as to activity occurring within the central portions of the nervous system.

The measured or recorded electrical responses which may be obtained are influenced by the locations of the "pick-up" or recording electrodes, the composition of the medium surrounding the nerve tissue under study and other factors. Great advantage has resulted from varying the method of recording or the environment of the nerve structure. Although discussion of the details of many of these studies is beyond the scope of this text, we will consider some records of electrical activity and some factors bearing upon the nature of the excitation and propagation of the nerve impulse.

If recordings of the nerve impulse are made, with two electrodes placed upon a nerve so that the area under each electrode changes from a resting to an active state at different times (i.e., out of phase), the upward and downward deflections constitute a *diphasic action potential* record. *Monophasic action potential* records may be obtained by placing one electrode on an injured portion of a nerve fiber or trunk or, in some species where the fiber size permits, in the interior of the fiber. Monophasic curves are of value for studying the magnitude, the direction and the time relations of the changes in the membrane under the electrode on the exterior or uninjured portion of the nerve. The diphasic action potentials represent the algebraic sum of the potentials occurring under the two electrodes at any moment; each spike represents the local monophasic variations which occur in sequence and cause a reversal in the direction of the current through the recording device.

The magnitude of the electrical disturbance is indicated by the size of the deflection. A timing device is used for simultaneous recording of the desired intervals, so that the durations and frequencies of specific events may be determined.

Other types of records which have been especially valuable have been measurement of the resistance of the nerve membrane to the flow of electricity (membrane impedance), and measurement of the electrical field around a nerve during rest and activity.

The electrical disturbance accompanying the nerve impulse should not be confused with the applied stimulus; it occurs when the nerve is stimulated by chemical, thermal and mechanical means as well as when electrical stimuli are used.

Some Characteristics of the Response of the Receptors. Objective studies of the characteristics of receptor end organs can be made by recording the resulting electrical disturbances which occur upon their stimulation in single nerve fibers or in groups of them. Certain specific properties of the end organs may be determined by this technic.

ADEQUATE STIMULI. Though receptors may be stimulated by a number of different kinds of environmental change, each type of receptor is especially sensitive to one type of stimulus. For example, while receptors for heat or touch-pressure may be stimulated electrically, heat receptors are especially sensitive to small increases in temperature and touch-pressure receptors are especially sensitive to small amounts of mechanical energy. Similarly, while action potentials will occur in the optic nerve as the result of a blow on the eye (mechanical stimuli), the sensory endings of the eye respond to only the minutest fraction of that amount of energy when radiant stimuli, in the form of visible light, are applied. This characteristic of exhibiting a low or minimum threshold for one specific type of stimulus is referred to as the *law of adequate stimuli*. Pain receptors, however, appear to be the exception, since they respond to many types of harmful or *nociceptive* stimuli, such as greater extremes of heat and cold, electrical currents, chemicals and mechanical energy. Whereas a heat receptor will respond to increases of 0.00015 gm. calories per cm.^{2} per second, applied for three seconds, pain receptors do not respond until heat is applied at a rate of 0.218 gm. calories per cm.^{2} per second for three seconds.

DISCHARGE OF THE RECEPTORS. Stimulation resulting from a sufficient and appropriate change of environment sets up an action potential which does not vary in magnitude with the intensity of the stimulation. The *magnitude* of the response in the nerve, then, depends only upon the physiologic state of the nerve tissues. The rate of discharge in any receptor, however, varies with the strength of the stimulus; weak stimuli give rise to a relatively low rate of firing, while stronger stimuli result in a higher rate of discharge.

The absolute rate of discharge of any receptor is of course limited by its refractory period, or the point at which it no longer responds to stimuli. If the duration of the recovery period of the receptor endings is longer than for the principal peripheral process of the ganglion cell, the mechanism underlying the relation of the rate of discharge and the intensity of the stimulus may be determined by the relative refractory period, or the point where conduction of stimuli slows. The stronger the stimuli, the earlier it would be effective during the relative refractory period; weaker stimuli would be ineffective until recovery was more nearly completed, and hence the rate of discharge would necessarily be reduced.

Whatever the initial rate of discharge, however, it will decrease to a greater or lesser extent during the time the stimulus is being applied. This decrease in the rate of discharge with continued application of a constant stimulus is a phenomenon known as *adaptation*. It is distinct from fatigue, since it sets in within a brief interval after the beginning of the discharge. Further, the initial rate of discharge can be brought about if a second stimulus is applied at a brief interval after the end of the first stimulus in which adaptation had occurred, whereas recovery from fatigue would require a longer period.

Naked nerve fibers adapt most quickly, as may be shown by the fact that one or at most two or three discharges occur from maximal stimulation. Touch receptors stimulated by bending a hair give rise to a volley of impulses which dies away in about one-fifth of a second. Pressure endings show a somewhat longer period of adaptation. The proprioceptors such as are involved in the maintenance of posture, however, adapt very slowly, continuing to discharge for many minutes or even hours. Pain endings also continue to discharge over such long periods of time that it appears questionable whether adaptation exists for this type of ending.

Characteristics of the Nerve Impulse. Nerve impulses in normal man are initated by a discharge of one or more receptors or as the result of some activity of the higher centers of the nervous system. The direction of conduction is from the axon, across the synapse, to the dendrites. Nerve impulses can also be brought about experimentally by direct stimulation of the nerve fiber or nerve trunk. Here the impulse starting from the point of excitation will travel with equal velocity in both directions. As long as the physiological conditions are constant, the response, or nerve impulse, will be constant in its intensity.

ALL-OR-NONE RESPONSE. If the nerve impulse were transmitted along the axon like a current of electricity it would become progressively weaker as it traveled away from the point of origin. The nerve impulse does not show any diminution of intensity as long as it is passing through normal nerve tissue. If a section of the fiber is depressed by drugs or by oxygen lack, the magnitude of the impulse decreases when passing through this area of altered physiologic conditions. However, upon reaching a normal area, the magnitude of the impulse regains its initial level. It may be likened to the burning of a trail of small, closely adjacent piles of gunpowder which would ignite uniformly and give a blaze of constant intensity along its course; dampening the powder at one point would slow the ignition and diminish the intensity of the flame. If the fire traveled over the dampened area it would blaze up to the original intensity when it again reached dry powder. Thus it may be said that a nerve fiber conducts by responding maximally at every point along its course for the existing set of physiologic conditions. It obeys the all-or-none law. Another indication of the all-or-none response in nerve is that the magnitude of the nerve impulse does not vary with strength of stimulus. We have learned previously that the receptors always behave the same way. If they respond to stimulus they respond by initiating an impulse which is maximum for the existing physiologic condition of the nerve fiber. Stimulation of nerve trunks, however, may result in a graded response. This may be explained on the basis of increasingly strong stimuli affecting greater numbers of nerve fibers.

SIGNIFICANCE OF REFRACTORY PERIOD. If a nerve fiber is subjected to continued stimulation by repeating effective electrical stimuli at a very rapid rate, it responds by a rapidly interrupted stream of impulses which are comparable to a stream of machine-gun bullets rather than to the continuous flow of a stream of water. We know, however, that if the rate is continually increased, a point will be reached where one stimulus will fall at the time the fiber is in a refractory state from the preceding stimuli, and the rate at which the nerve impulses are initiated will no longer show an increase.

While the refractory period of a nerve fiber sets the limit at which it can respond to repeated stimulation, the rates of discharge of normal physiologic stimuli in the body are well below this value. This would mean that the fiber could respond to every successive physiologic stimulus which would normally occur and in addition have a margin of safety in its ability to respond at a higher rate.

During the relative refractory period (altered physiologic conditions) the magnitude of the nerve impulse is diminished and the rate of conduction is slowed. The reduction in the rate of conduction would prevent the possibility of interference of a second impulse "catching up" to a previously initiated impulse and encountering nerve tissue in an absolute refractory state.

The Local Excitatory State. Rapidly repeated subthreshold stimuli result in a phenomenon quite different from that resulting from threshold stimuli. The subliminal stimulus, while not exciting a response in the nerve, leaves behind some effect. When another subliminal stimulus is applied before the effect of the first has worn off, the condition of the nerve at the point of stimulation approaches more closely the condition or state of excitability. The third or successive stimuli may build up in step fashion to the threshold for excitation. This is known as the *local excitatory state*. It differs from a nerve impulse in four respects:

1. It is capable of summation; that is, the excitatory effect may be modified by successive stimuli following the initial stimulus at extremely short intervals.

2. It is not followed by a refractory period.

3. The extent of the local change is proportional to the strength of stimulus. It does not follow the all-or-none law.

4. The excitatory state is not conducted along the nerve, but remains at the point of stimulation.

If the local excitatory state is raised by rapidly repeated stimuli it may reach the critical value necessary for initiating a nerve impulse. When a single stimulus is applied, the local excitatory state gradually diminishes over a period of about two ten-thousandths of a second and the affected area returns to its resting state.

Velocity of Nerve Impulses. The velocity of a nerve impulse is quite independent of the strength of the stimulus and is determined only by the size, type and physiologic condition of the nerve fiber. The type or group showing the highest velocities includes the larger myelinated nerve fibers. All the motor nerve fibers and the larger sensory fibers belong in this class. The rates of conduction of impulses in these myelinated nerve fibers of the central nervous system vary between 5 and 120 meters per second, depending upon the diameter of the fiber. If we record monophasic action potentials from a nerve trunk at successive points farther and farther from the point of stimulation, the deflection will show first a series of small elevations, and finally separate waves of lesser amplitude than the original spike. The separation of disturbances conducted at different rates increases as the distance from the point of stimulation becomes greater. This is similar to the situation which occurs in distance races in a track meet; the runners start in a group, but because of their different speeds we soon see a succession of individuals rather than a compact group. It has been determined that the smaller the diameter of the fiber within the central myelinated group, the slower the rate of conduction of the impulse. Myelinated nerve fibers of the autonomic system may conduct at rates between 3 and 15 meters per second. Unmyelinated nerve fibers have conduction rates of 0.6 to 2 meters per second.

Metabolism of the Nerve. Resting nerve consumes oxygen and gives off carbon dioxide. If placed in a solution containing either carbohydrate or fat, the quantity of the substance decreases, indicating that it is used by the nerve tissue. Both respiratory quotients and heat production have been measured for nerve by means of delicate instruments.

Activity increases both oxygen consumption and heat production. Coincident with the passage of the nerve impulse there is a small and rapid heat production, followed by two further periods of heat liberation during the recovery phase. The first of these periods occurs during the relative refractory period and the second after the nerve has regained normal excitability.

Nerve fibers appear remarkably resistant to fatigue because of their property of rapid recovery. However, it has been demonstrated that prolonged activity diminishes the irritability of nerve fibers, decreases the action potentials, rate of oxygen consumption and heat liberation, and prolongs the refractory period.

Nature of Excitation and Propagation of the Nerve Impulse. Although physiologists have made important recent advances in knowledge of excitation and propagation of the nerve impulse, our understanding of the mechanisms is far from complete. Combining the old and the newer experimental findings will help us to visualize at least some of the physiologic processes, even if we cannot draw firm conclusions as to their nature.

We know that if two electrodes connected to a sensitive galvanometer are placed at two points on the surface of an uninjured, resting nerve fiber there will be no difference in voltage between them. If, on the other hand, one electrode is placed on the outside of the fiber of an excised nerve, and the second electrode in the axoplasm inside the nerve, a potential difference of some 50 millivolts can be measured between the outside and the inside of the membrane. The interior of the nerve is electrically negative to the outside. The voltage difference is known as the *resting membrane potential.* This potential may be even greater in normal nerve lying undisturbed in the body. It appears that the membrane of a resting nerve, when uninjured and in a normal physiologic condition, effectively separates positive electrical charges on the outside and the negative charges on the inside, and so maintains the resting potential. When unlike electrical charges, or ions, are so distributed in an "electric double layer" the membrane is said to be "polarized." If we again place two electrodes on the outside of the nerve membrane, but this time injure the portion of the nerve under the second electrode, the membrane no longer acts as an electrical insulator in maintaining the 50 millivolt potential. The injured area acts as if the insulation had broken down and its electrode were in contact with the electrically negative interior of the fiber. The potential difference between the two electrodes is called the *injury* or *demarcation potential;* the positive current which flows in an external circuit toward the injured area is known as a *demarcation* or *injury current.* The fact that injury currents continue to flow indicates that a force is acting which maintains the potential difference across the membrane; ions which migrate are replaced so that the uninjured portion of the membrane continues to be polarized.

Several different theories have been advanced to account for distribution of electrical charges. We know that the axoplasm contains relatively large amounts of K^+, some protein anions, little Na^+ and scarcely any Cl^-. Outside the nerve there is little K^+, but relatively large amounts of Na^+ and Cl^-. It is also known that the membrane of the resting nerve fiber is selectively permeable to K^+ and Cl^-, but is impermeable to Na^+. The outward migration of K^+ and the inward migration of Cl^- along their respective gradients may account for the distribution of electrical charges. Another explanation which has been advanced is that polarization may be maintained chemically by separation and by binding the layer of cations outside and anions inside the membrane.

If energy is applied to the resting nerve with its polarized membrane, changes in the potential difference across the membrane will result. If the applied energy is small, the change in potential will be greatest at the point of stimulation and measurable, but of lesser value, at more distant points. The degree of change decreases not only with distance from the stimulated point, but with time. It thus appears that application of energy starts the process of depolarization of the nerve membrane locally, which affects more distant segments. If the local effect does not attain a critical value, a restoring process returns the membrane to its former state.

If, however, the energy of the stimulus brings about a sufficient change in potential and involves a sufficient expanse of nerve tissue, the disturbance is propagated as a nerve impulse. As the potential difference at the point of excitation changes from a negative value (say 50 millivolts) to zero, current flows along the interior of the fiber from the active region, out through the resting membrane and along the outside of the nerve, from the resting to the active area. In consequence, the potential difference across the resting membrane is reduced. The reduction in the membrane potential brings about a change in the permeability characteristics of the membrane. Sodium permeability increases from its former very small value about 150 times in one or two tenths of a millisecond and then returns to a low value in about one millisecond. The polarity of the membrane is reversed with the interior changing from its resting value of about —50 millivolts to about a +35 millivolts, i.e., a total change of about 85 millivolts. The potassium permeability also increases, but much

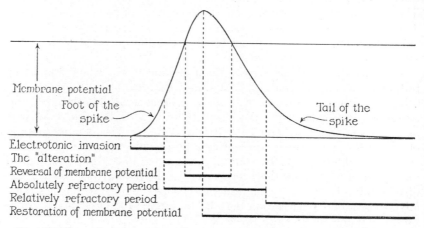

Fig. 37. The spike potential, really, is not a single simple event. This diagram relates spike potential to membrane potential, and to a number of the events that take place in association with conduction of a nerve impulse. As impulse approaches a given region of nerve, that region is progressively depolarized by electrotonic extension of impulse. When a critical level of depolarization is reached, "alteration" or nerve impulse proper occupies region, and lasts until spike potential reaches its peak. Phase of repolarization then begins. Region is absolutely refractory from onset of alteration until a major restoration of membrane potential has taken place; it is then relatively refractory during "tail" of spike potential. Since spike potential may exceed in voltage membrane potential, it is assumed that membrane potential may reverse during passage of an impulse. (David C. P. Lloyd in Fulton: Textbook of Physiology, Ed. 17.)

more slowly, reaching a maximum as Na^+ conductance falls from its peak and then returns to its original level as the resting potential is attained (see also Chemical Transmission of Nerve Impulses, p. 159).

The changes which have been briefly summarized may be related to the three phases of the action potential: the spike, the negative after-potential and the positive after-potential. The foot of the spike, as seen in the monophasic action potential, registers the original depolarization of the membrane associated with the flow of current within the fiber from the active to the inactive portion of the nerve. The alteration of polarity then occurs with the inflow of cations until an actual reversal results with the interior positive to the exterior. From the beginning of the period of alteration to the beginning of the tail of the spike the nerve is in the absolute refractory period. At the beginning of the spike tail, and coincident with the negative after-potential, the nerve is in the relative refractory period. Recovery to normal excitability is gradual and accompanies the restoration of the resting polarization of the nerve membrane.

SUMMARY

Nervous tissue shows a high degree of specialization in the two fundamental properties of protoplasm, irritability and conductivity.

In normal man, impulses are initiated by the receptors in response to changes in the external and internal environment.

Special methods are used in studying excitation and discharge of receptors and conduction of the nerve impulse. The electrical disturbances which accompany the nerve impulse can be recorded by cathode ray oscillographs or other suitable types of galvanometers, connected to the nerve by special electrodes.

The recorded response which is obtained is influenced by the location of the electrodes and the medium surrounding the nerve structure.

Two properties of receptors have been determined by studying the electrical disturbances which occur when afferent nerve fibers are stimulated: (1) each type of receptor is especially sensitive to one type of stimulus; (2) the sensory receptor endings obey the all-or-none law.

The rate of discharge of any receptor is limited by its refractory period.

Decrease in the rate of discharge following continued application of a constant stimulus is a phenomenon known as adaptation.

If a nerve fiber is stimulated at any point, the nerve impulse initiated will travel with equal velocity in both directions.

The local excitatory state is the change produced in the fiber by subthreshold stimuli. The second or successive stimuli become effective because of the persistence of the change within the fiber at the point of stimulation.

The velocity of a nerve impulse depends upon both the type and size of the nerve fiber. Conduction is most rapid in large myelinated fibers. The small medullated fibers and the nonmyelinated fibers show slower rates of conduction.

Activity of the nerve increases both oxygen consumption and heat production.

The resting potential and the nerve impulse are physicochemical phenomena dependent upon polarization and depolarization of the nerve membrane. Depolarization is brought about by application of sufficient energy to constitute an adequate stimulus. The disturbance of the physicochemical system involves an early rapid inward migration of Na^+, followed by a slower outward migration of K^+. With sufficient change in potential, involving an adequate expanse of nerve tissue, the disturbance is propagated as a nerve impulse.

QUESTIONS FOR DISCUSSION

1. How would the factors affecting permeability of the cell membrane be related to the nerve impulse?

2. What factors influence the velocity of the nerve impulse?

3. How does the local excitatory state differ from the nerve impulse?

Chapter
6

The Spinal Cord
and Spinal Nerves

GENERAL ORGANIZATION OF THE SPINAL CORD

THE SPINAL cord serves as a reflex center and as a structural and functional pathway for conducting and integrating afferent nerve impulses as they pass centrally from peripheral nerves toward the brain, or efferent impulses as they pass from the central nervous system toward the effector organs.

When we speak of a "center" in the nervous system, we are referring to an area where two, several or a great many neurons have functional connections which provide for integrated responses. In serving as a reflex center, the cord provides the connections and performs the functions necessary to carry out a series of events beginning with stimulation of a sensory receptor and terminating with an effector response. Theoretically, at least, this activity may be so limited as to involve only two neurons. Here, the afferent neuron process lies in the dorsal root, and the efferent neuron process in the ventral root of the same spinal nerve. A slightly less limited response may involve both right and left sides of a single segment of the cord, i.e., a section corresponding to one vertebra and associated with a single pair of spinal nerves. Spinal reflexes resulting from natural rather than experimentally applied stimuli more generally involve several levels or segments of

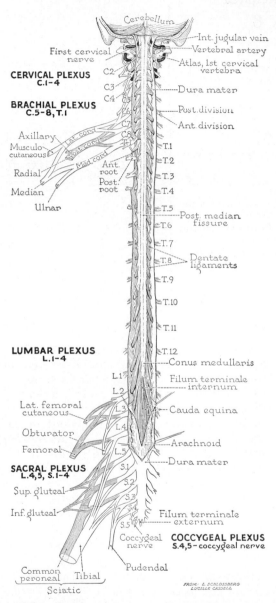

Fig. 38. The spinal cord and spinal nerves. The dura mater has been opened to show the spinal cord and nerve roots. The plexuses are represented diagrammatically. Only the main branches are shown.

the cord. Under some conditions, particularly strong stimulation may result in a spread of nervous activity throughout all segments of the cord.

The conducting and integrating functions of the cord become evident when more than two neurons are involved. One or many connector or internuncial neurons provide pathways between the two sides and the different segments or levels of the cord and between the various levels of the cord and the brain. Because of the multitude of interconnections of the neurons within the cord, an almost infinite variety of responses is possible. Further study will show, however, that in spite of the number and complexity of interconnections, there is an orderly arrangement of fibers which conduct between the various levels of the spinal cord and between the cord and the brain. It is more difficult to recognize the orderly arrangement of cell bodies and synapses within the cord. Evidence for the existence of orderly arrangement and knowledge of detailed architecture is provided by precise methods of physiologic and neurologic experimentation and clinical neurologic observation.

STRUCTURE

General Structure. The spinal cord occupies the upper two thirds of the vertebral canal. It is composed of thirty-one segments of nervous tissue, each bearing a pair of spinal nerves. It extends from the foramen magnum, where it is continuous with the medulla oblongata, to the level of the disc between the first and second lumbar vertebrae. The lower end tapers off to a point and is called the conus medullaris. Until the third month of fetal life the cord extends the entire length of the canal, but thereafter, because of the more rapid linear growth of the vertebral column, the spinal cord has the appearance of having been drawn upward within the canal. The disparity between the length of the spinal cord and vertebral canal increases the distance between the attachment of the various nerve roots and the intervertebral foramina through which the several nerves leave the vertebral canal. Therefore the nerve roots arising from the lumbar and sacral regions pass for some distance in the canal before making their exit. This bundle of nerve roots is descriptively called the *cauda equina* (Fig. 38).

White and Gray Matter. Examination of a cross section (Fig. 39) shows the spinal cord divided into right and left halves by the anterior median fissure and posterior median septum. A striking feature of the central portion of the section is an area of gray matter which follows the general form of the capital letter H. This gray matter is made up of cell bodies and their processes, which are largely unmyelinated fibers, held together by neuroglia. This central gray core is surrounded by white matter made up of cross sections of longitudinal columns of nerve fibers, most of which are myelinated, embedded in a network of neuroglia.

The two projections of the "H" extending backward or dorsally are called the *posterior columns* of the gray matter. In some microscopic sections, central processes of the spinal root ganglion cells may be seen

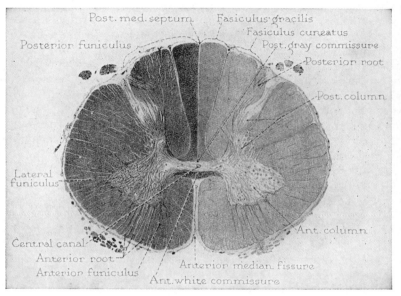

Fig. 39. Cross section of the spinal cord from the lower cervical region. (Sobotta and McMurrich.)

entering the posterior column; the dorsal root or afferent fibers branch, giving off rami which run in bundles or tracts to other levels of the cord or to the brain, or synapse with internuncial or connector neurons, or with ventral horn cells in the gray matter at the same level. The *anterior columns*, which form the ventral or forward projections of the letter H, contain the ventral horn cells, whose axons constitute the ventral root fibers of the spinal nerve which innervate the muscles. Some microscopic sections show these anterior root fibers passing out from the anterior columns. The *lateral columns* of gray matter, which are most prominent in the thoracic region of the cord, contain the cell bodies of the axons which, as preganglionic fibers, pass to the sympathetic ganglia; they form part of the motor innervation of the visceral organs. The band of gray matter forming the horizontal bar of the H is called the *central gray* or *gray commissure*. It encloses a small opening, the central canal, which divides the horizontal band into the anterior and posterior gray commissures, formed by fibers passing between the two halves of the spinal cord.

The anterior and posterior columns of gray matter divide the white matter of the cord into *anterior, lateral and posterior portions or funiculi*. These funiculi make up the ascending and descending fiber tracts;

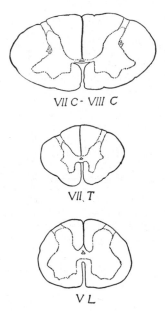

VII C- VIII C

VII. T

V L

Fig. 40. Outline drawings of sections through cervical, thoracic and lumbar segments of the human spinal cord. (Ranson, The Anatomy of the Nervous System.)

most of the fibers in these tracts are myelinated. The ascending tracts conduct sensory or afferent impulses to or toward the brain; the descending tracts conduct motor or efferent impulses from the brain.

The size and shape of the cord and the proportion of gray and white matter vary in different regions (Fig. 40). These variations are more easily understood if they are thought of in terms of both structure and function. As might be expected, the funiculi of the afferent pathways increase in size from caudal to cranial portions of the cord, since new afferent fibers are joining these tracts. The arrangement of the fibers is orderly; the details of the arrangement depend upon the course taken by the fibers. For example, if we consider the posterior funiculi, we find that the afferent fibers from the lower extremities are displaced

medially as they pass up the cord by the afferent fibers which enter
at successively higher levels. The medial funiculi of the posterior white
columns contain afferent fibers associated with receptors in the lower
extremities, while the more lateral portions of the posterior funiculi

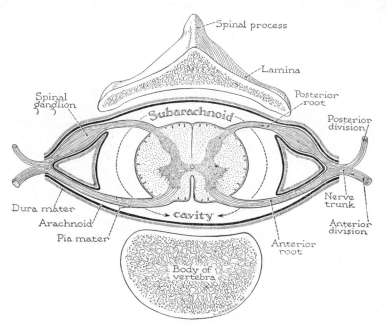

Fig. 41. Cross section of spinal cord, showing spinal nerves and membranes.

contain fibers associated with the receptors of the trunk and upper
extremities.

The over-all gradual decrease in the diameter of the cord from the
upper to the lower ends is determined, not only by increase of the
size of the afferent bundles as they ascend, but also by the decrease
in the descending bundles as they pass caudad. This results from
termination of fibers from the higher centers as they form connections
with other neurons of the effector pathways at successively lower levels.
There are two conspicuous enlargements of the cord, one in the cervical and the other in the lumbar region; the volume of the gray matter
is greatly increased at these levels by the many cell bodies of nerve
fibers supplying the arms and legs.

Spinal Nerves.   The thirty-one pairs of spinal nerves correspond to
segments of the spinal cord, and are classified as eight cervical, twelve
thoracic, five lumbar, five sacral and one coccygeal. As pointed out in

the previous discussion, the spinal nerves are formed by the fibers from the dorsal and ventral roots which join as they pass out through the intervertebral foramen. Spinal nerves continue for only a few millimeters before dividing into anterior and posterior branches. The roots and divisions are shown in Figure 41.

In general, the posterior divisions supply the muscles of the back acting on the vertebral column and the skin covering them. The anterior division is large and forms the main part of the spinal nerve. The muscles and skin of the extremities and the remaining areas of the trunk are supplied by anterior divisions.

The fibers of the nerve are grouped into bundles called funiculi, and each funiculus is ensheathed with connective tissue called perineurium. A looser connective tissue, the epineurium, containing blood vessels and lymphatics, binds the funiculi together and completely surrounds the nerve trunk.

In all regions except the thoracic the anterior divisions of the spinal nerves interlace to form networks of nerves, called *plexuses*. The plexuses thus formed are cervical, brachial and lumbosacral. In each instance, branches are given off from the plexus to the parts supplied. The branches are called nerves and receive special names. Figure 42 shows the distribution of spinal nerves.

The first four cervical nerves form the *cervical plexus*, which supplies structures in the region of the neck. One important branch is the phrenic nerve, which supplies the diaphragm.

The *brachial plexus* is formed from the fifth, sixth, seventh and eighth cervical and first thoracic nerves. This plexus supplies the upper extremity. Important branches are the radial, median and ulnar nerves of the arm.

The *lumbosacral plexus* is formed from the last thoracic and lumbar and sacral nerves. Its branches pass to the lower extremity. Its great nerves are obturator, femoral and sciatic.

The thoracic nerves do not form a plexus, but pass out in the intercostal spaces as the intercostal nerves. They supply intercostal muscles, upper abdominal muscles and the skin areas of the chest and abdomen.

Spinal Membranes. The spinal cord and attached nerve roots within the vertebral canal are surrounded by three coverings: dura mater, arachnoid, and pia mater (Fig. 41). The *dura mater* is a strong fibrous layer attached by loose connective tissue to the periosteum of the vertebral canal. The dural sheath extends below the end of the spinal cord as far as the second sacral segment. In its lower part it encloses the root fibers of the cauda equina. The *pia mater* is a thin, highly vascular membrane which closely invests the cord and nerve roots. Between the dura and pia mater lies the delicate *arachnoid* of

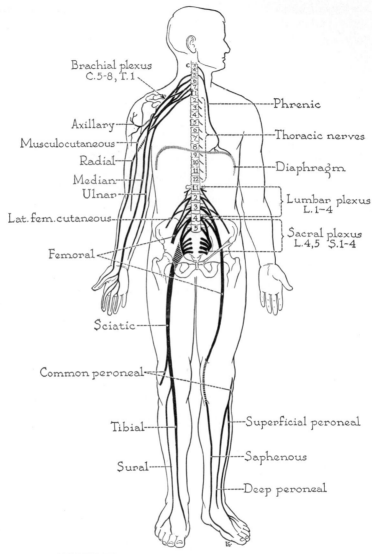

Fig. 42. Distribution of the spinal nerves.

spider-web thinness, as its name implies. The arachnoid and pia mater are separated by a considerable interval called the subarachnoid space, which contains the cerebrospinal fluid. The spinal cord, surrounded by the bony walls of the vertebral canal and suspended in a fluid bath, is well protected from injury.

The membranes of the cord are continuous through the foramen magnum with those covering the brain. These will be described later.

REFLEX ACTIVITY OF THE SPINAL CORD

We have seen that the architectural pattern of the spinal cord provides for responses which may involve one, several or all of its segments. We cannot, however, study the functional activity of the spinal cord itself without separating it from the influence of the higher centers. Our knowledge of the extent and limitations of independent activity of the spinal cord has developed through experimental studies on animals and from study of human beings whose cords have been severed by war or other forms of traumatic injury. Experimentally, it is very simple to prepare a "spinal" frog. Within a short time after decapitation, the spinal frog preparation responds to various applied stimuli. While experimental technics for making and caring for spinal preparations of higher animals are much more elaborate and difficult, they have added greatly to our knowledge of normal neurophysiology and to the under-standing and development of clinical neurology. The use of spinal preparations eliminates the possibility of influence of sensory effects of afferent stimulation, that is, sensation or conscious "feeling." The responses observed cannot be decreased or inhibited, augmented or modified in any manner by the higher centers, because either these centers or their connections with the spinal cord have been destroyed.

Before discussing some of the characteristics of the reactions of spinal preparations, it will be helpful to discuss two concepts which are impor-tant for an understanding of reflex activity, i.e., the reflex arc and reflex times.

Reflex Arc (Fig. 43). The general pattern of a spinal reflex arc includes:

1. A sensory receptor, i.e., the terminal branches of the peripheral process of an afferent neuron;
2. An afferent neuron, with its peripheral process, a cell body lying within a dorsal root ganglion, and a median or central process which enters the posterior gray column of the spinal cord;
3. A synapse or synapses with one or more internuncial neurons;
4. The internuncial neurons or connector cells which lie within the spinal cord;
5. A synapse with the dendrite of an efferent neuron which has its cell body in the ventral or anterior horn of the gray matter;
6. The axon of the efferent neuron, leaving the cord in the ventral root of a spinal nerve;

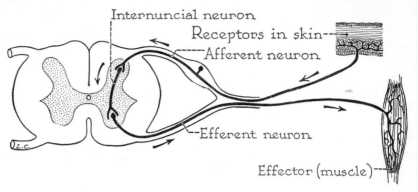

Fig. 43. Diagrammatic section through spinal cord and a spinal nerve to illustrate a simple reflex arc.

7. The neuromuscular junction;

8. The muscle, which is the effector organ.

In the simplest type of spinal reflex, such as the knee jerk, the afferent and efferent neuron may synapse directly without an intervening connector cell.

Reflex Time. If we initiate a reflex by stimulation of a sensory nerve ending, there is a delay before the muscle responds. Analysis has shown that the delay is determined by (1) the time of passage of the impulse along the afferent nerve, (2) the time for passage across the synapse or synapses, (3) the time for passage along the efferent nerve, and (4) the latent period of the muscle. The *central* or *reduced reflex* time is the time for passage of the impulse over that part of the reflex arc which lies within the spinal cord. The greater part of the reduced reflex time is consumed in transmission of the impulse across the synapse. In general, the longer reflex times indicate a greater number of synapses in the reflex arc.

Some Reflex Responses in the "Spinal" Animal. Profound spinal shock on the nervous system occurs immediately after section of the spinal cord or destruction of the brain; the spinal animal fails to respond even to stimuli of considerable intensity. The time for recovery is far greater for mammals than for amphibia, and increases as we go up in the animal scale. Frogs recover quickly and without any special care, but if mammals are used, the section must be made below the level of the spinal nerves which make up the phrenic nerve, or artificial respiration must be provided. Upon recovery, the two outstanding characteristics of the "spinal" animal are the apparent purposiveness and the predictability of the responses. Descriptions or, better yet, direct observation of some of the spinal reflexes reveals patterns so precise and so closely similar to those of a normal animal that they appear to be purposeful voluntary acts. If controlled stimuli are repeated, the fatality of the unconditioned reflex is demonstrated by precise repetition of the pattern of response; the variations which are characteristic of normal animals no longer occur.

Successful preparations will show *flexor reflexes*, that is, withdrawal from a harmful or potentially harmful stimulus, phasic and static *extensor reflexes* such as occur in the knee jerk and in maintenance of posture, *scratch reflexes* or rhythmic responses to touch or local irritation, and others. The detailed pattern and the intensity of these responses are determined by the characteristics of the stimuli. Several special characteristics of the sensory mechanisms and of spinal activity may be observed.

That afferent receptor mechanisms bear an accurate *local sign* is seen by the effective application of the limb to the exact site of the irritating stimuli. A "spinal" frog will brush off a bit of paper dipped in acid or some irritant substance and placed on any part of the body accessible to its legs; "spinal" cats will scratch the site of application of moderate irritating stimuli such as bending of hairs. If the brain were intact, the sensation would be referred to these points. The structure of the cord provides segmental arrangements and pathways which may result in appropriate movements even where there can be no consciousness or sensation.

The flexor reflex is a primitive, unconscious response that is so well established that it is difficult to control voluntarily. If we touch a hot stove or step on a sharp object, we behave in much the same manner as the "spinal" animal. An orderly, effective withdrawal of the part may start before we are conscious of the painful stimulus.

The intensity of the reflex responses depends upon the number of impulses arriving in the central nervous system. The number of impulses will depend upon (a) the strength of the stimulus applied to the receptor, since more intense stimuli give a greater rate of discharge of the receptor; (b) the duration of stimulation and rate of adaptation of the receptor, and (c) the number of end organs affected. As the intensity of stimulation is increased, *irradiation* occurs; this is a spread of nervous activity to other segmental levels through response of connector and effector neurons whose threshold of stimulation was not attained by lesser stimuli. A strong nociceptive stimulus to a hind leg of a "spinal" frog or mammal will not only cause flexion of the ipsilateral leg, but also extension of the contralateral hind leg; it may even involve the forelimbs and trunk. In addition, the activity may continue for a brief interval after the stimulus has been withdrawn; this phenomenon is known as *after-discharge*. It is believed to depend upon the time for passage of the impulse over relatively indirect and long pathways; the effect of some of the afferent impulses is delayed because of the increased central reflex time.

Afferent impulses are capable of bringing about *inhibition*, i.e., of preventing activity, as well as stimulation. When a muscle group is stimulated to contract, inhibitory impulses may pass to the motor neurons innervating antagonistic muscle groups and cause their active relaxation.

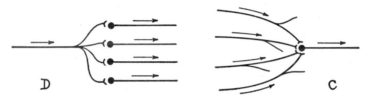

Fig. 44. Diagrammatic schemata of divergent mechanism (*D*) and of convergent mechanism (*C*). Arrows indicate direction of impulse conduction. (David P. C. Lloyd in Fulton: Textbook of Physiology, Ed. 17.)

The concepts of divergence and convergence enable us to visualize the possibilities for a wide variety of structural combinations which could determine the nature of individual responses. The *divergent* mechanism provides for excitation of two or more neurons by a single axon whose rami or branches form synaptic connections with them. The principle of *convergence* describes the structural arrangement whereby the axons of two or more neurons may converge and provide dual or multiple innervation of a single neuron (Fig. 44).

Convergence and divergence allow for many of the phenomena exhibited by the central nervous system. Let us visualize a pool of six ventral horn cells (Fig. 45A). We will assume that the fiber from an afferent nerve *a* synapses with two of these motor units; a fiber from nerve *b* synapses with two other motor units. Fibers from both *a* and *b* converge on each of the two remaining ventral horn cells providing for their dual innervation. If we should measure the strength of contractions resulting from intense stimulation of nerve *a* and nerve *b* separately, the sum of the work performed would be greater than the total work obtained by simultaneous stimulation. Since we have chosen an intensity of stimuli which, when applied to one nerve, will discharge the motor units having overlapping innervation, these motor units will be unaffected by impulses arriving over the other nerve. This phenomenon is known as *occlusion*.

Let us now assume another situation for the pool of the six ventral horn cells (Fig. 45B). Here, a moderate stimulus to the peripheral receptor of nerve fiber *a* will cause the discharge of one ventral horn cell and like stimulation of *b* will also discharge one motor unit. Stimulation of *a* is also assumed to have a subthreshold effect on three other ventral horn cells, two of which may also be affected subliminally by stimulation of *b*. If we now stimulate fibers *a* and *b* at the same time or in rapid succession, the impulses from one fiber may not only discharge one motor unit, but also set up a local excitatory state in the three neurons in its subliminal fringe. The discharge of the second fiber, if it occurs before the excitation in the two neurons with common innervation dies down, will bring about summation of subthreshold stimuli and these two neurons also respond. Thus stimulation of the first nerve contributing to the dual innervation provides for *facilitation,* so that an additional subliminal stimulus through the fibers of nerve *b* results in a discharge of the motor units. Facilitation allows for *spatial summation* of subthreshold stimuli, i.e., subliminal stimuli from different areas of the body.

If we increase the strength of stimulation so as to obtain a higher frequency of discharge of the receptor end organs of nerve *a*, facilitation may again occur by summation of successive stimuli, i.e., *temporal summation,* so that all four of the motor units with which it synapses will respond.

CONDUCTING PATHWAYS OF THE SPINAL CORD

The white matter of the spinal cord serves as a conducting pathway for the long *ascending* and *descending* tracts by which afferent impulses reach the brain and efferent impulses pass from motor centers in the brain to the anterior gray column cells of the cord and so modify muscular movement. The fibers are arranged in bundles which show a functional as well as an anatomic grouping. A bundle of fibers having the same origin, termination and function is called a fiber tract. The funiculi of the spinal cord are composed of a number of such tracts which have definite locations (Fig. 39). The origin means the location of the cell bodies giving rise to processes forming the tract. The termination refers to the point at which the axons forming the tract end.

We can follow the course of a tract in experimental animals by sectioning a part of the conducting pathway, observing all the deficiencies which appear upon recovery, and allowing degeneration of the fibers which have been separated from their cell bodies so that they may be identified in postmortem histologic sections. This procedure involves using the most refined surgical technics under conditions which parallel those in operating rooms for human patients. The experimental animals must be given the best postoperative care. All sensory and motor changes must be noted and related to specific areas of the body during the period which is allowed for degeneration to take place. In this way we learn that sensory receptors, located on either the same or the opposite side of the body, cease to function and that the response to one or several types of sensation is lost. Subsequent study of histological sections at various levels of the nervous system shows area of degen-

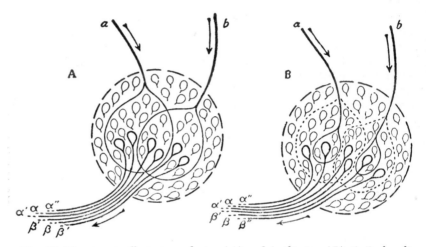

Fig. 45. Diagrams to illustrate *occlusion* (A) and *facilitation* (B). A, Broken line encloses a pool of neurons some of which are discharged by presynaptic path a, some by path b. Fields overlap so that when a and b are stimulated together the discharge is less (6 neurons in diagram) than sum of the discharges evoked by a and b severally (which would be 8 neurons). B, Broken line encloses a pool of neurons, some of which are discharged by presynaptic path a, some by path b. The subliminal fields of path a and path b are enclosed by dotted lines. These subliminal fields overlap. According to diagram B stimulation of a or b would cause discharge of 1 neuron each; the sum, 2 neurons; but, stimulated together, a and b cause 4 neurons to discharge because of summation in subliminal fringe. Two neurons are represented as remaining in subliminal fringe on combined stimulation of a and b. (From Sherrington, Proc. Roy. Soc., 1929, *105B*:332–362.)

eration which can be followed to determine whether the tracts continue on the same side of the cord throughout their course or whether they cross to the opposite side, and the direction and extent of displacement within the funiculi. We can also determine whether a single neuron or a chain of neurons make up the pathway between two levels of the nervous system. The experimental results on animals are carefully related to clinical and postmortem findings on man. Detailed, precise and orderly observation and careful recording, and analysis and summary of the findings of individual experiments over a period of many years afford us a background for interpreting the pathways of conduction and for understanding the structural and functional basis for sensory and motor deficits and pathologies. An example of sections at various levels, and a notation of their effects, are shown for lesions of motor and reflex paths (Fig. 46).

Pathways and Fiber Tracts. The successive links of an ascending (afferent) pathway are referred to as first order neurons, second order neurons, and so forth. The first order neuron is associated with the receptor end organ. The location of its synapse with the second order neuron varies with the pathway. In descending (efferent) pathways we speak of upper motor neurons and lower motor neurons. The lower motor neuron is associated with the effector organ, while the upper motor neuron includes the cells of origin and any intercalated or internuncial neuron which lead to the ventral horn cell, i.e., the cell body of the lower motor neuron.

The fiber tracts form a link in the pathway for conduction of afferent or efferent impulses between the higher centers and the cord. With some exceptions, the names of these tracts are sufficiently descriptive to indicate the funiculus in which they travel in the cord, the general location of the cells of origin, and the level of the location of the axon terminals which connect with the neurons making up the next succeeding link in the pathway. For example, we may conclude that, in the *lateral spinothalamic tract,* the fibers run in the lateral funiculi of the cord, that the cells of origin lie within the spinal cord, and that the terminal processes of its axons make their connections with other neurons at a thalamic level. Since it passes from the lower level of the spinal cord to the thalamus at the higher level, it is an ascending or afferent tract. The axon fibers of the *ventral corticospinal tract* lie in the ventral funiculus, its cells of origin in the cortex, and its terminal connections in the spinal cord. We would conclude from this that it was an efferent or descending pathway.

Description of specific pathways will be limited to several of the major ascending and descending tracts (Fig. 47). If the time allotted for study of the conducting pathways permits, the student is urged to refer to the standard texts on neurology and neuroanatomy for a more comprehensive treatment than is warranted in an anatomy and physiology text.

ASCENDING TRACTS. 1. FASCICULUS GRACILIS AND FASCICULUS CUNEATUS. These are the two major afferent fiber tracts which make up the posterior funiculus or dorsal white columns (Fig. 48). They are fibers of *first order neurons* which form the first link in the pathway for sensations of position, movement and touch-pressure. The cells of

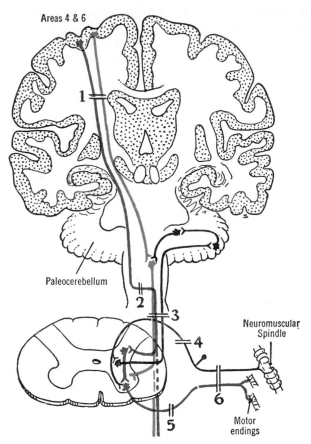

Fig. 46. Diagram illustrating lesions of the motor and reflex paths. *1*, A lesion at this point causes an upper motor neuron defect, the severity of which depends on the extent of the lesion. *2*, A lesion near the decussation of the pyramids affects only corticospinal fibers and produces a weakness or *paresis* on the opposite side of the body which is specially pronounced in the muscles concerned with skilled movements. *3*, A lesion in the lateral funiculus of the cord causes an upper motor neuron defect more severe than that at *1* because more descending fibers are cut. *4*, Section of dorsal root or roots causes loss of reflexes, anesthesia, hypotonia and ataxia, but not paralysis. *5*, Section of ventral root or roots causes lower motor neuron defect. *6*, Section of a spinal or peripheral nerve results in combined motor and sensory losses. (From E. Gardner: Fundamentals of Neurology. See Gardner's text for more detailed discussion.)

origin lie in the spinal root ganglia. Some of the peripheral processes of these neurons are associated with neuromuscular and neurotendinous spindles, Pacinian corpuscles and free nerve networks. All these receptors are proprioceptor nerve endings which, through their connections, give rise to the sense of position and movement. The peripheral processes of other posterior root cells of origin of fasciculi cuneatus and gracilis are associated with Meissner's corpuscles, which, upon stimulation, give rise to sensation of light or discriminative touch, and Pacinian corpuscles, which are concerned with deep or massive pressure. The central processes of the spinal ganglia cells enter the cord through the dorsal roots, where they divide to form reflex connections, short descending branches, and short and long ascending branches. The long ascending branches which make up the fasciculi gracilis and

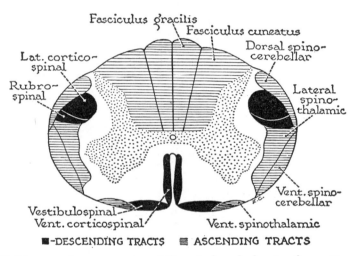

Fig. 47. Diagram of a cross section of the spinal cord, showing the position of the fiber tracts in the white matter.

cuneatus pass upward and terminate in the medulla on the same side of the cord; i.e., the fibers are uncrossed. The fibers of fasciculus gracilis which occupy the most medial position in the posterior columns, above the midthoracic region, come from the sacral, lumbar and lower thoracic segments. In consequence, they are associated with sense of position, movement and pressure-touch in the lower extremities and the lower part of the trunk. The fibers of fasciculus cuneatus which occupy the lateral positions in the posterior funiculus have their cells of origin in the upper five thoracic and cervical segments.

The terminal rami of fibers of these tracts are located in the nucleus gracilis and the nucleus cuneatus of the medulla oblongata. Here they form synapses with other neurons whose fibers cross to the opposite

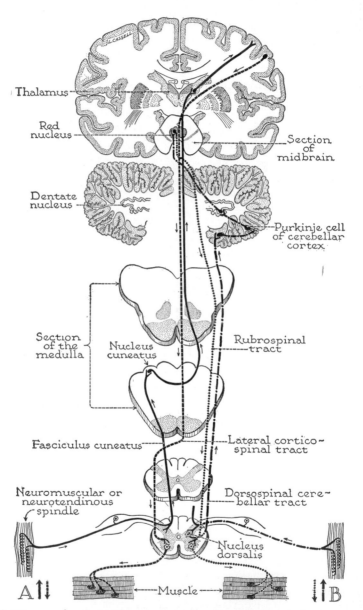

Fig. 48. Diagram showing pathways of muscle sense impulses. A, Conscious muscle
sense impulses. B, Unconscious muscle sense impulses.

side; the final link in the pathway is made up by neurons from the thalamus to the cerebrum. Thus, while the fasciculi cuneatus and gracilis are uncrossed, crossing of the second link in the chain of neurons results in the central representation of one side of the body lying in the cerebral hemisphere of the opposite side (Fig. 49).

A great deal of information is derived from sensory impulses conveyed over the dorsal columns. Our knowledge of the position and exact movement of the extremities eliminates the need for following them with our eyes when we are performing a task. We walk without looking at our thighs, legs or feet as long as the dorsal columns are intact. When we hit or kick an object, we look only at the object, since we know where our feet and hands are and can continuously adjust their route until contact is made. Sensation of touch-pressure enables us to recognize objects by feeling their shape and texture, and to be aware that an object or objects are touching our body at one or more points. Sensations of pressure enable us to discriminate between weights of objects. Because of the local sign of the receptors, we can identify the points on the body at which tactile stimuli or pressure is being applied.

2. VENTRAL SPINOTHALAMIC TRACTS. These tracts, which, like the fasciculi gracilis and cuneatus, convey impulses arising from stimulation of proprioceptor nerve endings and Meissner and Pacinian corpuscles, are formed by fibers of *second order neurons.* They ascend in the ventral funiculus (Figs. 47, 49). The first link in the pathway is the neuron whose cell body lies in the posterior root ganglion. The central fibers of the spinal ganglia may synapse in the dorsal gray matter with neurons whose axons leave the gray matter, cross to the opposite side of the cord and pass to the ventral spinothalamic tract in the contralateral ventral funiculus. A second route for the first link in the pathway is by way of the short ascending branches which pass up with the fibers of the posterior white columns and, after giving off collaterals, synapse with neurons in the gray matter at a higher segmental level; the axons of neurons cross the midline and join with the other fibers of the ventral spinothalamic tract. Thus the cells of origin of the second order neurons which make up the ventral spinothalamic tract lie in the gray matter of the opposite side. They terminate in the lateral nucleus of the thalamus. The third order neuron of the pathway passes between the thalamus and the homolateral cerebral hemisphere.

The structural arrangement which provides the uncrossed fasciculi gracilis and cuneatus and the crossed ventral spinothalamic tracts as pathways for afferent impulses of position and movement, touch and pressure, explains why hemisection of the cord does not result in a

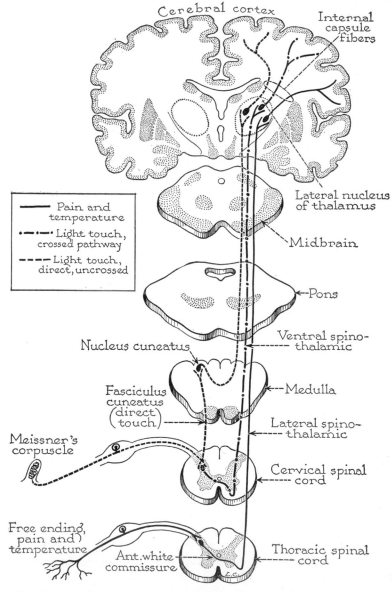

Fig. 49. Diagram of sensory mechanisms for pain, temperature and touch.

complete loss of these sensations; the crossed fibers provide for functional receptors after homolateral hemisection of the cord (Fig. 49).

3. DORSAL SPINOCEREBELLAR TRACTS. These tracts lie in the lateral funiculi. They are composed of fibers of *second order neurons*. The first link in the pathway between the neuromuscular spindles and the cerebellum is formed by the spinal ganglion cells. Rami of the central processes of these neurons pass to the nucleus dorsalis, which is located in the medial part of the posterior gray column. Here they synapse with the cells of origin whose axons pass to the outer margin of the lateral funiculus to form the spinocerebellar tract (Figs. 47, 48). The tracts are made up chiefly of cells of Clark's column (nucleus dorsalis) of the same side, although it is believed that cells of the dorsal nucleus of the opposite side may contribute some of the fibers. These second order neurons end in the cerebellum.

The spinocerebellar tracts, while an ascending or afferent pathway to the higher centers, cannot be called sensory, in that impulses traveling over this route do not reach consciousness (Fig. 48). The afferent impulses which arise in the neuromuscular receptors are those of "unconscious muscle sense" which, when integrated in the cerebellum, are concerned with muscular coordination.

4. LATERAL SPINOTHALAMIC TRACTS. These tracts are made up of second order neurons which constitute the second part of the pathway for pain and temperature. The peripheral processes of spinal ganglion cells which form the first link in the chain are associated with the free nerve endings which are the pain receptors, and the end bulbs of Krause and brushes of Ruffini which are the receptors for cold and heat, respectively. The central processes enter the cord in the medial division of the posterior roots, and pass up in the dorsal columns as short ascending branches. They give off collaterals to the gray matter at several levels before their terminal rami also enter the posterior gray columns. The collaterals and terminal rami synapse with the cells of origin of the lateral spinothalamic tract which lie in the dorsal portion of the posterior gray columns. Axons from the cells of origin pass to the opposite side of the cord and ascend without interruption in the lateral funiculi to end in the thalamus (Figs. 47, 49). The majority of the afferent neurons for pain and temperature impulses from the face send second order neurons whose fibers join with those from the cord to make up part of the lateral spinothalamic tract. The final link in the pathway for pain and temperature is made up of neurons passing from the thalamus to the cortex.

Since these tracts are crossed, hemisection of the cord results in loss of the sensations of pain and temperature on the opposite side of the body below the level of the section.

DESCENDING TRACTS.   The somatic efferent tracts have their cells of origin in the higher centers and terminate in the ventral gray columns of the spinal cord. Though such connections may afford an uninterrupted pathway between the higher level and the anterior horn cell of a motor unit, the more usual structural arrangement includes one or more intercalated neurons. The possibilities of the architectural arrangements should be borne in mind in considering integration and control of the effector muscles. Axons from a number of areas of the higher centers may have connections with a single ventral horn cell; in consequence, this cell with its peripheral process or axon in the ventral root of the spinal cord is called *the final common pathway.* Efferent impulses which reach the final common pathway may be either excitatory or inhibitory.

1. CORTICOSPINAL TRACTS.   The two corticospinal tracts (also called pyramidal tracts) form the great motor pathways from the cerebral cortex and carry impulses for voluntary movement. They are for the most part concerned with skilled voluntary movement requiring participation by a small number of muscle groups. Both tracts take their origin from the large pyramidal cells in (motor) Area 4 of the cerebral cortex. Just before entering the spinal cord, about four-fifths of the fibers undergo a decussation or crossing in the medulla oblongata. These decussating fibers, together with a lesser number of uncrossed fibers, form the large *lateral corticospinal tracts;* the remainder of the uncrossed fibers pass downwards to continue in the ventral funiculus as the *ventral corticospinal tracts* (Figs. 47, 48). The fibers of the ventral corticospinal tract which do not decussate in the medulla cross over a few at a time in the anterior white commissure at the successive levels of the cord at which they terminate; it is believed that a small number of these fibers do not cross at all. Fibers from both tracts end directly, or through intercalated neurons, on ventral horn cells. The lateral tracts supply muscles of the extremities. The fibers of the ventral tract convey motor impulses which reach the muscles of the trunk.

As in the afferent system, there is a crossed relation between cortical representation and peripheral structure. Cortical representation of the great majority of the efferent pathways is located on the side opposite to that of the effector muscles receiving the impulses. Lesions of the cortical areas or of the pyramids of the medulla result in a weakness in the opposite side of the body and marked decrement in performing precise movements (Fig. 46). The paralysis is not complete, however, because other fibers, which pass in the extrapyramidal tracts, remain. The results of lesions of the cord are more severe, since greater numbers of fibers may be involved. If inhibitory influences of the higher centers are interrupted, the reflex activity of the postural reflexes may be greatly exaggerated, and spastic paralysis results.

2. RUBROSPINAL TRACT.   This tract arises in the cells of the red nucleus of the midbrain. The fibers cross to the opposite side at once and descend in the lateral funiculus to end in relation to motor cells in the anterior columns of the cord. Since the red nucleus receives fibers from the cerebellum, the rubrospinal tracts may be said to carry impulses of unconscious muscle coordination, or, in other words, through it muscular movements are unconsciously adjusted to proprioceptive impulses.

3. VESTIBULOSPINAL TRACT.   This tract has its origin in the cells of the lateral vestibular nucleus of the medulla. It descends in the anterior funiculus without crossing and ends in the anterior columns around motor cells. This tract adjusts muscular movements to impulses received from the semicircular canals and so assists in the maintenance of muscle tone and equilibrium.

CONDUCTION AND INTEGRATION IN THE PERFORMANCE OF A SIMPLE TASK.   If we trace a typical impulse through the nervous system we shall see how the tracts of the spinal cord function as conducting pathways, and understand more clearly the operation of the nervous system as a whole. The course over which this impulse passes may be followed on the diagram in Figure 48.

The use of the muscles of the forearm and hand in carrying a suitcase requires almost constant adjustment of muscular movements. Although the act is initially consciously directed by the cerebral cortex, the details of these adjustments are largely automatic, and attention (consciousness) is centered mainly on where we are going rather than on the discrete muscular movements involved in supporting the burden while walking over uneven surfaces. These unconscious adjustments are made in response to proprioceptive impulses coming from muscles, joints and tendons of the arm and hand. Specialized receptors (neuromuscular and neurotendinous spindles) of afferent neurons receive impulses of position, stress or strain. The cell body of such a neuron is in the posterior root ganglion. Its axon enters the cord through the posterior root and, as previously described, divides into a long ascending and a short descending branch having collaterals and terminal rami. The impulse passes to a second neuron in the dorsal nucleus. The axon of this neuron carries the impulse by way of the dorsal spinocerebellar tract to the cerebellum. Connection is here made through internuncial neurons with the Purkinje cells of the cerebellar cortex. These large cells may be said to form the beginning of the efferent path. Their axons end in the dentate nuclei of the cerebellum. The cells of the dentate nucleus give rise to the great efferent tract from the cerebellum which reaches to the red nucleus of the midbrain. Here the impulse is relayed to the cells of origin of the rubrospinal tract, which descends in the lateral funiculus of the cord to end around motor cells in the anterior column. The axons of these cells pass out in the nerves of the brachial plexus to the muscles of the forearm and hand, and the impulses passing over them stimulate the muscles to contract.

The path traveled by this impulse is that of an elaborate neural arc with components comparable to a spinal reflex arc. It differs from a spinal reflex in that it involves many parts of the brain as well as the cord and many neurons instead of two or three. The principle, however, is the same and the response is reflex in nature; that is, it is an involuntary response to a stimulus.

Continuing with the same illustration, we know that we are conscious of sensations of stress and strain in the forearm and hand. What are the pathways by which the impulse reaches the conscious centers and by which the response is made?

The stimulus is received as before by special receptors in muscles, joints and tendons, and is carried by afferent neurons of the spinal nerves. The cell bodies of the neurons are in the posterior root ganglia, and their central processes pass into the cord in the posterior root. The impulse passes by way of the long ascending branches of the processes. These fibers form the fasciculus cuneatus, which ends in the medulla at the nucleus cuneatus. The axons of the cells of the nucleus cuneatus cross in the medulla and relay the impulse to the thalamus, from which it passes to the sensory area of the cerebral cortex by a third neuron. The impulse has now reached consciousness. Connection is established between the sensory area and motor area of the cerebrum by an internuncial neuron, and the impulse passes to the large pyramidal cells. The axons of these cells form the corticospinal tracts, the great motor pathways from the cerebrum. Since the impulse is destined for the muscles of the arm, it will be carried in the lateral corticospinal tract, which crosses in the medulla and ends in the cord around cells in the anterior column. These neurons carry the impulse by way of the nerves of the brachial plexus to the muscles of the upper extremity, and the position of arm is voluntarily changed. The diagram of these pathways (Fig. 48) shows that impulses which enter the cord on one side of the body pass to the opposite side of the brain. In like manner, the motor area on one side of the cerebrum controls movements of the opposite side of the body. Sensory and motor pathways both cross at some point in their course.

In tracing the course of these impulses, the object has been to show in a concrete way how a few of "the wheels go 'round." It is probable that any given impulse travels, not over one or two pathways as we have pictured it, but over many. It should be understood that the possibilities of the nervous mechanism are almost infinite.

SUMMARY

The spinal cord serves as a center for spinal reflexes and as a pathway for nerve impulses passing to and from the brain.

The spinal cord occupies the upper two thirds of the vertebral canal.

The cord consists of a central core of gray matter surrounded by white matter.

The gray matter is in the form of the capital letter H. The two forward projections are called anterior columns; the two extending backward are the posterior columns. The anterior and posterior columns are connected across the median plane by a band of gray matter called the central gray.

The cord shows conspicuous enlargements in the cervical and lumbar regions. The gray matter in these portions is increased because of the many cell bodies of nerve fibers supplying the arms and legs.

The thirty-one pairs of spinal nerves issue from the corresponding segments of the spinal cord that give them origin and are classified as eight cervical, twelve thoracic, five lumbar, five sacral and one coccygeal.

In all regions except the thoracic the anterior divisions of the spinal nerves interlace to form networks of nerves, called plexuses.

The spinal cord and attached nerve roots within the vertebral canal are surrounded by three coverings: dura mater, arachnoid and pia mater.

The cerebrospinal fluid is between the arachnoid and the pia mater.

In serving as a reflex center, the cord provides for the connections (synapses) between the afferent, internuncial, and efferent neurons of the reflex arc.

The predictability of response is an invariable characteristic of the "spinal" animal. The local sign relates the reflex response to the area stimulated.

Successful preparations will show flexor, extensor and scratch reflexes. Such phenomena as the local sign, irradiation and after-discharge may also be observed.

Reflexes may involve only one level of the spinal cord, or the impulses may spread upward or downward through internuncial neurons, producing an almost infinite variety of responses.

The white matter of the spinal cord serves as a conducting pathway for long ascending and descending tracts by which afferent impulses from the spinal nerves reach the brain, and those through which efferent impulses pass from motor centers in the brain to the anterior column cells of the cord to initiate and modify muscular movement.

Important ascending tracts are fasciculus gracilis, fasciculus cuneatus, dorsal spinocerebellar and lateral and ventral spinothalamic.

The descending tracts are lateral and ventral corticospinal, rubrospinal and vestibulospinal.

QUESTIONS FOR DISCUSSION

1. How are the right and left sides of the brain related to the right and left sides of the trunk and extremities?

2. What happens to the nerve impulse at synaptic connections? How is this related to convergence, divergence, spatial and temporal summation, occlusion?

3. In explaining the conscious act of removing your hand from a hot iron, follow the pathway of the nerve impulse from stimulation to response. What pathways are involved as you respond and then become conscious of the response and the pain?

Chapter 7

The Brain and Cranial Nerves

THE BRAIN is a suprasegmental monitoring apparatus concerned with all somatic and visceral functions. It serves as a center for integrating responses to sensory stimuli arriving by way of the ascending tracts of the spinal cord and of the cranial nerves, and to nervous activity of its various component parts. It contains centers (i.e., groups of neurons with their functional connections which provide for integrated responses; apexes of several functional neural arcs) which control respiration, circulation, temperature regulation and fine adjustment of voluntary movement, as well as areas for the senses of sight, smell, hearing, balance, touch and taste. It contains centers or areas for associative memory, which allow us to store, recall and make use of past experience through the establishment of the relatively simple condi-

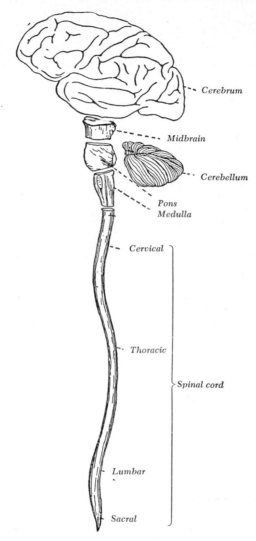

Fig. 50. Diagram illustrating the gross divisions of the central nervous system. (Morris, Human Anatomy, The Blakiston Co.)

tioned reflexes and through the more complex and less well understood process of learning.

The brain is defined anatomically as that part of the nervous system which lies within the cranial cavity of the skull. It arises in the embryo as a development of the head end of the neural tube. The canal extending throughout the length of the tube, which in the spinal cord is reduced almost to obliteration, widens out in the different parts of the brain to form spaces called *ventricles* which are filled with cerebrospinal fluid.

Differences in size, shape and function of the different portions of the brain assist in its division for convenience of description into three chief masses, the *brain stem*, the *cerebellum*, and the *cerebrum*. The parts of the brain stem from below upward are *medulla, pons* and *midbrain*. The cerebrum appears as a huge flowering outgrowth from the upper end of the stem. It covers most of the midbrain. The cerebellum develops as an extension from the lower part of the brain stem or hind brain. The main divisions of the central nervous system are shown in Figure 50.

PARTS OF THE BRAIN—STRUCTURE AND FUNCTION

Medulla. The medulla lies between the spinal cord and the pons (Fig. 51). Its structure closely resembles that of the cord. All the ascending and descending pathways of the cord are represented here. Some of the fiber tracts end in the medulla (fasciculi gracilis and cuneatus), while others pass through it, crossing from one side to the other without interruption (lateral corticospinal tract). The central canal of the cord opens out on the dorsal surface of the medulla into the large space, the fourth ventricle. The medulla contains the nuclei (i.e., a large group of cell bodies) of origin of the last four cranial nerves, nine to twelve inclusive. The reticular formation occupies a large portion of the medulla. Within the medulla are such vital centers as the cardiac, vasomotor and respiratory centers.

Pons. The pons lies above the medulla and in front of the cerebellum. It consists of a bridge of fibers which connect the halves of the cerebellum and join the midbrain above with the medulla below. The pons forms an important connecting link in the corticopontocerebellar path by which the cerebral hemispheres and the cerebellum are united. Nuclei of the fifth, sixth, seventh and eighth cranial nerves are located in the pons.

Midbrain. The midbrain is the short part of the brain stem which lies just above the pons (Fig. 51). It consists of a dorsal part, the tectum, and a ventral part, the cerebral peduncles. A canal, called the *cerebral aqueduct* (aqueduct of Sylvius), passes lengthwise through the midbrain to connect the third and fourth ventricles. The tectum presents two pairs of rounded elevations, the corpora quadrigemina, which serve as relay centers for visual and auditory reflexes. The *cerebral peduncles* are two large diverging stalks which pass into each half of the cerebrum (Figs. 51, 57). They are composed of bundles of fibers which form conducting pathways for impulses to and from the cerebrum. Nuclei of the third and fourth cranial nerves are located in the midbrain. The *red nucleus,* which contains the cells of origin of the rubrospinal tract, is in the forward part of the midbrain. Little is known about the red nucleus. While it plays a prominent role in rela-

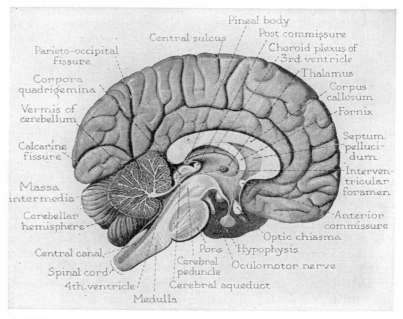

Fig. 51. Midsagittal section of the human brain. (Sobotta and McMurrich.)

tion to complex muscular movements in the cats, it is of less consequence in the higher species and may have little or no functional importance in man.

Cerebellum. The cerebellum lies in the posterior cranial fossa, covered by the tentlike roof of dura mater, the tentorium, which separates it from the posterior part of the cerebrum. It is composed of a middle portion, the vermis, and two lateral hemispheres (Fig. 51). The cerebellum is connected to the brain stem by three bands of fibers called *peduncles.* The superior cerebellar peduncle establishes connections with the midbrain. The middle cerebellar peduncle passes through the pons across the midline to unite the cerebellar hemispheres. The inferior cerebellar peduncle, which contains fibers of the dorsal spinocerebellar tracts of the cord, connects with the medulla. The outermost layer of the cerebellum is composed of gray matter. It is called the cerebellar cortex. The large Purkinje cells, which are important efferent neurons of the cerebellum, are in the cortex. There are some deeply placed masses of gray matter within the cerebellum. The dentate nuclei are the most important of these masses.

All activities of the cerebellum are below the level of consciousness. Its main function is that of a reflex center through which coordination

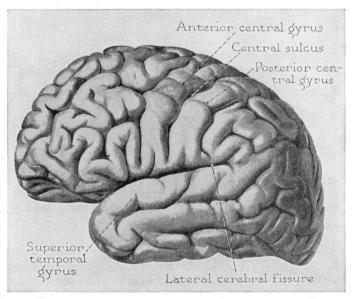

Fig. 52. Lateral view of the human cerebral hemisphere. (Sobotta and McMurrich.)

and refinement of muscular movements are effected and by which changes in tone and strength of contraction are related to maintaining posture and equilibrium.

Cerebrum. The cerebrum is the largest and most prominent part of the brain. The cerebrum is divided into right and left hemispheres by a deep cleft, the great *longitudinal fissure.* The cerebral hemispheres have an outer coating of gray matter called the cerebral cortex spread over an inner mass of white matter. There is a space or ventricle within each hemisphere which connects with the third ventricle through an opening, the interventricular (Monro) foramen. These two cavities are called the lateral ventricles.

THE CEREBRAL CORTEX. The cortex or gray mantle of the cerebrum is thrown into numerous folds called convolutions or *gyri* (Fig. 52).

The grooves between the convolutions are *sulci*. Such an arrangement makes it possible for a large surface area (estimated at about 220,000 square millimeters) to be contained within the narrow confines of the cranial vault. Deep sulci or fissures divide each hemisphere into distinct areas known as frontal, parietal, temporal and occipital lobes. The *central sulcus* (fissure of Rolando) separates the frontal and parietal lobes. The *lateral fissure* (fissure of Sylvius) separates the temporal lobe below from the frontal and parietal above. The *parietooccipital* fissure marks off the boundaries of the occipital lobe. There

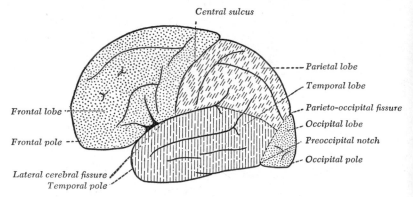

Fig. 53. Diagram of the lobes on the lateral aspect of the human cerebral hemispheres. (Ranson, The Anatomy of the Nervous System.)

are five lobes in each hemisphere: frontal, parietal, temporal, occipital, and insula. The insula lies within the lateral fissure and is not visible on the surface. The fissures and lobes with the exception of insula are shown in Figure 53.

LOCALIZATION OF FUNCTION IN THE CEREBRAL CORTEX. Our knowledge of cortical localization has been developed by observation of the effects of electrical and chemical stimuli and by experimental and clinical observation of the effects of removal or injury of various portions of the cortex (Figs. 54, 55). The responses to electrical stimulation may be either discrete and highly localized, such as those involving small muscle groups or sensation referred to a specific part of the body, or may be generalized responses. Other areas do not appear to be excitable by electrical or chemical means. There are, then, motor and sensory areas and association areas. The associative functions of the cerebral cortex are concerned with emotion and intellectual processes involving memory, reasoning and judgment. The cortex is subdivided into relatively limited areas which are referred to by number. The numerical designation will be mentioned in certain cases which

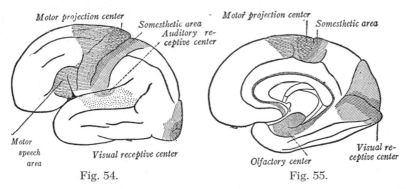

Fig. 54.   Fig. 55.

Fig. 54. Diagram of the localization areas or cortical projection centers on the lateral aspect of the cerebral hemisphere. (Ranson, The Anatomy of the Nervous System.)

Fig. 55. Diagram of the cortical projection centers on the medial aspect of the cerebral hemispheres. (Ranson, The Anatomy of the Nervous System.)

are frequently referred to in the scientific literature, so as to aid the student in his supplementary reading.

The motor area lies just in front of the central fissure in the anterior central convolution. Area 4, associated with voluntary movement, contains most of the large pyramidal cells which are the cells of origin of the corticospinal tracts. Responses of individual or small groups of muscles to electrical stimulation have shown that the cells are arranged along the convolution in an inverted order beginning with the motor cells for movement of the toes in the upper part at the great longitudinal fissure and ending with the motor projection for the face in the lower part of the gyrus near the lateral cerebral fissure. As would be expected, on the basis of what we have learned about the crossing of the fiber tracts, stimulation of cells in the right hemisphere causes movement of the muscles of the left side of the body.

The sensory or somesthetic area, designated as Areas 1, 2 and 3, is in the posterior central convolution. It is associated with cutaneous and deep sensibility, i.e., heat, cold, touch, pressure, muscle sense and pain. Localization shows the same general pattern as the immediately rostral motor area; i.e., sensory representation of the contralateral toes is located uppermost near the central longitudinal fissure with areas for the trunk, arm and face lying at successively lower levels nearer the lateral cerebral fissure. Various parts of the somesthetic area have been stimulated electrically in human patients requiring brain surgery under local anesthetic. The sensations which result are called *paresthetic,* i.e., numbness, tingling and constriction, which are interpreted as arising from specifically localized regions of the body. More refined or critical sensation depends upon other areas of the cortex. Pain does not result from stimulation of Areas 1, 2 or 3.

In addition, the cortex contains certain areas or centers concerned with hearing, seeing, smelling and verbalization (language mechanisms).

The *auditory area* is in the superior convolution of the temporal lobe just below the lateral fissure. The area is connected with the organ of hearing, and functions in interpretation of sound.

The *visual area* is in the calcarine fissure of the occipital lobe.

The *olfactory area* is located on the medial surface of the cerebral hemisphere in the hippocampal convolution and hippocampus. These areas are concerned with the sense of smell and probably taste. There are regions or areas whose destruction results in decrement or failure of the language mechanisms. These disorders are called aphasias. The areas include Area 44 (Broca's area), which lies in the posterior part of the inferior frontal convolution just anterior to the lower part of Area 6 (which is immediately rostral to Area 4), and parts of the association areas in the temporal and parietal lobes. Area 44 is concerned with muscular movements necessary in pronouncing words. Verbalization is a complex process which is bound up with the auditory, visual and writing centers. It involves memory of the sound of the spoken word and of the muscular movements made in pronouncing the word; in the literate it involves memory of the sight of the written word as well as of the muscular movements made in writing the word.

No definite function has been assigned to the remaining portions, but it is assumed that they are concerned with intellectual processes involving memory, reasoning and judgment.

THE ELECTROENCEPHALOGRAM (Fig. 56). The electrical activity of the brain may be recorded by means of an oscillograph connected to electrodes placed upon various areas of the scalp. Evidence of cortical activity is seen by changes in the pattern of the "brain waves" as the result of any attempt to see detail if the eyes are open, mental activity in general, apprehension, or attention to loud noises or brain injury. The alpha waves, or slow, fairly regular waves with a frequency of 8 to 12 per second occurring in successive trains which last one to thirty seconds, are often obtained from the occipital area. The beta waves of 18 to 32 per second are more common from frontal and parietal areas. The student is referred to a neurology or a standard advanced physiology text for a more detailed discussion of the electroencephalographic patterns.

THE CONDITIONED REFLEX. The cerebrum is essential to the establishment of conditioned reflexes which play an important part in habit formation and reactions of human beings. In the unconditioned reflexes which have already been discussed, a stimulus brings about the response without previous training, and the response is specific for the stimulus. Thus chemical and mechanical stimuli from food in the mouth bring about salivation. In conditioned responses previous training is necessary for forming associations, and the stimulus may be neutral or quite unrelated to the response. Salivation from visual and olfactory stimuli associated with the presentation of food is a familiar example. Even thinking of sucking a lemon is sufficient to cause saliva-

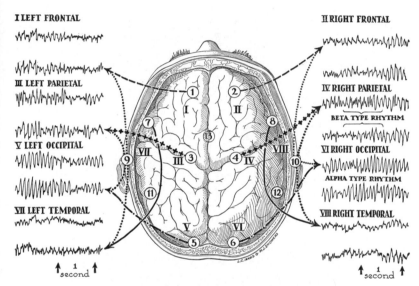

Fig. 56. Diagram of electroencephalogram: 1, 2, 3, etc., are relative locations on the brain of electrodes placed on the subject's scalp. These may be used in several combinations; one combination is shown above where 1, 2, 3, etc., are attached to 9, 10. The regions of the brain represented by records of electrical waves are indicated by Roman numerals. Typical alpha rhythm of 8–12 waves per second and beta rhythm of 18–32 waves per second are shown.

tion if the taste of a lemon is familiar. If puppies are allowed to see and smell meat, no salivation will occur if they have been kept on a milk diet and are unfamiliar with meat as a food.

In the conditioned reflex, the response which would normally accompany or follow the unconditioned stimulus occurs when neutral stimuli which have been associated with that response are given. Experimentally, such widely diverse responses as constriction of the pupil, sleeping or vomiting have been elicited by the ringing of a bell. Previous training has established the association of the ringing of the bell with the unconditioned stimuli bringing about these responses. Formation of conditioned responses may be easily recognized when observing reactions of young children. Conditioned reflexes may also be observed in many routine responses of adults. Examples of such reactions are applying the brakes or shifting gear when driving, turning out lights when leaving a room, and "automatically" sorting objects such as surgical instruments.

FIBER TRACTS. The white matter of the cerebrum consists of fiber

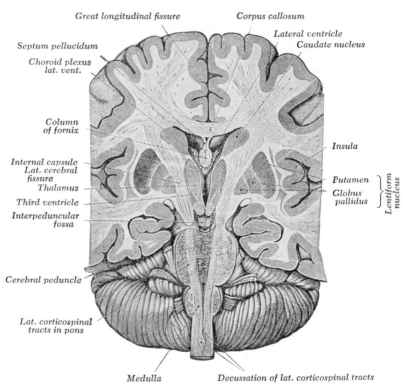

Fig. 57. Section through the brain in the axis of the brain stem. (Toldt.)

tracts which may be grouped into three divisions: (1) the association tracts, (2) the commissural tracts, (3) the projection tracts.

The *association tracts* connect adjacent and distant convolutions of the same hemisphere, so that each convolution has a possible connection with every other one.

The *commissural tracts* are composed of fibers which connect the two hemispheres. The principal commissural tract is the corpus callosum. Its upper surface can be seen in the floor of the great longitudinal fissure (Fig. 57). These tracts function to correlate the action of the two halves of the brain. When the two hands and arms are used together as in tossing balls, so that several are kept in the air at the same time, the use of the commissural fibers of the corpus callosum is necessary to coordinate the movements of the two extremities.

Projection tracts include the system of fibers which connect the cerebral cortex to other parts of the central nervous system. The corticospinal tracts are examples of projection fibers (Fig. 57).

THE BASAL NUCLEI.   Embedded in the white matter of the cerebral hemispheres are deeply placed gray masses which constitute the basal nuclei, commonly called the basal ganglia (Fig. 57). The thalamus and the corpus striatum form the important nuclei.

The *thalamus* is a large ovoid structure situated at the base of the cerebrum. It is composed of two conspicuous nuclear masses, separated by a deep median cleft, the third ventricle. The two parts arc connected by a bridge of gray matter, called the massa intermedia. The thalamus is an important relay station in which sensory pathways of the cord and brain stem form synapses on their way to the cerebral cortex. Evidence indicates that the thalamus acts also as a center of primitive uncritical sensation. Electrical stimulation causes a feeling that "something is happening" which gives rise to an exaggerated sensation of pleasure or pain.

The *corpus striatum* is composed of the caudate nucleus, lentiform nucleus and the internal capsule. The broad band of fibers of the internal capsule separates the lentiform nucleus on the lateral side from the caudate nucleus and the thalamus on the medial. There is a lack of agreement among neurologists regarding the functions of the corpus striatum. One view is that these nuclei exert a steadying effect upon voluntary movements, but are incapable of initiating such movements.

THE HYPOTHALAMUS.   The hypothalamus lies beneath the thalamus and forms the floor and part of the lateral wall of the third ventricle. It contains the temperature-regulating centers. The center for controlling heat-loss functions, such as sweating and panting, is located in the anterior part; the other center, for preventing heat loss by vasoconstriction and for increasing heat production by shivering, is in the posterior part. Through connections with the posterior lobe of the pituitary gland, the hypothalamus plays an important part in the regulation of water, fat and carbohydrate metabolism. There is some evidence that a center for controlling sleep is present in the hypothalamus. Certain emotional manifestations are probably produced by the hypothalamus when it is released from the control of the cerebral cortex.

MENINGES

The membranes covering the brain are the same as those covering the cord: namely, dura mater, arachnoid and pia mater (Fig. 58).

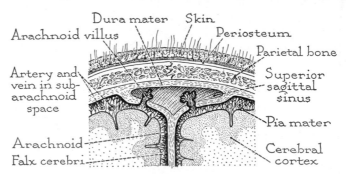

Fig. 58. Meninges (after Netter).

Dura Mater. The dura mater is adherent to the inner surface of the cranium where it serves the double function of an internal periosteum and a covering for the brain. Two conspicuous folds of dura mater, the falx cerebri and the tentorium cerebelli, are given off from the deep surface.

The *falx cerebri* is a sickle-shaped partition which passes in the great longitudinal fissure between the hemispheres. Its inferior border arches over the corpus callosum.

The *tentorium cerebelli* forms a roof for the posterior cranial cavity and separates the cerebellum from the posterior part of the cerebrum.

The dura mater consists of two layers which separate along certain lines to form venous channels, sinuses, for the return of blood from the brain (Fig. 222, p. 349). The more important sinuses are the superior sagittal sinus along the superior border of the falx cerebri, the inferior sagittal sinus on the inferior border, the straight sinus where the falx cerebri joins the tentorium, the transverse sinus along the occipital and temporal bones, and the cavernous sinus in the region of the sella turcica.

Arachnoid. The arachnoid membrane is a fine membrane loosely disposed over the surface of the brain. It does not dip down into the sulci between convolutions. The arachnoid membrane forms finger-like projections, called villi, which penetrate the walls of the venous sinuses and extend into them. The subarachnoid space, like its counterpart in the spinal cord, contains the cerebrospinal fluid.

Pia Mater. The pia mater is closely adherent to the surface of the brain and is carried down into the sulci between convolutions. The pia mater lines the ventricles and forms the choroid plexuses of these spaces.

CEREBROSPINAL FLUID

The cerebrospinal fluid is a clear, slightly viscous liquid circulating in the subarachnoid space about the brain and spinal cord. Its chemical composition is somewhat similar to that of lymph and closely resembles that of the aqueous humor of the eye. About 150 cc. are found in the subarachnoid space under pressure equivalent to that of 110 mm. of Ringer's solution. It forms a watery cushion for the brain and spinal cord, thus protecting them from injury. Since it contains

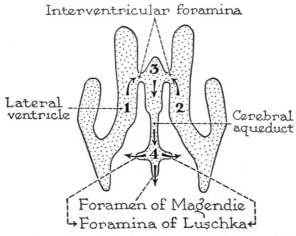

Fig. 59. Diagram of ventricles and course of cerebrospinal fluid.

nutrient substances and waste products, the cerebrospinal fluid apparently plays an important part in metabolism also.

This fluid is formed principally in the choroid plexuses of all four ventricles. Choroid plexuses are highly vascular tufts of tissue found on the roofs of the third and fourth ventricles and portions of the wall of each lateral ventricle. Fluid formed in the lateral ventricles passes (Fig. 59) through the interventricular foramina (Monro), where it is joined by the fluid produced in the third ventricle, to pass through the cerebral aqueduct (Sylvius) into the fourth ventricle. The fluid from all four ventricles passes from the roof of the fourth ventricle through the foramen of Magendie and foramina of Luschka to the subarachnoid space.

It slowly circulates down the posterior surface of the spinal cord and up the anterior surface of the cord and brain to the arachnoid villi. These villi are minute finger-like processes of the arachnoid projecting into the venous sinuses on the superior surface of the brain. As the cerebrospinal fluid reaches the arachnoid villi it is absorbed into the venous sinuses and systemic circulation.

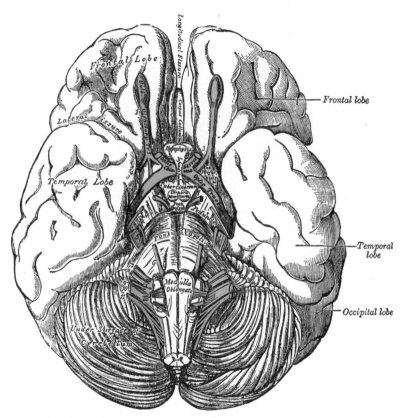

Fig. 60. The base of the brain, showing cranial nerves. (Gray, Anatomy of the Human Body, Lea & Febiger.)

CRANIAL NERVES

In the early discussion of nervous tissue it was noted that the cerebrospinal nerves form a part of the peripheral portion of the nervous system. Cerebrospinal nerves, as the name implies, include the spinal and cranial nerves. Cranial nerves are designated as those, attached to the brain, which pass through the foramina of the skull. Twelve pairs symmetrically arranged are distributed mainly to the structures of the head and neck. Because of their diversity of function, the nerves have been given names as well as numbers. Most of the nerves have motor and sensory roots, but a few have sensory roots only. The sensory components have their cell bodies in ganglia outside the brain; the cell bodies of the efferent components are in nuclei within the brain. Table 3 (p. 126) presents a summary of the principal features of the cranial nerves.

Olfactory Nerve. The olfactory nerve fibers are the central processes (axons) of the bipolar cell bodies situated in the olfactory area of the mucous membrane of the nose. As the axons pass upward from their cell bodies, they form plexuses in the mucous membrane. The fibers from the upper parts of these plexuses collect into about twenty filaments on each side. These filaments pass through the openings in the cribriform plate of the ethmoid bone and synapse with the cells of the olfactory bulb (Fig. 60). From the olfactory bulb, fibers pass inward to the hippocampus of the cerebrum mediating the sense of smell.

Optic Nerve. Like the olfactory nerve, the optic nerve is purely sensory. Its function is to carry the impulses for the sense of sight. This nerve is composed of the central processes (axons) of the ganglion cells of the retina. The fibers emerge from the eye in a single trunk through the choroid and sclerotic coats, a little to the nasal side of the center (Fig. 74, B, p. 142). The optic nerve traverses the orbital fat and passes through the optic foramen into the cranial cavity, and then backward and medialward to the chiasm. Here the optic fibers undergo partial decussation; those from the nasal half of the retina cross to the opposite side, while those of the temporal half continue to the thalamus uncrossed (Fig. 77, p. 149). Both groups of fibers form synapses in the thalamus with neurons which convey the visual impulses to the calcarine fissure in the occipital lobe.

Oculomotor Nerve. This nerve contains both sensory and motor fibers. Sensory fibers arise from all but two of the extrinsic eye muscles, forming the superior and inferior branches of the oculomotor nerve. These banches become one trunk as the nerve passes into the cranial cavity through the supraorbital fissure. The superior branch carries afferent impulses from the superior rectus and levator palpebrae muscles; the inferior branch carries the afferent impulses from the medial rectus, inferior rectus and inferior oblique muscles. Efferent fibers from the Edinger-Westphal nucleus of the midbrain run to the ciliary ganglion, where they synapse with neurons supplying the iris and ciliary muscle within the eye. The oculomotor nucleus just ventral to the Edinger-Westphal nucleus sends efferent fibers to the extrinsic orbital muscles mentioned above. The oculomotor nerve, then, provides for muscle sense and movement in most of the muscles of the eye, constriction of the pupil and accommodation of the eye (Figs. 74, 75, pp. 142, 143).

Trochlear Nerve. This is the smallest of the cranial nerves. It supplies muscle sense and the impulse for movement to the superior

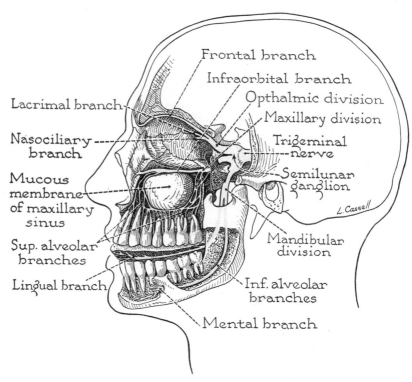

Fig. 61. Diagram showing distribution of the trigeminal nerve.

oblique muscle of the eye. The afferent fibers from the superior oblique muscle pass through the supraorbital fissure into the brain. Like the oculomotor nerve, the efferent component has its origin in the midbrain (trochlear nucleus), from which the motor impulses go to the superior oblique muscle.

Trigeminal Nerve (Figs. 61, 62). Following the smallest cranial nerve is the largest or trigeminal nerve. It is composed of a large sensory root, and a smaller motor root. It is sometimes called the great sensory nerve of the head because it supplies the sense of touch, pain, heat and cold to the skin of the face and scalp and the mucous membranes of the head. The ophthalmic division sends sensory fibers to the skin of the upper eyelid, side of the nose, forehead and anterior half of the scalp. In addition, it supplies the lacrimal gland, cornea (pain only) and the conjunctiva. The maxillary division mediates sensory impulses from the skin of the cheek, anterior temporal region,

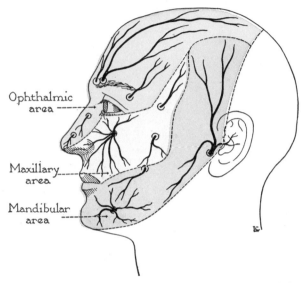

Ophthalmic
area

Maxillary
area

Mandibular
area

Fig. 62. Diagram showing skin areas supplied by three divisions of the fifth cranial nerve. (Redrawn from Gray.)

upper lip, upper teeth and mucous membranes of the nose. The mandibular division carries sensory impulses from the side of the head, chin, mucous membrane of the mouth, lower teeth and anterior two thirds of the tongue. The cell bodies of these three divisions are located in the semilunar (Gasserian) ganglion. From the semilunar ganglion the ophthalmic division runs through the supraorbital fissure, the maxillary through the foramen rotundum, and the mandibular through the foramen ovale. The main trunk of the fifth nerve passes from the semilunar ganglion into the pons.

The smaller motor root has its origin in the pons, and runs underneath the semilunar ganglion to become part of the trunk of the mandibular division of the trigeminal nerve. Motor fibers supply the muscles of mastication.

Abducens Nerve. This cranial nerve completes the innervation of the extrinsic eye muscles by supplying afferent and efferent fibers to the

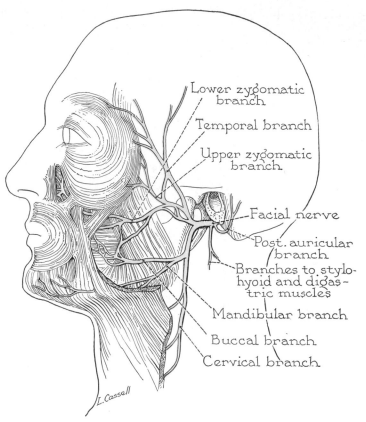

Fig. 63. Diagram showing distribution of the facial nerve. (Redrawn and modified from Cunningham.)

lateral rectus muscle for muscle sense and motion. From the lateral rectus, impulses pass into the cranial cavity through the supraorbital fissure to the pons. Outgoing motor impulses follow the same path.

Facial Nerve. The seventh nerve consists of motor and sensory divisions; of the two, the motor (in contrast to number five) is the larger. From the taste buds of the anterior two thirds of the tongue afferent fibers pass to their cell bodies in the geniculate ganglion. The axons of geniculate neurons enter the cranial cavity through the internal acoustic meatus. Their termination is in the medulla, where they synapse with cells going to the cerebral cortex and giving the sensation of taste.

The motor division arises in the lower part of the pons, leaves the cranial cavity through the internal acoustic meatus and the facial canal, and finally passes out of the skull by way of the stylomastoid foramen. Portions of the efferent nerve supply the muscles of facial expression

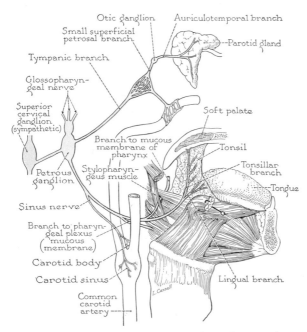

Fig. 64. Diagram showing the distribution of the glossopharyngeal nerve. (Redrawn and modified from Cunningham.)

for motion. Other portions go to the submaxillary, sublingual and lacrimal glands for secretion. The efferent distribution to the facial muscles is shown in Figure 63.

Acoustic Nerve. This cranial nerve has two parts known as the vestibular and cochlear nerves. Both divisions are confined to carrying impulses for sensation from the inner ear. Afferent fibers of the cochlear nerve arise in the cochlea and pass to their cell bodies in the spiral ganglion near the cochlea. The axons of these neurons run through the internal acoustic meatus and terminate in the medulla. Synapses with neurons there continue the communication of impulses for the sensation of hearing to the cerebral cortex.

The vestibular nerve mediates the impulses for equilibration. Connections are made in the medulla with neurons of the vestibulospinal tract and with neurons which relay impulses to the cerebellum. The

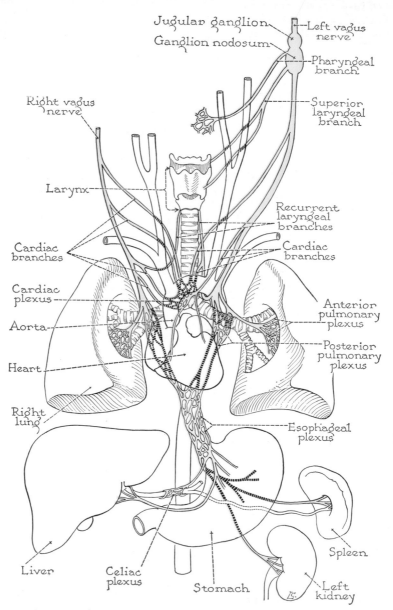

Fig. 65. Diagram showing the distribution of the vagus nerve. (Redrawn and modified from Cunningham.)

nerve arises in fibers from the semicircular canals, utricle and saccule of the internal ear (Fig. 70, B). The cell bodies of these neurons lie in juxtaposition to the spiral ganglion in the vestibular ganglion. The vestibular nerve enters the cranium through the internal acoustic meatus, and at this point joins the cochlear nerve to become one trunk, the acoustic nerve.

Glossopharyngeal Nerve (Fig. 64). By afferent fibers the glosso-pharyngeal nerve provides for reflex control of the heart, taste and swallowing reflexes. These impulses are initiated by stimulation of the carotid sinus, taste buds of the posterior third of the tongue and mucous membrane of the pharynx, soft palate and tonsils. The afferent neurons, whose cell bodies are found in the jugular and petrosal ganglia, enter the skull and pass into the medulla by way of the jugular foramen.

Efferent fibers to the muscles of the pharynx (for swallowing) and the parotid gland (for secretion) originate in cell bodies in the medulla. They follow the path of the afferent fibers from the brain to the structures which they innervate.

Vagus Nerve (Fig. 65). The tenth cranial nerve has the most exten-sive distribution of any in this series, since it goes to structures in the thorax and abdomen as well as in the head and neck. Afferent impulses are obtained from the mucous membrane of the larynx, trachea and bronchi, lungs, arch of the aorta, esophagus and stomach. It is through this innervation that the reflex control of respiratory rate and acces-sory respiratory reflexes (coughing, sneezing), reflex inhibition of heart rate and the sensation of hunger are facilitated. Briefly, sensory fibers run to their cell bodies in the jugular ganglion and ganglion nodosum, and thence to the medulla through the jugular foramen.

Cell bodies of the efferent component lie in the medulla. Their fibers leave the skull in the jugular foramen, pass through the jugular gan-glion and ganglion nodosum, and at the root of the neck the right and left vagi traverse divergent paths. In general, the branches of the vagi are meningeal, auricular, pharyngeal, superior laryngeal, superior and inferior cardiac, recurrent laryngeal, bronchial, esophageal, pericardial and abdominal. As can be noted in the diagram of distribution, the right and left vagi come together in certain areas of the thorax and abdomen to form a plexus or network of nerve fibers about certain structures that they innervate. Some of the structures supplied by motor fibers include muscles of the larynx, heart, smooth muscle of the stomach and small intestine, smooth muscle of the trachea, bronchi and bronchioles, glands of the stomach and pancreas. This portion of the vagus nerve provides for swallowing, speech, inhibition of the heart, peristalsis, contraction of the musculature in the respiratory tract and secretion of certain glands of the digestive system.

Accessory Nerve (Fig. 66). The eleventh cranial nerve consists of two parts called bulbar and spinal divisions. Afferent and efferent components carry muscle sense and motor impulses for the palate muscles, sternocleidomastoid and trapezius muscles. Entering the skull

Table 3
The Cranial Nerves

NUM-BER	NAME	EXIT FROM SKULL	STRUCTURES SUPPLIED BY AFFERENT FIBERS (FUNCTION)	STRUCTURES SUPPLIED BY EFFERENT FIBERS (FUNCTION)
I	Olfactory	Cribriform plate	Mucous membrane of upper third of nasal passage (Smell)	None
II	Optic	Optic foramen	Retina of eye (Sight)	None
III	Oculomotor	Supraorbital fissure	Levator palpebrae Superior rectus Medial rectus Inferior rectus Inferior oblique (Muscle sense)	Same group of eye muscles (Eye movement) Ciliary muscle (Accommodation) Iris (Constriction of pupil)
IV	Trochlear	Supraorbital fissure	Superior oblique (Muscle sense)	Superior oblique (Motion)
V	Trigeminal	Three divisions: Ophthalmic-supraorbital fissure Maxillary-foramen rotundum Mandibular-foramen ovale	Skin of face and anterior one half of scalp Mucous membranes in head Teeth Anterior two thirds of tongue (Pain, cold, heat, touch) Chewing muscles (Muscle sense) Cornea of eye (Pain) Lacrimal gland (Reflexes)	Muscles of mastication (Muscle movement)
VI	Abducens	Supraorbital fissure	Lateral rectus (Muscle sense)	Lateral rectus (Motion)
VII	Facial	Internal acoustic meatus Stylomastoid foramen	Taste buds of anterior two thirds of tongue (Taste) Muscles of facial expression (Muscle Sense)	Muscles of facial expression (Motion) Submaxillary gland Sublingual gland (Secretion) Lacrimal gland
VIII	Acoustic	Cochlear division—internal acoustic meatus Vestibular division—internal acoustic meatus	Cochlear division spiral organ (Hearing) Vestibular division Utricle Saccule Semicircular canals (Equilibrium)	None
IX	Glossopharyngeal	Jugular foramen	Carotid sinus (Cardiac reflex) Mucous membrane of pharynx, soft palate, tonsils, posterior one third of tongue (Swallowing reflex) Taste buds posterior one third of tongue (Taste)	Muscles of pharynx (Swallowing) Parotid gland (Secretion)

Table 3
The Cranial Nerves

NUM-BER	NAME	EXIT FROM SKULL	STRUCTURES SUPPLIED BY AFFERENT FIBERS (FUNCTION)	STRUCTURES SUPPLIED BY EFFERENT FIBERS (FUNCTION)
X	Vagus	Jugular foramen	Mucous membrane of larynx, trachea, bronchi (Respiratory reflex) Lungs (Reflex control) Arch of aorta (Reflex inhibition of heart) Stomach (Hunger)	Muscles of palate, pharynx, esophagus (Swallowing) Muscles of larynx (Speech) Heart (Inhibition) Smooth muscle of stomach and small intestine (Peristalsis) Smooth muscle of trachea, bronchi, bronchioles (Contraction) Glands of stomach and pancreas (Secretion)
XI	Spinal accessory	Jugular foramen	Palate and neck muscles (Muscle sense)	Sternocleidomastoid Trapezius Palate muscles (Motion)
XII	Hypoglossal	Hypoglossal foramen	Muscles of tongue (Muscle sense)	Muscles of tongue (Motion)

through the jugular foramen, afferent fibers terminate and efferent fibers arise in the medulla.

Hypoglossal Nerve. From the medulla the hypoglossal nerve runs dorsal to the vertebral artery through the hypoglossal foramen to the inferior surface of the tongue. Both muscle sense and motion are provided for the muscles of the tongue by the hypoglossal nerve.

SUMMARY

The brain is composed of cerebrum, cerebellum, medulla, pons and midbrain.

The medulla lies between the spinal cord and the pons. It serves as a conducting pathway for tracts carrying impulses to and from the higher centers and contains such vital centers as the cardiac, vasomotor and respiratory centers.

The pons consists of a bridge of fibers which connect the halves of the cerebellum and join the midbrain above with the medulla below.

The midbrain is composed of the corpora quadrigemina and the cerebral peduncles. The corpora quadrigemina serve as relay centers for the visual and auditory reflexes. The cerebral peduncles are composed of bundles of fibers which form conducting pathways for impulses to and from the cerebrum.

The cerebellum serves as a reflex center through which muscular movements maintaining posture and equilibrium are coordinated.

The cerebrum is divided into right and left hemispheres by the great longitudinal fissure.

Each hemisphere is divided into five lobes: frontal, parietal, temporal, occipital, and insula.

Certain functions are localized in definite regions of the cerebral cortex. These comprise the motor, sensory, auditory, visual, speech and olfactory areas. It is assumed that the remaining portions are

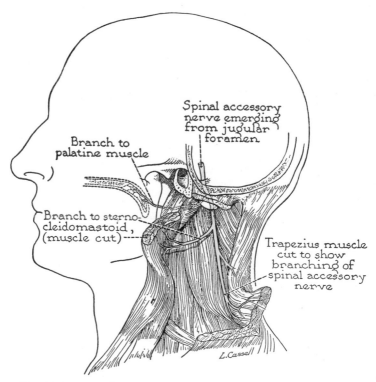

Fig. 66. Diagram showing distribution of the spinal accessory nerve.

concerned with intellectual processes involving memory, reasoning and judgment.

The fiber tracts of the cerebrums are the association, the commissural and the projection tracts.

The basal nuclei include the thalamus, the lentiform and the caudate nuclei.

The thalamus is a relay station for impulses passing to and from the cerebral cortex. It serves as a center of primitive sensation through which the individual becomes vaguely conscious of pleasurable or painful sensations.

The hypothalamus contains the temperature-regulating centers; through connections with the posterior lobe of the pituitary gland, it plays an important part in the regulation of water, fat and carbohydrate metabolism.

The cerebrospinal fluid is formed in the choroid plexuses of all four ventricles. It passes into the subarachnoid space of the brain and cord through foramina in the roof of the fourth ventricle and is absorbed into the veins of the brain and the venous sinuses of the dura mater.

The twelve pairs of cranial nerves supply structures of the head and neck region. The vagus nerves pass into the thorax and abdomen to supply the viscera.

QUESTIONS FOR DISCUSSION

1. While at a football game the following sequence of events occurred: You *saw* the halfback running down the field; *turned* your head to follow the play; *listened* to the cheers of the crowd and *shouted* your own; *clapped* your hands as the touchdown was made; *sat* down and *ate* a hot dog. Name localization areas, tracts of the cerebrum and cranial nerves involved.

2. Compare the reflexes involving cranial nerves and the reflexes involving spinal nerves.

Chapter 8

The Special Senses

IN THE DISCUSSION of cutaneous, deep and visceral sensations and their pathways some special characteristics of the sensory mechanisms were stressed. We have learned that the receptors may respond to several types of stimulation, but have the lowest threshold for a specific type of stimulus; for example, the eye responds to minute amounts of radiant energy, and the ear to sound waves of low intensity. Sensory nerve endings adapt to continuous stimulation by decreasing their rate of discharge. They display a local sign through which the stimulus is referred to a specific location. Further, if the central nervous system is intact, each receptor always signals its characteristic sensation regardless of the type of stimulus applied; a blow on the eye or ear results in our "seeing stars" or "hearing" a "ringing."

We have also learned that sensation, as interpreted at the thalamic level, cannot be localized or identified. There is only a noncritical level of awareness that something pleasurable or painful is happening. The somesthetic area of the cortex, though concerned with localization, depends upon association areas for interpretation of the qualities of a sensation.

Everyday experience demonstrates that consideration of each sensation separately is an oversimplification which, while convenient for the presentation, does not give a sufficiently complete picture of the extent of interaction of the various portions of the cortex. Combinations of visual, auditory, superficial, deep and visceral sensations may be simultaneously involved in determining comfort or discomfort; the combination of taste, smell, vision and touch may indicate the palatability of a food; touch, pressure, heat and pain may all be felt upon coming in contact with a solid object. Further, it is not only the modalities of sensation, but also their relative intensities in combination which, interpreted upon the basis of past experience, determine our subjective and objective reactions.

So far we have considered senses related to the present or immediate environment, stimulated by environmental changes acting directly on or within the body. We will now consider the special senses which, taste excepted, respond to more distant environmental changes and hence are concerned with the "immediate future." These telereceptors or distance receptors are end organs of the cranial nerves.

SMELL AND TASTE

The receptor organs for taste and smell may be classed as chemical receptors responding to stimulation by chemical substances dissolved in the secretions of the mouth and nose.

Sensory Mechanism for Smell. The olfactory epithelium is in the upper part of the nasal cavities on the surface of the superior conchae and upper part of the septum (Fig. 67). Ciliated cells constitute the end organs of the olfactory nerve. The neuron as a whole, rather than its peripheral process, serves as the olfactory receptor organ. The olfactory epithelium is kept moist by the secretions of the mucous membrane. Aromatic substances entering the nose in gaseous form must diffuse through the respiratory air into the quiet air (Fig. 68) of the olfactory area. Little is known about the quality of odors. Adaptation to odors is rapid.

The axons of the bipolar cells constitute the fibers of the olfactory nerve which pass upward through the cribriform plate of the ethmoid bone to form synaptic connections with the mitral cells of the olfactory bulbs. From these cells the impulses are transmitted by way of the anterior commissure and fornix to the hippocampus and hippocampal gyrus in the temporal lobe of the cerebral cortex.

Sensory Mechanism for Taste. The receptors for taste are the taste buds, located chiefly on the tongue, but present also in the pharynx, on the epiglottis, and roof of the mouth. Those on the tongue are located in the vallate and the fungiform papillae. While the taste buds give rise to four qualities of taste, they have the same general structure (Fig. 69). They are composed of clusters of cells submerged in

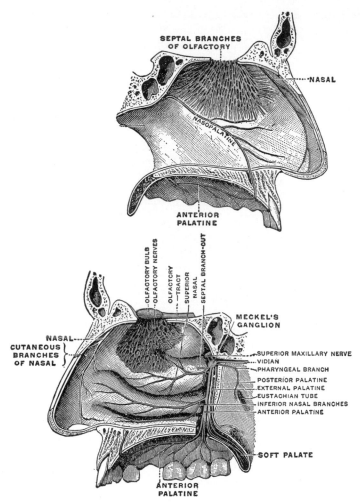

Fig. 67. Nerves of the nasal septum and outer nasal wall (olfactory). (Testut.)

the epithelium, but communicating with the surface through a small pore.

Although taste sensations are numerous, only four qualities are recognized: bitter, sour, salty, and sweet. The supposition is that the four different kinds of taste buds are concerned with the four fundamental taste sensations. The distribution of the taste sensations over the surface of the tongue supports this conception. Bitter taste is localized at the base of the tongue, sour along the sides, and salty and sweet near the tip.

The many taste sensations which we experience are the result of (a) the fusion or blending of the fundamental qualities, (b) the combination of some exteroceptor sensation in the tongue with the taste sensation, or (c) reinforcement of taste by smell. Concerning the last,

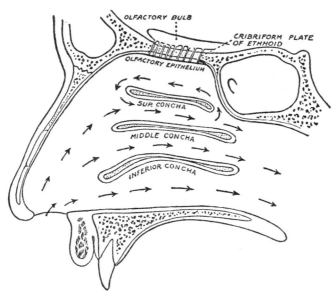

Fig. 68. Section through nasal fossae. The arrows show direction of air currents through nose in inspiration. (Starling, Human Physiology, J. & A. Churchill Ltd.)

the oral and nasal cavities communicate freely through the pharynx and are frequently stimulated by the same substances. Many sensations which we describe as taste are really odors. Coffee tastes flat when the olfactory sense is destroyed; food seems tasteless when we have a head cold.

The afferent neurons for taste sensations from the anterior two thirds of the tongue pass in the facial or seventh cranial nerve and those from the posterior third in the glossopharyngeal or ninth cranial nerve. The axons of these nerves enter the brain stem and end in the nucleus of the solitary fasciculus. The course of the internuncial neurons is uncertain, but the sensory area is the hippocampal gyrus in the temporal lobe.

HEARING AND EQUILIBRIUM

The ear is concerned with the functions of hearing and equilibrium. On the basis of structure it is divided into three parts: external ear, middle ear, and internal ear (Fig. 70*a*). The first two portions serve to conduct sound waves to the receptor in the internal ear.

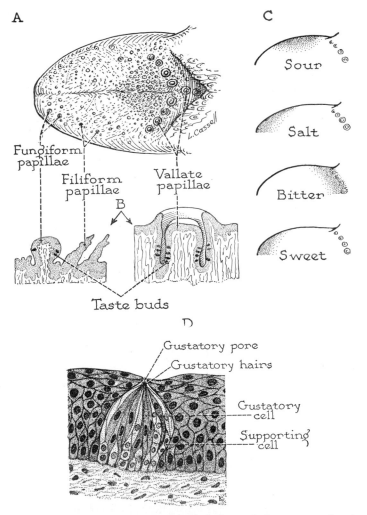

Fig. 69. Receptors for taste. *A*, Dorsal surface of the tongue, showing taste papillae. *B*, Three types of papillae in section and enlarged. *C*, Areas of maximum sensibility to four primary taste qualities. *D*, Vertical section of a taste bud.

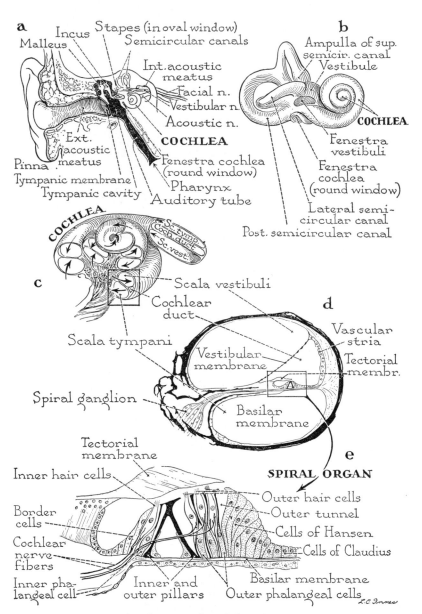

a

Incus Stapes (in oval window)
Malleus Semicircular canals
Int. acoustic
meatus
Facial n.
Vestibular n.
Acoustic n.
COCHLEA
Fenestra cochlea
(round window)
Pharynx
Auditory tube
Ext. acoustic meatus
Pinna
Tympanic membrane
Tympanic cavity

b

Ampulla of sup.
semicir. canal
Vestibule
COCHLEA
Fenestra
vestibuli
Fenestra
cochlea
(round window)
Lateral semi-
circular canal
Post. semicircular canal

COCHLEA

Sc. tymp.
Coch. duct
Sc. vest.

c

Scala vestibuli
Cochlear duct
Scala tympani
Vestibular membrane
Spiral ganglion
Basilar membrane

d

Vascular
stria
Tectorial
membr.

Tectorial membrane
Inner hair cells

e

SPIRAL ORGAN

Outer hair cells
Outer tunnel
Cells of Hansen
Cells of Claudius
Basilar membrane
Outer phalangeal cells

Border cells
Cochlear nerve fibers
Inner phalangeal cell
Inner and outer pillars

Fig. 70. The external, middle and inner ear.

The External Ear (Fig. 70a). The pinna and the external acoustic meatus constitute the external ear. The *pinna,* the expanded portion composed of cartilaginous framework covered with skin, projects from the side of the head and serves to collect and direct sound waves into the external acoustic meatus. The *external acoustic meatus* is a canal a little over an inch in length which leads from the outside to the ear drum or tympanic membrane, which separates the external ear from the middle ear. The canal is lined with skin which presents many fine hairs and sebaceous glands near its orifice. Along the upper wall are modified sweat glands, the ceruminous glands which secrete the ear wax or cerumen. The hairs and cerumen help to prevent the entrance of foreign particles and insects into the ear.

The Middle Ear (Fig. 70a). The tympanic cavity, or middle ear, is a small air cavity located in the petrous portion of the temporal bone. The *auditory tube,* or Eustachian tube, which connects the cavity with the nasal pharynx, serves as an air channel by which air pressure within the cavity is equalized with that outside. Equalization of pressures is aided by swallowing; this accounts for the practice of offering chewing gum or peppermints to promote salivation and hence swallowing during the descent and landing of an airplane. Through the posterior wall is an opening into the mastoid antrum and mastoid cells. Two openings covered with membrane (the round and oval windows) separate the cavity from the inner ear. A chain of three small bones extends across the cavity from the tympanic membrane to the oval window. Derived from their shape, their names are *hammer* (malleus), *anvil* (incus) and *stirrup* (stapes). The malleus is attached to the drum membrane; the stapes fits into the oval window. Vibrations set up in the tympanic membrane by sound waves reaching it through the external auditory meatus are transmitted to the inner ear through the ossicles which bridge the cavity.

The Internal Ear. The internal ear contains the essential organs for hearing and equilibrium. It consists of bony and membranous portions. The bony part is called the *osseous labyrinth* and is composed of a series of canals tunneled out in the petrous portion of the temporal bone (Fig. 70b). The *membranous labyrinth* lies within the osseous labyrinth. It conforms to the shape of the osseous labyrinth, but is much smaller.

The osseous labyrinth is filled with a liquid called *perilymph;* the membranous labyrinth contains *endolymph.* The parts of the bony labyrinth are cochlea, vestibule and semicircular canals. The vestibule occupies a central position between the cochlea in front and the semicircular canals behind. The cochlea is concerned with hearing, the vestibule and semicircular canals with equilibrium.

The *cochlea* resembles a snail shell. It is in the form of a spiral wound two and one half times around a central axis called the modiolus. A cut through the cochlea from apex to base shows five cross sections of the tube (Fig. 70c, d). Examination of the cross section shows the tube to be divided into three compartments. A bony lamina projecting from the modiolus, together with the basilar membrane, forms a partition which divides the tube into upper and lower passageways. The upper passage is the scala vestibuli; the lower passage is the scala tympani. The two connect at the apex by a small opening. The scala vestibuli ends at the fenestra vestibuli or oval window, the scala tympani at the fenestra cochlea or round window. They are filled with perilymph. Between these two canals is the cochlear canal filled with endolymph. It is bounded above by the vestibular membrane and below by the basilar membrane. The *basilar membrane* consists of tightly stretched fibers which increase in length from base to apex. Resting on the basilar membrane is the *spiral organ,* the receptor for hearing, composed of a number of columnar cells with cilia on their free borders. These are the hair cells. Over them projects the tectorial membrane. The fibers of the cochlear nerve are in contact with the hair cells. These structures are shown in Figure 70e.

Physiology of Hearing. Sound waves coming to the ear through the external acoustic meatus set the tympanic membrane in vibration. The chain of ossicles transmits the vibration to the oval window. The mechanical characteristics of the systems of ossicles are well adapted for the transfer of air-borne vibration to pressure waves in a fluid system. The area of the tympanic membrane is nearly thirty times as great as that of the oval window, so that the total pressure is brought to bear on a smaller surface area; the amplitude of the excursion is reduced, since the piston-like movement of the tympanum results in a rocking-like movement of the stapes. When the vibrations of the stapes impinge upon the oval window, the whole fluid system is set in motion. The vibrations of the perilymph begin in the scala vestibuli and pass through the opening in the apex of the cochlea to the fluid in the scala tympani. Descending over this course, the force of the wave expends itself against the membrane of the round window. From this point on the knowledge of the mechanism of hearing is incomplete. Our current concept is that a sound will set a portion of the basilar membrane into vibration. This portion may be limited in extent if the sound is of low intensity; broader areas become involved as the intensity is increased. In any case there is one point of maximum excursion of the membrane, so that the nerve fibers associated with this point will fire at the highest frequency. It is the hair cells in contact with the tectorial membrane which are stimulated by vibration and which set up impulses in the acoustic nerve which pass to the auditory area in the temporal lobe, where sound is perceived.

In general, the *intensity*, that is, the loudness, of sounds within the audible range is related to the magnitude of the sound waves. Physiologically, differences in intensity are described in terms of the ratio of the intensities of two sounds. The standard or reference intensity for describing loudness is the lowest intensity at which a sound of a frequency of 1000 cycles per second can be heard by a person with

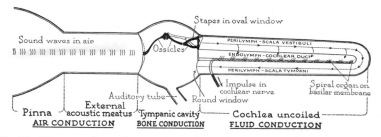

Fig. 71. Diagram of sound transmission from the air to impulse in cochlear nerve. Dotted lines indicate the position of the ossicles and various membranes after inward displacement of the tympanic membrane.

normal hearing. The power or physical equivalent of this intensity is 0.0002 dyne per cm.^{2}. Since the range of energy between the threshold intensity and the loudest tolerable intensity is 1 to 1,000,000,000,000, logarithmic units are used to express the ratios: the term *decibel* or one-tenth of a bel is customarily used. For example, if we compare two sounds, and state that the loudness of the second sound is 1 bel, or 10 decibels, we mean that the intensity of the second sound is 10 times that of the first sound; if it is 2 bels or 20 decibels it is 100 times louder (you will remember that the log of 10 is 1; the log of 100 is 2).

In general, *pitch* is determined by the frequency of the sound waves, i.e., the number of vibrations per second. The pitch is said to be high when the frequency is high. The normal ear can hear frequencies of from 16 cycles per second to 20,000 cycles per second.

In speaking of intensity and pitch we have qualified the discussion by use of the term "in general." Space does not permit discussion of the exceptions, but such qualification is necessary for relating the physical characteristics of vibration to physiological sensations such as "loudness" and "pitch." As might be expected in the case of sensory mechanisms, loudness is determined by the rate of discharge of neurons, and pitch is a form of localization depending on the portion of the basilar membrane responding maximally.

Localization of sound, that is, recognition of the direction of its source, depends upon the differences in the time (or phase) of sound waves reaching the two ears. Movements of the head and body are used in detecting these differences. The detection of the source is called *binaural* localization. It is an important telereceptor function for warning of danger at a distance.

Pathway for Hearing. The hair cells of the spiral organ (organ of Corti) form the receptors for sound waves. The afferent pathway is composed of at least three units. Neurons of the first order are afferent neurons which constitute the fibers of the cochlear division of the acoustic nerve. The cell bodies of these neurons are in the spiral ganglion. Their axons terminate in the dorsal and ventral cochlear nuclei of the medulla, where they form synaptic connections with neurons of the second order. The tract formed by the second neurons transmits impulses to the thalamus. From the thalamus auditory impulses pass in the sublenticular portion of the internal capsule (Fig. 57, p. 114) to the cerebral cortex. The auditory area is in the superior temporal gyrus of the temporal lobe.

Equilibrium. The saccule, utricle and semicircular ducts contain the receptors for the senses of position and movement of the head.

The *saccule* and *utricle* form the portion of the membranous labyrinth located in the vestibule. They contain sensory hair cells in contact with particles of calcium carbonate called *otoliths*. Changes in the position of the head cause the otoliths to exert a pull on the hair cells which results in their stimulation. The hair cells connect with the fibers of the vestibular nerve. The utricle and perhaps the saccule are concerned with static equilibrium, that is, with the relationship of the body (really the head) with the pull of gravity. These impulses aid us in maintaining static posture.

The *semicircular ducts* form the membranous labyrinth of the semicircular canals. Each ear has three semicircular canals placed at right angles to each other in the three planes of space. They are called posterior, superior and lateral semicircular canals. Within each is the corresponding semicircular duct. All are filled with endolymph. There are groups of hair cells called *cristae ampullaris* in the dilated portion (ampulla) of each duct (Fig. 72). Agitation of the fluid occasioned by movements of the head stimulates the hair cells, and impulses are initiated in the vestibular nerve endings. The semicircular ducts are the sense organs of dynamic equilibrium and are concerned with initiating body-righting reflexes.

Impulses from the otoliths and from the receptors in the ampullae of the semicircular canals are augmented by impulses from other postural receptors. Images or successions of images on the retina provide a source of information as to our position in relation to the external environment. If sensations from the labyrinths and the eyes tell us we are disoriented, we may adjust the position of the head to its normal relation to outside objects. If the body is not aligned with the head, the proprioceptor nerve endings in the neck are stimulated and discharge. In addition, the superficial and deep receptors in the feet signal

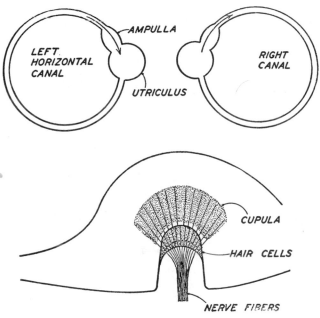

Fig. 72. The sense organs of dynamic equilibrium. *Above:* Horizontal semicircular canals. Rotation of an animal to the left causes movement of fluid (endolymph) in these canals to the right (indicated by arrows), because of inertia of the fluid. Movement of fluid in this direction stimulates the sensory end organ of the left canal. *Below:* End organ (the crista) of the ampulla of a semicircular canal. (Carlson and Johnson, The Machinery of the Body, University of Chicago Press.)

the relation of the feet and body to gravitational forces. Impulses from these many sensory receptors, located on widely different areas of the body, alter integration in the higher centers, converge upon the final common pathway and bring about the effective and coordinated response of the antigravity muscles which enable us to retain or to recover our normal orientation in space.

VISION

The Eye and Associated Structures. The eye is, in many ways, comparable to a camera. Some of its structures form an optical system which bends or focuses the light rays from outside objects, located at various distances, to form sharp images within the eye. Other structures, comparable to the film of a camera, react to these light rays which make up the image and set up nerve impulses giving rise to the sensations of form, contrast and color by which the objects are recognized. The eye, however, is an exceedingly adaptable, highly complex camera which may seem to work automatically, since we are seldom aware of the adjustments for distance, amount of light and the position or location of the object. The associated structures which protect the eye and aid in its function are the orbital cavities, the eyelids, the lacrimal apparatus and the eye muscles.

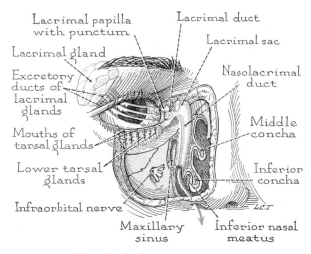

Lacrimal papilla with punctum

Lacrimal gland

Excretory ducts of lacrimal glands

Mouths of tarsal glands

Lower tarsal glands

Infraorbital nerve

Maxillary sinus

Lacrimal duct

Lacrimal sac

Nasolacrimal duct

Middle concha

Inferior concha

Inferior nasal meatus

Fig. 73. The lacrimal apparatus.

Outer Parts of the Eye. The eyeballs, lying in the anterior part of the orbital cavities, are protected above and at the side by the prominent margins of the orbits and below by the zygomatic bones and medially by the bridge of the nose.

The Eyelids. The eyelids are placed in front of the eyeball (Fig. 74). They are formed of muscular tissue attached to dense fibrous plates which give shape to the lids. Externally, they are covered by skin, and internally, by mucous membrane, called conjunctiva, which is reflected upon the anterior surface of the eyeball. Hairs project from the free margins to form the eyelashes. Along the margin of the lids are the tarsal or Meibomian glands; these glands secrete an oily liquid which keeps the lids from becoming adherent. The muscular tissue of the lids forms sphincters, the orbicularis oculi muscles, which close the eyelids. The levator palpebrae superiorus muscle raises the upper eyelid. The origin is the posterior part of the orbit above and in front of the optic foramen; the insertion is the upper eyelid (Fig. 75).

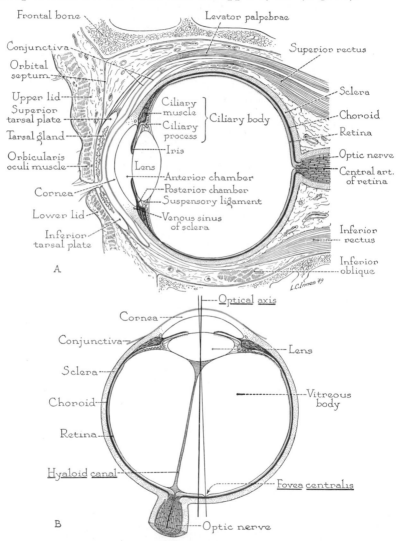

Fig. 74. *A*, Vertical section of the anterior part of orbit and contents. *B*, Horizontal section of right eye. Underlined labels indicate structures which are not shown in the vertical section above.

The Lacrimal Apparatus (Fig. 73). The anterior surface of the eye is protected by a constant stream of tears secreted by the lacrimal gland lying above the eye. The excess secretion is drained off from the eye through the nasolacrimal duct into the nose. The tears pass into the duct through two small openings at the medial corner of the

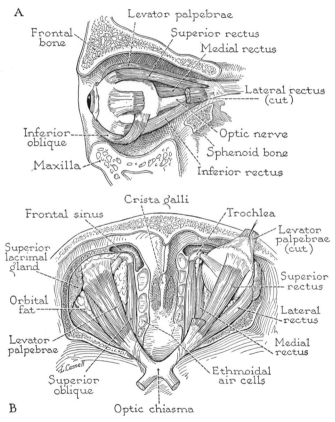

Fig. 75. Muscles of the orbit. *A,* Lateral view. *B,* Superior view. (Modified after Sobotta; Grant, An Atlas of Anatomy, Williams & Wilkins Co.)

eye. In this way the surface of the eye is kept moist and free from irritating particles.

The Extrinsic Eye Muscles. Each eyeball is attached to six muscles which hold it in place and control its movements. There are four straight or rectus muscles, superior, inferior, lateral and medial, and two oblique muscles, superior and inferior (Fig. 75). All except the inferior oblique arise from the apex of the orbit near the optic foramen. The inferior oblique arises from the medial margin of the orbit. The six muscles are inserted into the outer coat of the eyeball. The tendon of the superior oblique muscle passes through a cartilaginous ring or pulley attached to the upper and inner part of the orbit to reach its attachment on the eyeball. The movements of the muscles of both

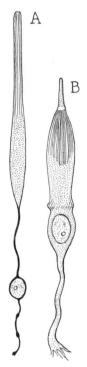

Fig. 76. Visual cells from the human retina: *A*, rod, and *B*, cone. (After Greeff.)

eyes are coordinated so that both eyes move together to focus on a single field of vision.

The Structure of the Eyeball (Fig. 74). The eyeball is roughly spherical in shape. Its walls are formed of three layers: an outer fibrous coat, a middle vascular coat, and an inner nervous coat.

The fibrous coat has two parts, the sclera and the cornea. The *sclera* invests the eye except for a small area in front. It is tough and opaque and gives form to the eyeball. The *cornea* is the clear, transparent tissue which completes the coat anteriorly.

The vascular coat or uvea has many blood vessels and is concerned chiefly with nutrition of the eye. There are three parts: choroid, ciliary body, and iris. The *choroid* contains a rich plexus of blood vessels and a large amount of dark brown pigment. It is continuous with the ciliary body in front. The ciliary muscle and ciliary process make up the *ciliary body,* which projects into the cavity of the eye at the sclero-corneal junction to form a circular band. The ciliary muscle forms the main part of the ciliary body. The longitudinal fibers arise from the sclera near its junction with the cornea and pass backward to be inserted into the choroid. Other muscle fibers radiate from the sclera into the ciliary body. The ciliary muscle functions in accommodation of the eye. The ciliary processes consist of fibers which radiate from the free border of the ciliary muscle and give attachment to ligaments supporting the lens. The *iris,* or colored portion of the eye, is a muscular diaphragm which is attached at its circumference to the ciliary body and has an opening (the pupil) in the center. It controls the amount of light admitted to the eye. Its circular fibers, when stimulated, produce constriction of the pupil; its radial fibers contract to dilate the pupil. The ciliary muscle and the circular fibers of the iris are supplied by the third cranial nerve.

The nervous coat or retina forms the lining layer of the eyeball. It contains the rods and cones (Fig. 76), which are specialized cells sensitive to light rays. The rods and cones are connected with the optic nerve. The *optic nerve* leaves the eye slightly to the nasal side of the center. The point is marked by a white circular area called the *optic disc.* Since there are no rods or cones in this area, it is called the blind spot. Near the center of the posterior pole is a yellowish spot called the *macula lutea.* In the center of the macula lutea is a small depression, the fovea centralis. At this point the rods are absent, but cones are greatly increased in number. It is the region of keenest vision. The retina receives blood from the central artery, a branch of the ophthalmic artery. It passes through the center of the optic nerve and appears at the center of the optic disc, where it divides into branches.

The *crystalline lens* lies just behind the pupil and iris. It is held in position by the suspensory ligaments, which are attached to the ciliary processes. The iris separates the anterior and posterior chambers. The posterior chamber is the small recess between the iris in front and the lens and suspensory ligament behind. Posterior to the lens is the large cavity of the eye filled with a jelly-like material called the vitreous humor. The aqueous humor fills the space anterior to the lens. It is commonly believed that the aqueous humor is secreted by the ciliary process. From the posterior chamber it permeates the vitreous body and passes forward between the iris and the lens, through the pupil into the anterior chamber. Drainage from the anterior chamber is mainly by way of the spaces of Fontana and the venous sinus at the junction of the cornea and sclera. However, the drainage function of the sinus venosus sclerae is now held to be doubtful, and it is possible that the fluid in the anterior chamber is resorbed by the blood vessels of the iris and other veins.

Physiology of Vision. REFRACTION. In vision, rays of light reflected from an object must enter the eye, be brought to a focus on the retina, and the nervous impulses initiated by the image must be carried to the visual areas in the occipital lobes, where it is assumed they are interpreted. In coming to a focus on the retina, rays of light reflected from objects must be bent. This bending of light rays is called refraction. A ray of light is refracted when it passes from a medium of one density into a medium of a different density. When passing from a less dense to a denser medium it is bent toward the perpendicular, and when passing from a denser to a less dense medium it is bent away from the perpendicular. The degree of ability of a substance to bend rays of light is referred to as the *refractive index.*

The refractive index of air is taken as the standard and is said to be 1; accordingly the refractive index for water is 1.33. The refracting media of the eye are the cornea, aqueous humor, lens and vitreous humor. All except the lens have the same refractive index as water. The lens has a refractive index of 1.42. A ray of light passing into the eye receives its greatest refraction as it enters the cornea from the air; further refraction occurs as it enters and leaves the lens.

In the normal or emmetropic eye the optical system is adequate for bringing rays from distant objects (i.e., objects at a distance of more than 20 feet) to a sharp focus on the retina, so that no activity of the eye muscles is necessary for adjustment. If, however, a person is nearsighted (myopic) or far-sighted (hypermetropic), the rays will come to focus in front of or behind the retina, respectively. Near-sighted people whose eyes have a greater than normal anterior-posterior diameter wear lenses which diverge the light rays; far-sighted people, i.e., those with eyeballs having a relatively short anterior-posterior diameter, wear convex lenses which converge the entering rays.

ACCOMMODATION. Rays of light from objects close at hand require a greater degree of bending or refraction in order to bring them to a focus on the retina. This necessitates an adjustment of some part of the refracting media. The structure of the lens admits of such an adjustment. It is an elastic organ held in place by the suspensory ligaments, which in turn are attached to the ciliary processes. Contraction of the ciliary muscle pulls the choroid forward and causes the ciliary processes to project farther inward, and thus releases tension on the lens. Since the lens is highly elastic, release of tension causes it to become more nearly spherical in shape. The greater the convexity of the lens surface, the greater the index of refraction. By this mechanism rays of light from near objects are brought to a focus on the retina. Contraction of the ciliary muscle is associated with near vision and may account for the sense of strain sometimes experienced after long periods of close work.

The elasticity of the lens changes with age. The near point, i.e., the shortest distance at which an object can be seen distinctly, moves further and further away as we grow older, since the lens becomes progressively less elastic and hence cannot assume so great a curvature. This explains why older people tend to hold a paper or the printed page at a distance and, for correct vision, must wear glasses as an artificial aid in focusing nearby objects sharply on the retina.

FUNCTIONS OF RODS AND CONES. The rods and cones are the specialized receptor organs of the eye. The adequate stimuli for these end organs is the radiant energy of the visible spectrum. The rods are associated with vision under conditions of low illumination; this is called *scotopic* vision and enables us to get around fairly well at night once the eyes have become adapted to darkness. Vision is improved fairly rapidly, but complete dark adaptation may require twenty to thirty minutes. Night vision is not discriminative; we see no detail or color, but rather vague outlines of forms of objects which are more readily detected when they are moving. Under higher levels of illumination, peripheral vision—that is, vision resulting from light rays falling on the peripheral areas of the retina which contain only rods—signals the presence of stationary or moving objects. When the eyes are then turned so that the rays fall upon the central area of the retina, we can see fine details of form, contrast and color. Discriminative, or *photopic,* vision is a function of the cones. Whereas impulses from many rods or from a number of rods and cones may converge on a single neuron, the cones in the fovea centralis, or region of highly discriminative vision, may have direct line connections, i.e., connections which consist of one bipolar (second order neuron) cell and a single cone (first order neuron). The third order neurons, or ganglion cells, may synapse with many of the second order neurons, or may form connections through bipolar cells with only one or two cones.

The visible spectrum is a relatively narrow band of wavelengths between the longer infra-red waves and the short ultraviolet waves. The chemical changes which stimulate the end organs are brought about by absorption of light of various wavelengths by light-sensitive pigments. The pigment of the rods, which is called *rhodopsin,* has the characteristic of maximum absorption of green light; this pigment is chemically unstable under conditions of high illumination, a fact which accounts for loss of rod sensitivity in daylight vision. It is suspected, although not proved, that there is a photosensitive substance *iodopsin* associated with cone vision. The cones have greatest sensitivity to the red-green portion of the spectrum.

Recognition that vision is the result of photochemical reactions dependent upon absorption of light of various wavelengths aids us in understanding the three important factors determining retinal response: (1) the *wavelength*, (2) the *state of adaptation* of the eye, i.e., the chemical state of the pigments, and (3) the *quantity of light* falling on the retina, which is determined by the intensity and duration of the stimulus.

Visual acuity is a specific term for the ratio 1 over the least angle which must be subtended to recognize a white area between two black lines, i.e., an area of stimulation between two unstimulated areas. It describes the ability to see fine detail. To use the example of Luckiesh and Moss in their book "Science of Seeing," if we should progressively decrease the size of the letters on a printed page, the detail and finally the letters themselves would eventually become invisible; here we have gone beyond the limits of visual acuity. Reference to the three factors determining retinal response listed in the preceding paragraph should indicate to you that visual acuity is not a fixed value, but may vary with adaptation, quantity of light and wavelength.

JUDGMENT OF DISTANCE.   An effective telereceptor provides information as to separation between man and the stimulus at a distance. In vision, not less than eleven clues are provided. Interpretation of these clues is dependent, however, upon experience and associative memory. The clue provided by the slight differences in the images of a single object falling on the two retinas, which are separated by a distance of about 60 mm., is important for judging the distance of near objects. This ability to see part of the way around or see "two sides" of an object because of the separation of the eyes is called *stereoscopic vision*. Further, we judge distance by the size of the retinal image of familiar objects and by perspective, which is illustrated by the sides of a street appearing to come closer together as we gaze into the distance. Near objects appear to move greater distances than far objects as we move our head from side to side; near objects may also overlap or blot out parts of more distant objects. Clues are also provided by sensory endings in the eye muscles which contract in accommodation and convergence when viewing near objects.

THE VISUAL PATHWAY.   The regions from which objects are seen are called the visual fields. The visual field of each eye is divided into

a right and left half. The medial half is called the nasal visual field;
the lateral half is called the temporal visual field. The retina is divided
in the same way: nasal half of the retina and temporal half of the
retina. Rays of light from objects in the temporal visual field fall on
the nasal half of the retina; accordingly, rays of light from objects

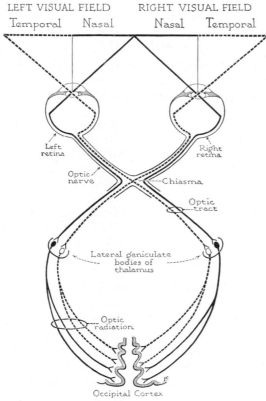

LEFT VISUAL FIELD   RIGHT VISUAL FIELD
Temporal   Nasal   Nasal   Temporal

Fig. 77. The visual pathway.

in the nasal visual field fall on the temporal half of the retina. It will
be noted in the diagram (Fig. 77) that the fibers from the nasal halves
of two retinas cross in the *optic chiasm*, while fibers from the temporal halves of the retinas pass uncrossed to the visual cortex of the
same side. Both crossed and uncrossed fibers synapse in the thalamus,
from which point the fiber tracts pass to the visual areas in the occipital lobes of the cerebrum. Thus the visual cortex in the left cerebral

hemisphere receives visual impulses from objects in the temporal visual field of the right eye and the nasal visual field of the left eye.

This description of the visual pathway includes all parts of the sensory mechanism for vision and is seen to consist of a receptor, the rods and cones of the retina; an afferent pathway made up of optic tracts from retinas to thalamus; and thalamocortical tracts from the lateral geniculate body of the thalamus to the visual area of the cerebral cortex, located in the calcarine fissure of the occipital lobe.

SUMMARY

The receptors for the special senses, i.e., vision, hearing, taste and smell, are the end organs of the cranial nerves.

Each receptor signals its characteristic sensation regardless of the type of stimulus applied.

The olfactory receptors are in the nasal mucous membrane. Little is known about the quality of odors. Adaptation to odors is rapid.

Four qualities of taste are recognized: bitter, sour, salty, and sweet. Many sensations which we describe as taste are really odors.

On the basis of structure the ear is divided into three parts: external ear, middle ear, and internal ear. The first two portions serve to conduct sound waves to the receptor in the internal ear.

The external ear consists of the pinna and external auditory meatus.

The middle ear or tympanic cavity is separated from the external ear by the tympanic membrane. The auditory tube and mastoid antrum are related structures.

The internal ear contains the essential organs for hearing and equilibrium. The parts of the bony labyrinth of the internal ear are cochlea, vestibule and semicircular canals. The cochlea contains the spiral organ, the receptor for sound waves. The vestibule is concerned with static equilibrium, the semicircular canals with dynamic equilibrium.

The organ of vision is the eyeball. Structures associated with it are the orbital cavities, the eyelids, the lacrimal apparatus and the eye muscles.

The walls of the eyeball are formed of three layers: an outer fibrous coat, a middle vascular coat, and an inner nervous coat.

The fibrous coat consists of the sclera and the cornea.

The middle vascular coat is composed of choroid, ciliary body and iris.

The iris separates the anterior and posterior chambers.

Vitreous humor fills the posterior chamber; aqueous humor, the anterior chamber. The aqueous humor is probably secreted by the ciliary process.

The nervous coat or retina forms the lining layer of the eyeball. It contains the rods and cones, which are specialized cells sensitive to light rays.

The crystalline lens lies just back of the pupil and iris. It is held in position by the suspensory ligaments which are attached to the ciliary processes.

In vision, rays of light reflected from an object must enter the eye and be brought to a focus on the retina.

Rays of light are refracted as they enter the cornea and as they enter and leave the lens.

The refractive power of the eye must be increased to bring light rays from near objects to a focus on the retina.

The eye meets this requirement by contraction of the ciliary muscle, which releases the tension on the lens and causes it to become more nearly spherical.

In the normal or emmetropic eye the optical system is adequate for bringing rays from distant objects to a sharp focus on the retina; no contraction of the ciliary muscle is required.

The rods are concerned with colorless and twilight vision; the cones with perception of color and bright daylight vision.

The nerve fibers from the nasal halves of the two retinas cross in the optic chiasm, while fibers from the temporal halves of the retinas pass uncrossed to the visual cortex of the same side.

QUESTIONS FOR DISCUSSION

1. Beginning with the external ear, list the structures which sound waves must pass to reach the receptor. Follow light waves through the eye to the receptor.

2. State the relationship between: Special senses and somesthetic senses; special senses and kinesthetic senses; special senses and exteroceptors and proprioceptors.

Chapter 9

The Autonomic
Nervous System

THE TERM *visceral nervous system* may be used to include both the autonomic nervous system, which was originally defined as being composed only of efferent fibers, and the visceral afferent fibers, which convey (*a*) afferent impulses from viscera which do not reach the level of consciousness, (*b*) organic sensation such as hunger, nausea, distention and sexual sensations, and (*c*) pain. In our discussion of the autonomic nervous system we shall consider the associated visceral afferents together with the motor fibers (traditionally the autonomic fibers).

By definition, the term "autonomic" implies self-control and independence of outside influences. So the autonomic nervous system has often been given the alternate names of involuntary or vegetative nervous system. However, the implication that the autonomic system functions free of influence from higher centers is incorrect. There is a present tendency to look upon the autonomic system as a convenient division for study, and a functional portion of the entire nervous system, rather than a clearly segregated unit.

ARCHITECTURE OF THE AUTONOMIC SYSTEM AND
ASSOCIATED VISCERAL AFFERENTS

The autonomic nervous system is divided into a craniosacral (parasympathetic) division and a thoracolumbar (sympathetic) division. The names indicate the portions of the central nervous system to which each is related.

Efferent neurons characterizing this system are known as *pregangli-onic* and *postganglionic fibers*. Cell bodies of the preganglionic fibers lie within the central nervous system. The preganglionic fibers are myelinated or white fibers and pass out of the central gray matter to synapse with the cells of the postganglionic unmyelinated or gray fibers in outlying tissue. Cell bodies of postganglionic fibers lie in ganglia of three types. The *vertebral* group of ganglia is found on either side of the vertebral column close to the bodies of the vertebrae. They form a series of some twenty-two ganglia connected together in a chain or trunk extending from the base of the skull to the coccyx.

Prevertebral ganglia lie in the thorax, abdomen and pelvis near the aorta and its branches. Three large prevertebral ganglia, named accord-ing to their position near the respective arteries, are the celiac, superior and inferior mesenteric.

Terminal ganglia are small aggregations of ganglion cells which lie upon or within the walls of the organ which they innervate.

The chain of vertebral ganglia is connected to each of the spinal nerves by one or more strands of delicate fibers called *rami communi-cantes*, or communicating branches. A *gray ramus* from the autonomic trunk runs to each spinal nerve. It is made up of postganglionic un-myelinated efferent fibers. *White rami* are limited to the thoracic and first three or four lumbar nerves. These rami are composed of visceral afferent and preganglionic myelinated efferent fibers.

The visceral afferent fibers have their cell bodies in the posterior root ganglion or in comparable ganglia near the brain, just as do any other sensory nerves. Generally associated with sympathetic afferent nerves are the reflex afferents which convey impulses (a) which do not reach the level of consciousness and (b) which give rise to sensa-tion of pain as the result of stretching or distention, smooth muscle spasm and chemical irritation. Afferent fibers which convey impulses giving rise to organic sensations travel in the parasympathetic (cranio-sacral) nerves. Certain somatic afferent nerves such as the phrenic and upper lumbar spinal nerves give rise to referred pain (appearing to arise at a source different from the area in which the disorder occurs).

Craniosacral Division. The bodies of the preganglionic cells of this division are located in the midbrain, medulla and sacral portion of the spinal cord. Preganglionic fibers from the midbrain run in the oculomotor nerve; from the medulla in the facial, glossopharyngeal and vagus nerves; in the sacral portion of the cord from the anterior column of the second, third and fourth sacral segments of the cord through the anterior roots of the corresponding spinal nerves.

The axons of these cells synapse in terminal ganglia with post-ganglionic fibers. Because of the close relation of the efferent neurons

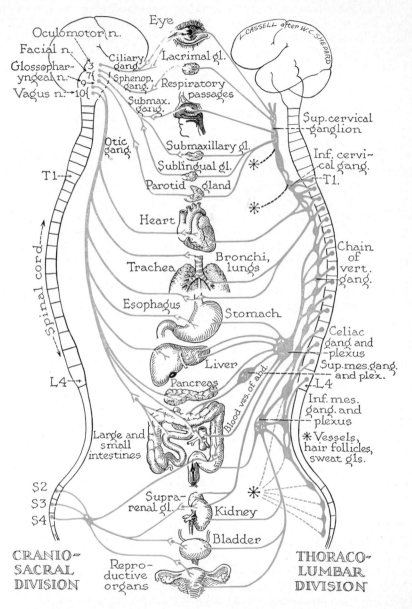

Fig. 78. Diagram of the autonomic nervous system. The craniosacral division is shown in blue, the thoracolumbar division in orange.

Table 4

Functions of the Autonomic Nervous System

ORGAN	CRANIOSACRAL EFFECTS: CONSERVATION AND RESTORATION OF ENERGY	THORACOLUMBAR EFFECTS: EXPENDITURE OF ENERGY
Eye { Iris / Ciliary muscle	Contraction of circular fibers Contraction accommodates for near vision	Contraction of radial fibers Relaxation
Lacrimal gland	Secretion	
Cerebral blood vessels	Dilatation	Constriction
Salivary glands	Secretion — large amount of thin watery saliva	Secretion — thick viscid and scanty saliva
Respiratory passages	Secretions stimulated, blood vessels dilated	Secretions inhibited, blood vessels constricted
Bronchi	Constriction	Dilatation
Heart	Inhibition	Acceleration
Coronary arteries	Constriction	Dilatation
Stomach { Wall / Sphincter / Glands	Increased tone, motility Inhibition Secretion	Inhibition Contraction Inhibition
Intestine { Wall / Internal anal sphincter	Increased tone, motility Inhibition	Inhibition Contraction
Liver	Inhibits glycogen breakdown Secretion of bile	Increases glycogen breakdown
Pancreas	Stimulates secretion of pancreatic enzymes and hormones	Diminishes enzyme secretion
Adrenal gland—medulla		Secretion
Blood vessels of abdominal and pelvic viscera		Constriction
Urinary bladder { Wall / Sphincter	Contraction Inhibition	Inhibition Contraction
Uterus—nonpregnant		Inhibition
Uterus—pregnant		Contraction
Blood vessels of external genitalia	Dilatation	Constriction
Sweat glands		Secretion
Blood vessels of skin		Constriction
Erector muscles of hair follicles		Contraction

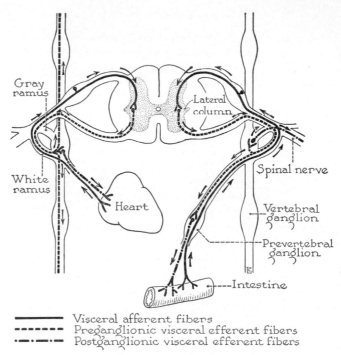

Visceral afferent fibers
Preganglionic visceral efferent fibers
Postganglionic visceral efferent fibers

Fig. 79. Diagram of reflex arc of the autonomic nervous system.

with the organs innervated, the responses of the craniosacral division of the autonomic system are usually limited rather than widespread.

Thoracolumbar Division. The bodies of the preganglionic cells of this division are located in the lateral column of gray matter of the spinal cord from the first thoracic to the third lumbar segment. These fibers leave the cord by way of the anterior roots of the corresponding spinal nerves and pass through the white ramus to connect with postganglionic neurons in the vertebral or prevertebral ganglia.

A preganglionic fiber may control a number of postganglionic fibers. For example, it has been found that there are about thirty-two cell bodies of postganglionic fibers in the superior cervical ganglion (a vertebral ganglion) to every preganglionic fiber in the chain of vertebral ganglia. Such an arrangement would explain the widespread responses to stimulation in the thoracolumbar system.

Autonomic Reflex Arc (Fig. 79). The reflex arc of the autonomic system follows the same general pattern as the reflex arc of the central nervous system:

1. A receptor, the afferent ending.

2. The visceral afferent neuron, a conductor carrying impulses to the brain or spinal cord.
3. A synapse with a connector neuron.
4. The connector or preganglionic neuron transmitting impulses to cells in vertebral, prevertebral or terminal ganglia.
5. A synapse with an efferent neuron.
6. An efferent or postganglionic neuron carrying impulses from the ganglia.
7. An effector, i.e., cardiac muscle, smooth muscle, or gland.

The essential difference in the two patterns is that the cell bodies of the efferent neurons of the autonomic system lie outside the spinal cord. As a consequence, the connector neuron leaves the central nervous system to synapse with the outlying efferent neuron. The possibility of a two-neuron arc does not exist for the autonomic system.

The diagram of the autonomic reflex arc (Fig. 79) presents three possibilities for the course of the preganglionic fiber of the thoracolumbar division after it has entered a vertebral ganglion. (1) The fiber may synapse with cells in this ganglion. (2) It may pass up or down the chain of vertebral ganglia for some distance and terminate in a ganglion at a higher or lower level. (3) The neuron may pass through the vertebral ganglion to synapse in a prevertebral ganglion.

FUNCTIONS OF THE AUTONOMIC SYSTEM

The autonomic system governs the activities of such visceral structures as heart, lungs, digestive tube, glands, blood vessels, uterus, urinary bladder and certain endocrine organs. As previously explained, it does not function automatically as an independent unit in the sense of controlling the organs from ganglia unrelated to the central nervous system, but control is exerted from centers within the central nervous system—cerebral cortex, hypothalamus and medulla. It is now generally agreed that the hypothalamus controls the finely adjusted balance that is effected between the craniosacral and thoracolumbar functions of the autonomic system. The forepart of the hypothalamus has craniosacral control centers, while the posterior part has thoracolumbar control centers. Interaction between the two parts permits the integration necessary for such functions as heat regulation and water metabolism.

The autonomic nervous system performs the important function of maintaining the constancy of composition of the internal environment. Through its manifold activities the autonomic nervous system works to resist forces which tend to alter the internal environment. Regulation of the body fluids in respect to composition, temperature, quantity and distribution is brought about through the action of this system on circulatory, respiratory, excretory and glandular organs. For example, the liver, pancreas and adrenals, which are controlled by autonomic influence, are important in the regulation of blood sugar; sweat glands aid in the control of temperature; and the regulation of heart action and of the caliber of blood vessels determines the distribution of the internal fluid environment.

Most visceral structures receive fibers from both divisions of the autonomic system, and effects exerted by the two types of fibers on a given organ are antagonistic. Thus the heart rate is slowed by the craniosacral division (vagus) and accelerated by the thoracolumbar division. In general, the craniosacral system is concerned with conservative and restorative processes, while the thoracolumbar division governs processes involving an expenditure of energy. In the craniosacral division the slowing of the heart rate, constriction of coronary arteries, contraction of the pupil for protection of the eye from intense light, action of the liver inhibiting glycogen mobilization, and effects on the gastrointestinal tract favoring digestion and absorption through which energy supplies are restored, furnish evidence of conservative activities controlled by this division.

The thoracolumbar division has been called the emergency mechanism of the body because it is brought into activity by conditions which call for unusual effort on the part of the body to perform work or to resist threatened dangers. In such crises the thoracolumbar division is stimulated, and, since this division supplies secretory fibers to the suprarenal glands, the hormone epinephrine is added to the blood, and this in turn augments the action of this division. A review of the actions of the thoracolumbar division will show how well these bodily reactions fit an animal (or man) to meet emergencies demanding defense or flight:

1. A rise in arterial blood pressure by acceleration of heart rate, increase in force of cardiac contractions and constriction of arterioles, especially in skin and splanchnic areas; dilatation of coronary arteries and blood vessels in contracting muscles brings about a state of maximum efficiency in the circulatory system.
2. Stimulation of glycogen breakdown in the liver releasing large amounts of glucose into the blood stream insures a fuel supply for active muscles.
3. Increase in oxygen content of the blood (slight contractions of the spleen may discharge red blood cells for oxygen carriage).
4. Dilatation of bronchi and inhibition of secretions of respiratory tract permit an increase in oxygen intake.
5. Decrease in coagulation time lessens danger from hemorrhage.

CHEMICAL TRANSMISSION OF NERVE IMPULSES

Autonomic effects are produced by the nerve ending liberating chemical substances which transmit the nerve impulse and activate the effector organs. The substance *acetylcholine* is elaborated at all the synapses between preganglionic and postganglionic fibers in the autonomic nervous system, and by the nerve endings of the postganglionic fibers of the craniosacral division of the autonomic system. It is thought that this substance may be formed or released by the internal current flowing from an active segment of peripheral nerves, and may be responsible for the changes in the nerve membrane which are associated with the propagation of the nerve impulse. The substance *sympathin* is liberated by the nerve endings of the postganglionic fibers of the thoracolumbar division. Acetylcholine is rapidly destroyed by enzymes of the blood and tissues called cholinesterases. This explains why stimulation of the vagus does not cause widespread and chaotic craniosacral effects. Sympathin is destroyed by oxidation, but much more slowly than acetylcholine.

SUMMARY

The visceral nervous system includes autonomic (motor) fibers and associated visceral afferent fibers.

The autonomic nervous system supplies nerves to smooth muscle, cardiac muscle and glands; in fact, to all tissues except striated muscles.

The autonomic nervous system is divided into a craniosacral division and a thoracolumbar division.

The reflex arc of the autonomic system is similar to the reflex arc of the central nervous system, except that the cell body of the postganglionic neuron lies in a ganglion outside the central nervous system.

The ganglia of the autonomic system may be divided into three groups: vertebral, prevertebral, and terminal ganglia.

The bodies of the preganglionic cells of the craniosacral division are located in the midbrain, medulla and sacral portion of the cord. The axons end in terminal ganglia on or within the walls of the structure supplied.

The cell bodies which give rise to the preganglionic neurons of the thoracolumbar division are located in the lateral column of the gray matter of the cord from the first thoracic to the third lumbar segments. The axons terminate in vertebral or prevertebral ganglia.

Most visceral structures receive fibers from both divisions of the autonomic system, and the effects exerted by the two types of fibers on a given organ are antagonistic.

In general, the craniosacral division is concerned with conservative and restorative processes, while the thoracolumbar division governs processes involving an expenditure of energy.

QUESTIONS FOR DISCUSSION

1. Describe your appearance and physiologic reactions when you are thoroughly frightened. How are these related to the autonomic nervous system?

2. How is the function of the thoracolumbar portion of the autonomic system related to summation, facilitation, and convergence?

3. What roles are played by acetylcholine in the transmission of nerve impulses?

Unit
3

THE ERECT AND MOVING BODY

IN THIS UNIT interest is centered upon the bony framework of the body and the muscles attached to it.

The development and growth of bony tissue furnish an important background for this study. The microscopic structure of muscular tissue is related to the type of contraction and is therefore included. Physiology of muscle describes the properties of muscle, analyzes muscle action and discusses the source of energy for muscular contraction.

The importance of the skeleton as a basis for muscle attachment is given considerable emphasis.

The attachment of muscles to the bony framework makes possible the maintenance of posture and the movements of the parts of the skeleton.

Chapter
10

The Skeletal System

Composition and Function. The bones of the body constitute the organs of the skeletal system. Together they form the supporting framework of the body, they serve as the basis of attachment for the muscles, in certain regions of the body they protect delicate structures, they supply calcium to the blood, and they are important in the formation of blood cells (for hemopoietic function, see p. 300).

Bones may be considered as *organs* because (1) they are made up of several kinds of tissue—osseous tissue, cartilage, fibrous tissue, nervous and vascular tissues; and (2) they function as integral parts of the skeletal system as a whole.

Bone Formation and Development. The skeleton of the young embryo is composed of fibrous membranes and hyaline cartilage. The formation of bone begins in these two tissues in the eighth week of embryonic life. Bone formed in a membrane is called intramembranous bone; bone formed in cartilage is called endochondral bone. It is important to understand that these terms indicate solely the method by which the bone starts to develop; they do not imply any difference in structure once the bone is fully formed.

INTRAMEMBRANOUS OSSIFICATION. This is the simpler, more direct type of bone formation. The flat bones of the face and cranial vault and a part of the clavicle form in membrane. In the area in which

162

bone formation is about to begin, *mesenchymal* cells congregate and many small blood vessels are present. The mesenchymal cells cluster to form long strands which run in all directions. Delicate bundles of fibrils, produced by the secretory action of the cells, form the axis of each elongated group. In a short time the fibrous axis is well defined and the cells are arranged in a layer around the outside of the strand. The fibers of the axis become saturated and cemented together with a collagenous substance called *osseomucoid*. The fibers are then less distinct, and in a short time they are masked to such an extent that the strand has a homogeneous appearance. This organic fibrous material forms a preliminary framework in which calcium salts are deposited. The framework is sometimes called *ossein* or *osteoid*. As soon as the deposit of calcium salts begins, the osteoid becomes true bone matrix and the mesenchymal cells are then called *osteoblasts* (bone-formers). When an original strand is completely invested with bone matrix it is called a *trabecula*. With the deposit of successive lamellae of bone, some of the osteoblasts become entrapped in their own secretions. Such cells are called *osteocytes*, and the spaces in the bone matrix which they occupy are called lacunae.

As the trabeculae in any ossification center grow, they soon touch each other and fuse. The pattern formed by the coalescence of the trabeculae resembles a latticework (Latin, *cancellus*), and bone showing this structure is accordingly called primary cancellous bone. Between the trabeculae are the marrow spaces. They contain mesenchymal elements which are gradually converted into marrow. Layers of compact bone form on the outer and inner surfaces by periosteal ossification. In this process, layers of the original mesenchyme condense to form *periosteum* shortly after bone forms at the inner centers. Osteoblasts from the inner surfaces of the periosteum deposit layers of cancellous bone. Much of the newly formed bone is destroyed and resorbed. In the surface areas the dissolving bone is replaced at a rapid rate; and by means of considerable internal reconstruction, bone of the compact type is formed. The cancellous bone at the inner ossification center also undergoes reconstruction; some bony strands are resorbed, while osteoblasts reinforce and construct other parts of the meshwork. Large multinuclear cells, called *osteoclasts* (bone-destroyers), are usually present in areas where bone destruction is taking place; but there is no positive evidence that they are actually responsible for bone destruction. The bones of the skull, when fully formed, consist of inner and outer *tables* of compact bone joined by the mass of spongy bone called *diploe*.

Table 5
Summary of Intramembranous Ossification

1. In the ossification centers, mesenchymal cells cluster together in long strands.
2. Collagenous fibers form the axis of the cell strands. The fibers are cemented together with osseomucoid to form a homogeneous framework called ossein or osteoid.
3. Osteoid becomes true bone when calcium salts are deposited in the framework.
4. A fibrous strand completely invested with bone matrix is called a trabecula. Trabeculae coalesce to form primary cancellous bone with marrow filling the open spaces.
5. The mesenchyme enclosing the ossification center differentiates into periosteum, which forms parallel plates of bone on the outer and inner surfaces of the center.
6. Bone at the surface is transformed into compact bone, and some reconstruction also occurs at the inner ossification center.
7. The final form of the bone consists of outer and inner tables of compact bone connected by cancellous bone.

ENDOCHONDRAL OSSIFICATION. This type of bone formation involves the same processes as intramembranous ossification, but these processes are preceded by an initial period of cartilage destruction. The endochondral course of development occurs in most of the bones of the body; namely, the bones of the thorax, the limbs, the greater part of the bones of the skull and the hyoid bone. These bones are represented in the embryo by temporary cartilaginous models. Bone begins to form in the eighth week of embryonic life, and at birth a large part of the skeleton is composed of bone (Fig. 80).

The process occurring in a long bone is typical. Figures 81 and 82 show stages in the ossification of the tibia. The contour of the cartilaginous model suggests the general form of the future bone (A). There is a central shaft called the *diaphysis* with an *epiphysis* at each end. The cartilage model is covered with *perichondrium*. Bone formation begins in an area surrounding the center of the diaphysis. The fibroblasts of the perichondrium adjoining the cartilage enlarge, become osteoblasts and begin the formation of bone, depositing a ring or collar of bone surrounding the middle of the diaphysis (B). As soon as the perichondrium begins to form bone, it is called periosteum. While the periosteal bone is forming, changes take place in the cartilage of the diaphysis; the cartilage cells swell into vesicles, and the matrix between them calcifies. Portions of the periosteum, fibrous tissue, and blood vessels, penetrate the collar of spongy bone and make their way into the interior of the altered cartilage. The calcified cartilage matrix surrounding the cartilage cells dissolves, and large spaces are opened up which soon become filled with embryonic marrow (E). These spaces are the primary marrow spaces. Cells of the embryonic marrow become osteoblasts and begin to form layers of bone about the remnants of cartilage matrix. Some cartilage cells also become osteoblasts; others degenerate. The osteoblasts form columns or trabeculae of spongy bone, and the cartilage matrix is gradually absorbed. Osteo-

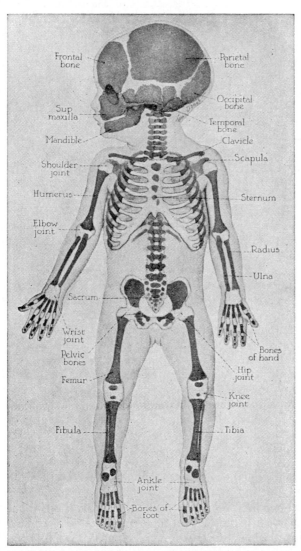

Fig. 80. Osseous development of infant at birth. (Courtesy of S. H. Camp & Co.)

clasts are also formed and can usually be seen in places where the newly formed bone is being resorbed.

Meanwhile the cartilage has grown steadily so that the whole model has increased in size. The periosteum has deposited successive layers of bone on the outside, gradually extending the collar toward each epiphysis. In the interior of the cartilage the process of cartilage destruction and endochondral bone formation has extended from the center of the diaphysis toward the epiphyses. As these areas of cartilage disintegration become removed somewhat from the center, the cartilage cells show a more definite arrangement and are seen in regular rows (E). Before long, mesenchymal elements of the periosteum invade the cartilage of the epiphyses and establish secondary ossification centers. In the tibia a center appears in the proximal epiphysis soon after birth and distally in the second year (F, G). The process is similar to that occurring in the diaphysis and results in spongy bone.

Plates of cartilage, known as epiphyseal cartilage, lie between the diaphysis and epiphysis at the *metaphysis*. This cartilage persists for some time, and provides for the growth in length of the bone. Cartilage grows by cell division on the epiphyseal side of the disc; it is destroyed and replaced by bone on the diaphyseal border, so that the disc remains approximately the same thickness. The metaphysis, or growth zone, is composed of the epiphyseal cartilage disc, a zone of calcified cartilage, and a zone of spongy bone deposited on the trabeculae of cartilage matrix. The process extends progressively, and the bone increases in length as the growth zone continues to move away from the center.

All bone is spongy when it is first formed; but later, by processes of bone destruction and resorption, the bone at the surface is reconstructed into the compact type. To accomplish this, the irregular channels in the spongy bone are enlarged; and concentric lamellae of bone are laid down on the inside to construct the Haversian systems. In the center of the diaphysis extensive dissolution of bone sculptures out a cylindrical space which is the medullary cavity. Eventually the cavity extends into the spaces of the spongy bone near the epiphysis. The design of the growing bone is suited to support body weight and muscular activity, and in every instance maximum strength is gained from a minimum of osseous tissue. Reconstruction of bone continues throughout adult life, though at a greatly diminished rate. The reconstruction of bone in adult life adjusts the pattern of structure to change in the mechanical conditions. It is also associated with supplying calcium to the plasma. Since calcium becomes available to the blood from the bone only by the destruction of the bone matrix, continuous

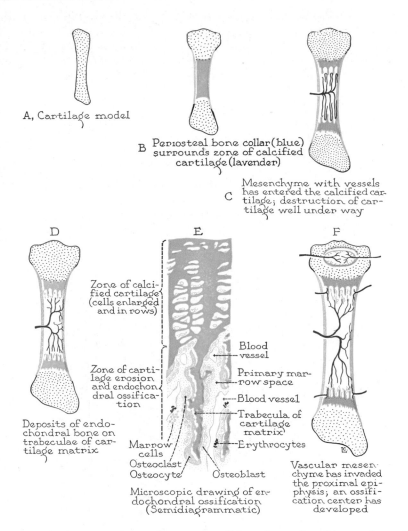

A, Cartilage model

B Periosteal bone collar (blue) surrounds zone of calcified cartilage (lavender)

C Mesenchyme with vessels has entered the calcified cartilage; destruction of cartilage well under way

D

E

F

Zone of calcified cartilage (cells enlarged and in rows)

Zone of cartilage erosion and endochondral ossification

Deposits of endochondral bone on trabeculae of cartilage matrix

Marrow cells
Osteoclast
Osteocyte   Osteoblast

Microscopic drawing of endochondral ossification (Semidiagrammatic)

Blood vessel

Primary marrow space

Blood vessel

Trabecula of cartilage matrix

Erythrocytes

Vascular mesenchyme has invaded the proximal epiphysis; an ossification center has developed

Fig. 81. Ossification and growth in a typical long bone, the tibia, as shown in longitudinal sections. Part I, Early stages.

reconstruction of bone supplies the "physiologic turnover" by which the calcium level is maintained in the plasma.

Ossification is complete when the cells of the cartilage cease to divide and the discs are entirely replaced with bone. The epiphyses are then united with the diaphysis, and growth in length is no longer possible. In the tibia this union occurs in the distal epiphysis at the age of seventeen, and in the proximal one about the twentieth year (*H, I*). Growth in the circumference of the bone is accomplished by layers of bone formed by the periosteum. Ossification is not complete in all the bones of the body until about the twenty-fifth year.

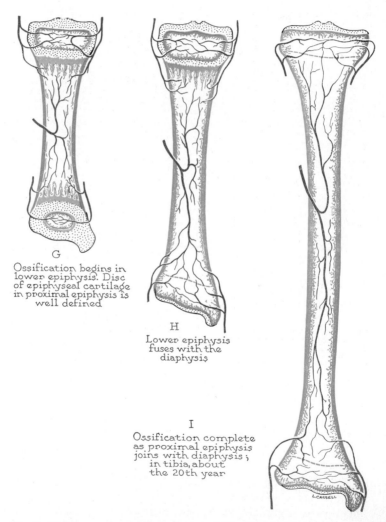

G

Ossification begins in lower epiphysis. Disc of epiphyseal cartilage in proximal epiphysis is well defined

H

Lower epiphysis fuses with the diaphysis

I

Ossification complete as proximal epiphysis joins with diaphysis; in tibia, about the 20th year

L. CASSELL

Fig. 82. Ossification and growth in a typical long bone, the tibia, as shown in longitudinal sections. Part II, Late stages.

Table 6

Summary of Endochondral Ossification

1. The greater part of the embryonic skeleton is formed of hyaline cartilage.
2. The cartilage model of the future bone is covered with perichondrium, which soon changes to periosteum.
3. In a long bone the osteoblasts of the periosteum deposit a collar of bone around the middle of the diaphysis. Cartilage destruction begins, cells swell, and matrix calcifies.
4. Elements of the periosteum (vascular mesenchyme) burrow into the altered cartilage; cartilage matrix between the cells dissolves, and opens up primary marrow spaces which become filled with marrow.
5. Cells of the embryonic marrow and some cartilage cells become osteoblasts and deposit bone around cartilage remnants. Osteoclasts are usually present.
6. The cartilage grows steadily, increasing the size of the model, and the periosteum continues to add successive layers of bone around the outside.
7. Within the cartilage the areas of cartilage destruction and bone formation extend toward the epiphyses. Later, ossification centers appear in the epiphyses.
8. Discs of epiphyseal cartilage between diaphysis and epiphyses remain for some time and provide for growth of the bone in length.
9. Growth is complete when cartilage cells cease to divide and epiphyseal cartilage is replaced with bone.
10. Bone grows in circumference by layers laid down around the outside by the periosteum.
11. Bone on the surface is transformed into compact bone by processes of resorption and internal reconstruction. In the center of the diaphysis extensive dissolution and resorption of bone forms the medullary cavity.
12. Ossification is not complete in all the bones of the body until about the twenty-fifth year.

Structure of Bone. The structure of a long bone is shown in Figure 83. Compact bone is found on the exterior of all bones and cancellous bone in the interior. In the long bones of the extremities the epiphyses are composed of the spongy type bone covered by a thin layer of compact bone. The diaphysis is made up almost entirely of compact bone, most of which is composed of Haversian systems and their interstitial lamellae. A set of lamellae, known as inner and outer circumferential lamellae, runs parallel to the surface of the bone on the interior and exterior. Extending throughout the center of the diaphysis is a cavity containing marrow.

The surface of the bone is covered by a fibrous membrane or *periosteum*. It has an outer fibrous layer composed of dense fibrous tissue with blood vessels and an inner osteogenetic layer containing many fibroblasts. The periosteum is attached to the surface of the bone by fibers, called fibers of Sharpey, which extend from the osteogenetic layer into the bone tissue. A thinner, more delicate membrane, the *endosteum,* which resembles periosteum in structure, lines the medullary cavity.

Bone is well supplied with blood. If we strip the periosteum from a fresh specimen of bone we see blood oozing from minute pores on the surface of the bone. At these points, blood vessels from the peri-

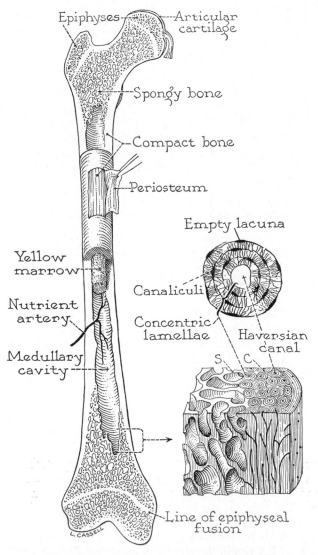

Fig. 83. Diagram of the structure of a long bone. S, On inset, indicates spongy bone; C, compact bone. (Inset adapted from Toldt.)

osteum enter the bone and pass through channels, *Volkmann's canals,* to enter and leave the Haversian canals of Haversian systems.

The lymph fluid from the blood vessels of the Haversian canals reaches all parts of the Haversian system through the circulatory tract formed by the canaliculi and lacunae. The circulation of the fluid in a Haversian system is probably independent of those of neighboring systems. In a long bone, an artery enters the marrow cavity through an opening, *the nutrient foramen,* which is usually near the center of the shaft. This nutrient artery divides into branches which run through the marrow and supply it. Other arteries penetrate the bone through Volkmann's canals to enter the Haversian canals. Branches of the nutrient artery connect with arteries of the compact and cancellous bone. In this way, blood vessels entering the bone from the periosteum are united with blood vessels entering from the marrow cavity, so that through the Haversian systems nutritive materials and calcium salts of the blood penetrate to all parts of the tissue. In the short, flat, irregular bones composed largely of spongy bone, several large openings in the surface transmit vessels which penetrate deep into the marrow spaces and resemble the nutrient arteries of long bones.

Bone marrow is found filling in the spaces of spongy bone and the medullary cavity of long bones. It is composed of a supporting framework of reticular tissue in which there are blood vessels and blood cells in various stages of development. In the adult, there are two kinds of marrow, red and yellow. Red blood cells and some white blood cells are formed in the red bone marrow. In the newborn, all marrow is red; in the adult it is found in spongy bone, such as the proximal epiphyses of long bones, in the sternum, ribs, vertebrae and diploe of the cranial bones. Yellow marrow, which contains many fat cells, is in the medullary cavity of long bones. Bone marrow aids in the nutrition of bone.

Anatomic Terminology. Examination of the surface of a bone reveals projections and depressions of various types. Table 7 lists the descriptive terms in frequent use:

Table 7
Anatomic Terms in Frequent Use

PROJECTIONS

Process—a general term for any bony prominence
Spine or spinous process—a sharp projection
Tubercle—a small rounded projection
Tuberosity—a large rounded projection
Trochanter—a very large process
Crest—a prominent ridge

Condyle—a rounded or knuckle-like process for articulation
Head—an enlargement at the end of a bone beyond the constricted portion, or
 neck

DEPRESSIONS

Fossa—a pit or hollow
Groove—a furrow
Sulcus—a furrow
Sinus—a cavity within a bone; also used to designate grooves on the inner surface
 of the skull
Foramen—a hole or opening in a bone
Meatus—tubelike passageway

DIVISIONS OF THE SKELETON

The bones of the body fall into two main groups (Fig. 84): those
comprising the axial skeleton, and those forming the appendicular
skeleton. The former is made up of the bones of the skull, vertebral
column and thorax; the latter consists of the upper and lower extremities.

The number of bones in the skeleton varies at different ages. At birth
the human body contains about 270 bones. This number is slightly
reduced during infancy by the union of some of the separate segments
to form single bones, but from then on through puberty and adolescence
the number increases steadily as the epiphyses and bones of wrists and
ankles develop. After adolescence reduction is again brought about by
a gradual union of independent bones. Ultimately the adult human
skeleton consists of 206 bones.

The number of bones in the axial and appendicular divisions of the
skeleton is listed below:

Axial Skeleton
Skull 29
         Cranium, 8; face 14,
         ear ossicles 6, hyoid 1
Vertebral column* 26
Thorax (sternum and ribs)................. 25
                                            ⎯
         Total axial 80
Appendicular Skeleton
Upper extremities 64
Lower extremities 62
                                            ⎯
         Total appendicular 126
                                                        ⎯
         Total all bones........................... 206

* Twenty-six bones when the nine or ten terminal segments which fuse to form
the sacrum and coccyx are counted as two bones.

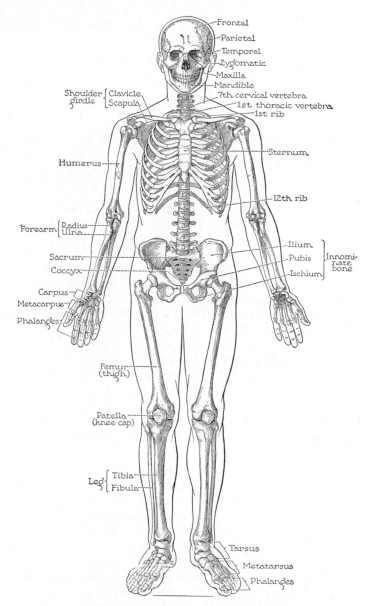

Fig. 84. Anterior view of human skeleton.

The Axial Skeleton

Bones of the Skull. The bones of the skull form the cranium, or brain case, and the face (Fig. 85):

BONES OF THE CRANIUM (8)	BONES OF THE FACE (14)
Single bones:	Single bones:
Occipital	Mandible
Frontal	Vomer
Sphenoid	Paired bones:
Ethmoid	Maxillae
Paired bones:	Zygomatic
Parietal	Lacrimal
Temporal	Nasal
	Inferior nasal conchae
	Palatine

The bones of the cranium form the floor and domelike vault which enclose the brain. On looking at the skull from the side (Fig. 86), it appears that the frontal bone forms the anterior part of the cranium and the occipital bone the posterior part, the parietal bones form the superior and lateral walls of the vault, while a portion of the temporal bone forms the lower part of the lateral wall in the center.

THE CRANIUM. Examining the base of the skull in Figure 87, we note that the sphenoid bone occupies the key position. Extending transversely through the center of the skull, it joins anteriorly with the orbital plates of the frontal bone and posteriorly with the central part of the occipital bone. Both frontal and occipital bones curve far underneath toward the center, forming considerable portions of the base of the skull. Wedgelike parts of the temporal bone fit between the occipital and sphenoid bones. The ethmoid bone separates the cranial cavity above from the nasal fossae below.

The *occipital* bone forms the posterior part of the floor and vault of the cranium (Figs. 87, 88, 91). In the middle of the inferior surface is a large opening, the foramen magnum, through which the spinal cord passes to make connection with the brain stem. On either side of the foramen magnum, externally, are two oval-shaped processes, the condyles (Fig. 88). These processes are curved anteroposteriorly, resembling rockers. Fitting into shallow depressions on the upper surface of the atlas (the first cervical vertebra), they form a joint allowing nodding movements of the head. Just above each condyle and visible on either side of the foramen magnum are the hypoglossal foramina. On the posterior part of the external surface is a projection called the external occipital protuberance, and extending out from it on either side are curved ridges, the superior nuchal lines, and a short distance below are the inferior nuchal lines. On the inner surface (Fig. 87) are well-defined grooves for the transverse sinuses.

The *frontal* bone (Fig. 85) forms the forehead, the anterior part of the cranial vault and the greater part of the roof of the orbits. On either side of the nose, where the frontal and orbital portions of the bone meet, there is a sharp curved border, the supraorbital margin. Toward the

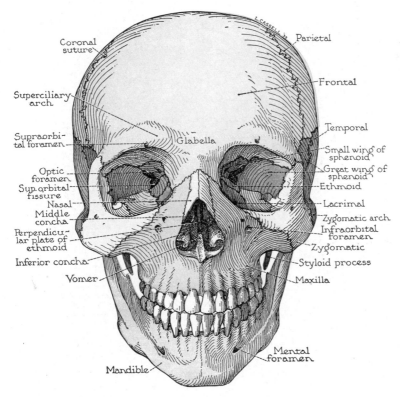

Fig. 85. Anterior view of the skull.

medial part each margin is crossed by a groove, the supraorbital notch, which transmits the supraorbital nerve and artery. Occasionally the notch is converted into a foramen. Above the margin are two ridges, the superciliary arches, which give prominence to the eyebrows. In the middle, just above the nose and between the ridges, is a smooth area called the glabella. Inside the bone in the position corresponding with the superciliary arches are two cavities, the frontal sinuses. These are air sinuses.

The *parietal* bones (Figs. 86, 89, 90) form a large part of the superior and lateral walls of the cranium. The two bones meet in the midline to form the sagittal suture. On the inner surface along the line of the suture is a groove for the superior sagittal sinus, called the sagittal sulcus.

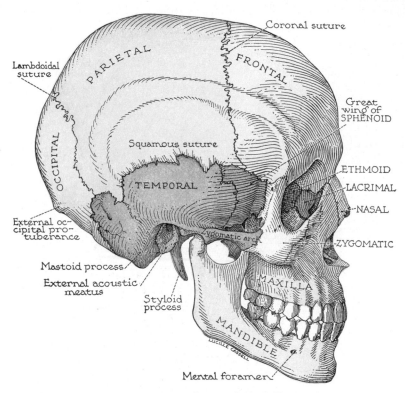

Fig. 86. Lateral view of the skull.

The *temporal* bones form part of the base and lateral wall of the cranium. Viewed from the side (Fig. 86), the external surface presents an important landmark, the external acoustic meatus. This canal forms part of the passageway leading to the middle ear and is a convenient point of reference in describing the parts of the temporal bone. Above the meatus is a thin, fan-shaped sheet of bone, the squamous portion (Fig. 92); backward and slightly below is the mastoid portion. The tympanic part is a curved plate which forms the inferior and lateral walls of the acoustic meatus. The petrous portion extends inward and forward from the meatus, forming a prominent elevation on the floor of the cranial cavity. It is best recognized in a view of the base of the skull from above (sec Fig. 87). The petrous portion is hard and rock-like, as its name implies, and in the interior are cavities containing the specialized organs of hearing and equilibrium. The internal acoustic meatus on the posterior wall of the petrous elevation transmits nerves leading to these structures. The zygomatic process, a conspicuous bar of bone, projects forward from the lower part of the squamous portion

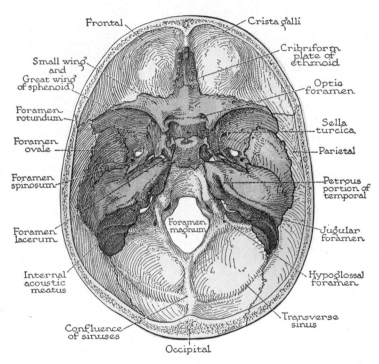

Frontal · Crista galli · Cribriform plate of ethmoid · Small wing and Great wing of sphenoid · Optic foramen · Foramen rotundum · Sella turcica · Foramen ovale · Parietal · Foramen spinosum · Petrous portion of temporal · Foramen lacerum · Foramen magnum · Jugular foramen · Internal acoustic meatus · Hypoglossal foramen · Confluence of sinuses · Transverse sinus · Occipital

Fig. 87. View of base of skull from above.

and joins with the zygomatic bone of the face to form the zygomatic arch. Below the zygomatic process and just in front of the external acoustic meatus is a depression, the mandibular fossa (Fig. 88), which receives the condyle of the mandible. The inferior surface of the temporal bone is rough, and from it extends a sharp projection, the styloid process. Between the styloid process and the mastoid process is an opening, the stylomastoid foramen. The mastoid portion contains the mastoid process and the groove for the transverse sinus. The mastoid process is the conspicuous bony prominence just behind the external ear. The interior of the process contains spaces, the mastoid air cells, which communicate with the middle ear. On the inner surface of the mastoid portion is a groove for the transverse sinus which is continuous with that of the occipital bone (Fig. 87).

The *sphenoid* bone (Figs. 87, 93) forms the central part of the base of the cranium. It is bounded by the ethmoid and frontal bones

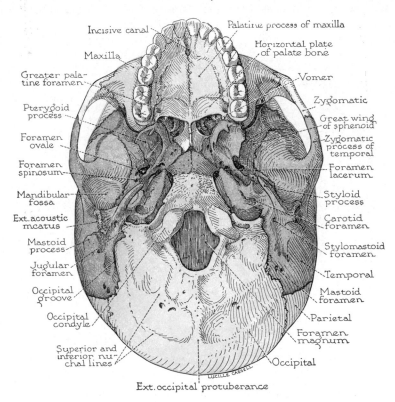

Incisive canal
Palatine process of maxilla
Maxilla
Horizontal plate of palate bone
Greater palatine foramen
Vomer
Pterygoid process
Zygomatic
Great wing of sphenoid
Foramen ovale
Zygomatic process of temporal
Foramen spinosum
Foramen lacerum
Mandibular fossa
Styloid process
Ext. acoustic meatus
Carotid foramen
Mastoid process
Stylomastoid foramen
Jugular foramen
Temporal
Occipital groove
Mastoid foramen
Occipital condyle
Parietal
Superior and inferior nuchal lines
Foramen magnum
Occipital
Ext. occipital protuberance

Fig. 88. View of base of skull from below.

anteriorly and the temporal and occipital posteriorly. It has been compared to a bird with wings outspread and feet dependent. It presents a body, two great wings, two small wings and hanging feet (the pterygoid processes). The body extends from its connection in front with the ethmoid through the midline to its union posteriorly with the occipital bone. In the center of the superior surface of the body is a hollow called the sella turcica, or Turk's saddle, which holds the hypophysis, or pituitary body. In the interior of the body are two large cavities, the sphenoidal air sinuses (Figs. 89, 90). The great and small wings extend laterally from the sides of the body. The small wings form a small part of the posterior part of the orbits. In the orbital portion of each small wing is an opening, the optic foramen, which transmits the optic nerve. The great wings form part of the floor and lateral walls of the orbits (Fig. 85). Each great wing is perforated by several openings: foramen rotundum, foramen ovale and foramen spinosum. At

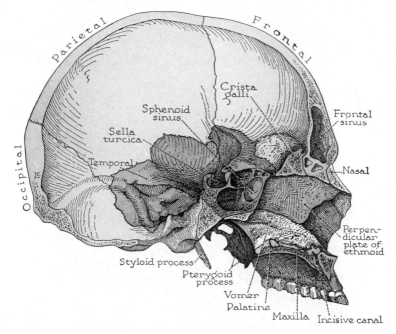

Fig. 89. Left half of skull, showing parts of nasal septum.

either side of the body where the lesser wings overhang the greater wings there are irregular, slitlike openings, the superior orbital fissures. The pterygoid processes (Figs. 88, 93) consist of medial and lateral plates. They extend downward from the sides of the body. The medial plate forms part of the lateral wall of the nose; the lateral plate forms the back part of the framework of the upper jaw.

The *ethmoid* bone (Figs. 87, 94) is located in the anterior part of the base of the cranium, between the two orbits, at the roof of the nose, and it contributes to each of these cavities. The main parts are a perpendicular plate, a horizontal plate and two lateral masses. The perpendicular plate descends into the nasal cavity in the midline, forming the superior part of the nasal septum (Figs. 85, 89, 94). The horizontal or cribriform plate extends at right angles to the perpendicular plate on either side, in which situation it roofs in the nasal fossae and joins the corresponding portion of the floor of the cranial cavity (above). The cribriform plates have perforations through which pass nerves of smell to the mucous membrane of the nose. Extending into the cranial cavity as an upward extension of the perpendicular plate is a process called crista galli. The lateral masses are attached to

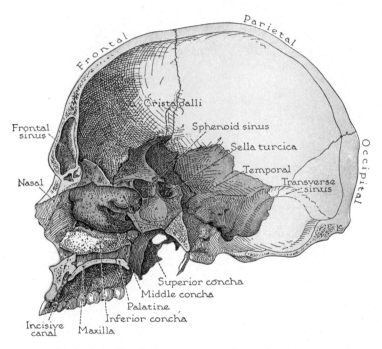

Fig. 90. Right half of skull, showing conchae on lateral nasal wall.

the margins of the cribriform plates. They are composed of the orbital plates, superior and middle conchae, and ethmoidal cells. The orbital plates, or lamina papyracea, are thin, rectangular sheets of bone which form the main part of the medial wall of the orbits. The medial surface of the lateral mass, forming the lateral wall of the nose, presents two scroll-shaped convoluted masses, the superior and middle conchae. Between the lamina papyracea and the superior and middle conchae is an intricate, honeycombed arrangement of bone which consists of many spaces or compartments called the ethmoidal cells. These are air spaces which connect with the nasal cavity, and collectively they comprise the ethmoid sinus.

THE FACE. The bones of the face (Fig. 85) appear suspended from

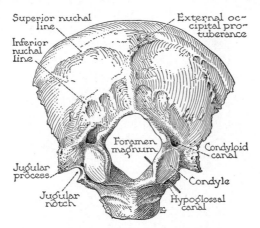

Fig. 91. The occipital bone, external surface.

the middle and anterior parts of the brain case. While it is convenient for purposes of study to divide the bones of the skull into those of the cranium and those of the face, it is evident that some of the bones

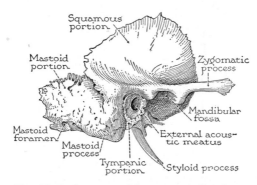

Fig. 92. Right temporal bone, external surface.

of the cranium, particularly the frontal and ethmoid, also contribute to the framework of the face.

The *maxilla* (Fig. 85) has been described as the key to the architecture of the face, since all bones of the face except the mandible touch it. This bone meets its fellow in the midline to form the whole of the upper jaw. Each bone shares in forming the floor of the orbit, the lateral and inferior walls of the nasal cavities and the hard palate (Fig. 88). The lower border of the bone which contains cavities for the teeth is the alveolar process. In the body of the bone is a large air space, the maxillary sinus or antrum of Highmore. The opening just below the orbit on the external surface is the infraorbital foramen.

The *mandible* (Fig. 95), or lower jaw, consists of a central horizontal portion, the body, which forms the chin and supports the teeth, and

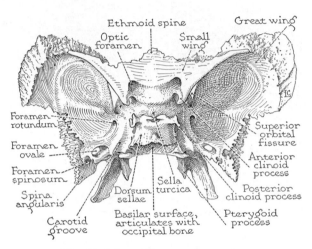

Fig. 93. Sphenoid bone, upper surface.

two perpendicular portions, the rami, which project upward from the back on either side. The body is curved and presents on its upper border the alveolar process for the teeth. Just below the first bicuspid, about halfway between the upper and lower margins of the jaw, is the mental foramen. Each ramus has a condyle for articulation with the mandibular fossa of the temporal bone and a coronoid process for attachment of the temporal muscle. The angle of the mandible is at the point of union of the posterior and inferior borders of the ramus. On the medial surface of the ramus is an opening, the mandibular foramen (Fig. 96), through which pass the vessels and nerves for the teeth. The terminal branches emerge through the mental foramen to supply the chin. At the base of the mandible where the body joins the ramus is a groove for the external maxillary artery. The symphysis marks the junction between the two halves of the mandible.

The *zygomatic* bone (Figs. 85, 86) forms the prominence of the cheek and outer margin of the orbit. It joins with the zygomatic process of the temporal bone to complete the zygomatic arch.

The *lacrimal* bone forms a small part of the medial wall of the orbit. It lies between the lamina papyracea of the ethmoid bone and the frontal process of the maxilla. The orbital surface is divided into two

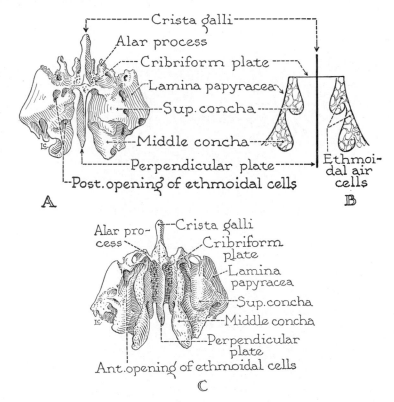

Fig. 94. *A*, Ethmoid bone from behind. *B*, Diagram of the parts of the ethmoid bone. *C*, Ethmoid bone from in front and below.

parts by a vertical ridge, the posterior lacrimal crest. In front of the crest is a longitudinal groove which joins with a corresponding groove on the maxilla to form the lacrimal fossa. The crest ends below in a hooklike projection which curves forward to articulate with the maxilla and complete the upper orifice of the nasolacrimal duct.

The *nasal* bones are thin, rectangular pieces of bone which form the upper part of the bridge of the nose; the lower part is composed of cartilage.

The *inferior nasal concha* (Fig. 90) is an elongated, curved bone placed horizontally along the lateral wall of the nasal fossa below the superior and middle conchae, which are parts of the ethmoid.

The *palatine* bones (Fig. 88) are situated at the back part of the nasal cavities between the maxillae and the pterygoid processes of the sphenoid bone. Each consists of a horizontal and vertical plate

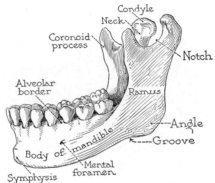

Fig. 95. The mandible as seen from the left side.

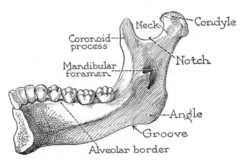

Fig. 96. Inner surface of right half of the mandible.

(Fig. 97). The union of the horizontal plates in the midline forms the posterior part of the hard palate. These bones help to form the walls of three cavities, the floor and lateral walls of the nasal cavities, the floor of the orbits, and the roof of the mouth.

The *vomer* is a thin bone, shaped like a ploughshare. It forms the back and lower part of the nasal septum (Figs. 85, 89).

The *hyoid* bone (Fig. 98) is a U-shaped bone suspended by ligaments from the styloid processes of the temporal bones. It is not a bone of the skull, but is considered here for convenience. It may be felt in the neck between the mandible and the larynx. It consists of a central portion, the body, and two projections or horns on each side, the great and small cornua.

SPECIAL FEATURES PERTAINING TO THE SKULL AS A WHOLE.   SUTURES. The sutures are the lines of union of the cranial bones. The sagittal suture is in the midline between the parietal bones. The coronal suture

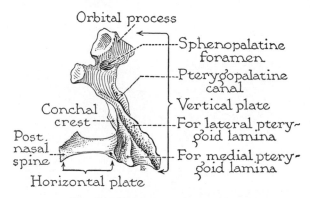

Fig. 97. Right palate bone from behind.

is at right angles to the sagittal suture and separates the frontal and two parietal bones. The lambdoidal suture marks the boundary line between the occipital and parietal bones. The squamous suture is between the parietal bone and the squamous portion of the temporal. At birth the frontal bone consists of two parts which later become

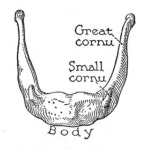

Fig. 98. Hyoid bone, front view.

fused to form the single bone, but occasionally this suture persists as a line of division between the halves of the frontal bone. It is called the interfrontal or metopic suture.

FONTANELS.   The spaces between the converging bones in which intramembranous ossification is incomplete at birth are called fontanels.

The newborn infant usually has six fontanels, found at the angles of the parietal bone. The anterior fontanel (Fig. 99) is diamond-shaped. It lies at the junction of the frontal and parietal bones. This fontanel usually closes about the eighteenth month. The posterior fontanel (Fig. 99), lying at the junction of the occipital and parietal bones, is triangular in shape. It is smaller than the anterior fontanel and closes usually by the second month. The anterolateral (Fig. 100) fontanels lie at the junction of the frontal, parietal, temporal and sphenoid bones.

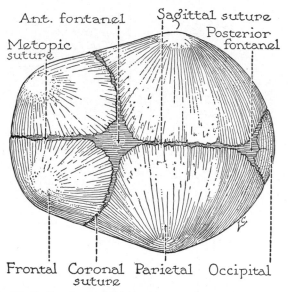

Fig. 99. Skull at birth, showing anterior and posterior fontanels.

They close usually by the third month. The posterolateral fontanels (Fig. 100) lie at the junctions of the parietal, occipital and temporal bones and do not close completely until the second year.

The incomplete ossification of the bones of the skull at birth points to an adaptive mechanism for childbirth. During labor the bones of the skull override each other, and the infant's skull, being reduced in its diameters, accommodates itself to the size of the birth canal to a considerable extent.

SINUSES.   The air sinuses, or paranasal sinuses, are cavities within the bones which communicate with the nose. The paranasal sinuses are the frontal, maxillary, sphenoid and ethmoid. They are lined with mucous membrane which is continuous with that of the nose, and they contain air. The blood sinuses are channels in the external membrane covering the brain which convey venous blood from the brain. Those which lie against the cranial bones make impressions or grooves on the inner surface of the bone. Examples of venous sinuses are the superior sagittal and transverse sinuses.

NASAL SEPTUM.   The nasal septum (Figs. 85, 89, pp. 175, 179) is the median vertical partition which divides the cavity of the nose into two nasal fossae. The perpendicular plate of the ethmoid forms the upper part, the vomer the lower, and the septal cartilage completes the anterior portion.

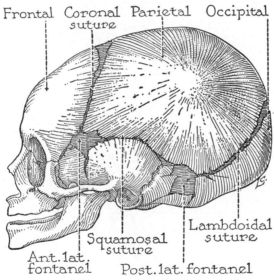

Fig. 100. Lateral view of the skull at birth.

ORBITAL FOSSAE OR ORBITS.   The orbit (Fig. 85) is the bony socket for the eyeball. It is formed by the frontal, zygomatic, ethmoid, sphenoid, lacrimal, maxillary and palatine bones. The fossa is cone-shaped, with the apex directed backward and somewhat medialward. Near the apex are two openings, the optic foramen and the superior orbital fissure.

Bones of the Vertebral Column.   The *spine* or vertebral column, a part of the axial skeleton, is a strong flexible rod which supports the head, gives base to the ribs and encloses the spinal cord. The thirty-three (or occasionally thirty-four) bones composing the spinal column are called *vertebrae.* These are divided into five groups according to their distinguishing characteristics. The cervical region has seven vertebrae; the thoracic, twelve; the lumbar, five; the sacral, five; the coccygeal, four or five. In the adult the vertebrae of the sacral and coccygeal regions are united into two bones, the sacrum and the coccyx.

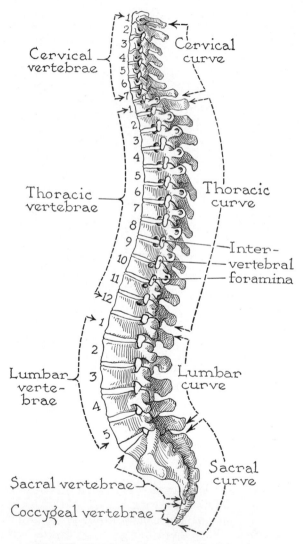

Fig. 101. Vertebral column from the left side.

A lateral view of the vertebral column (Fig. 101) shows four curves, alternately convex and concave ventrally. In fetal life the vertebral column is uniformly curved so that it is concave ventrally. In the thoracic and sacrococcygeal regions these concavities persist, providing space for accommodation of the viscera. The two convex curves are the cervical and the lumbar. The cervical curve appears when the infant learns to hold his head erect, usually about the third month; the lumbar curve appears when the child has learned to walk, between the twelfth and eighteenth months. The thoracic and sacrococcygeal curves present in the fetus are therefore primary; the cervical and lumbar appearing after birth are secondary and compensatory.

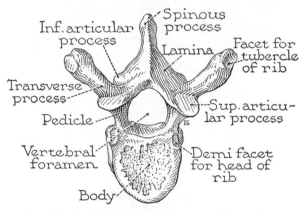

Fig. 102. Sixth thoracic vertabra viewed from above.

A TYPICAL VERTEBRA. The vertebrae differ in size and shape, but in general show a uniform plan of structure. The sixth thoracic vertebra exhibits this typical structure (see Fig. 102). A vertebra is composed of the following parts: a weight-bearing portion, the body; a part that protects the spinal cord, the neural arch; three levers on which muscles pull, the spinous process and right and left transverse processes; and four processes or projections, the articular processes, which restrict movements.

The body is the central mass of bone which forms the anterior part of the vertebra. The pedicles or pillars of the arch are two short, thick columns which extend backward from the body to meet with the laminae in the formation of the neural arch. The body and neural arch enclose a foramen, the vertebral foramen. Seven processes arise from the arch: one spinous, two transverse, two superior articular and two inferior articular. Extending backward from the point of union of the two laminae is the spinous process. Projecting laterally at either side from the junction of lamina and pedicle are the transverse processes. The articular processes arise near the junction of the pedicle and lamina, the superior processes project upward, and the inferior project downward. The surfaces of the processes are smooth, the inferior

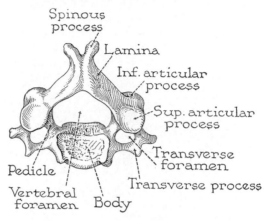

Fig. 103. Fourth cervical vertebra from above.

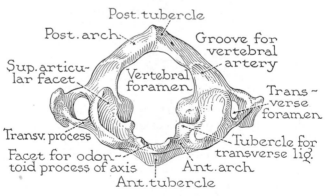

Fig. 104. First cervical vertebra or atlas from above.

articular processes of the vertebra above fitting into the superior articular processes of the vertebra below. These are true joints, but the contact established serves to restrict movement, preventing forward displacement of an upper vertebra on a lower.

DISTINGUISHING FEATURES OF DIFFERENT REGIONS. CERVICAL REGION (Fig. 103). All vertebrae of this region have foramina in the transverse processes; those of the upper six vertebrae transmit the vertebral artery. The spinous processes are short; the third, fourth and fifth are bifurcated, while the seventh is unusually long and may be felt as a prominence at the back of the neck. In general, the bodies of the cervical vertebrae are small, and the vertebral foramina large and

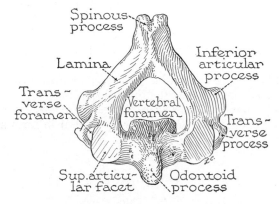

Fig. 105. Second cervical vertebra, axis or epistropheus, from above.

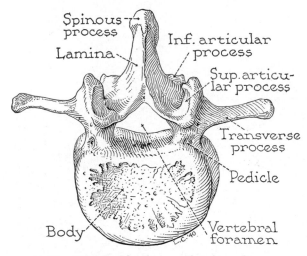

Fig. 106. Third lumbar vertebra from above.

somewhat triangular in outline. The first cervical vertebra, the *atlas*, has no body but is composed of an anterior and a posterior arch and two lateral masses (Fig. 104). The superior articular processes articulate with the condyles of the occipital bone. The second cervical vertebrae is the *epistropheus* or axis (Fig. 105). A process, the *dens* (odontoid process), on the upper surface of the body, forms a pivot about which the atlas rotates. The dens represents the separated body of the atlas which has fused with the epistropheus.

THORACIC REGIONS (Fig. 102).   The presence of facets for articulation with the ribs is the distinguishing feature of this group. All processes of the thoracic region are larger and heavier than those in the cervical region. The spinous process is directed downward at a sharp angle. The vertebral foramen is circular.

LUMBAR VERTEBRAE.   The bodies of the lumbar vertebrae are large and heavy. The superior articular processes face inward; the inferior articular processes face outward (Fig. 106).

SACRAL VERTEBRAE.   The *sacrum* (Fig. 119, p. 204) is composed of five fused and modified vertebrae. It is triangular in form and is fitted

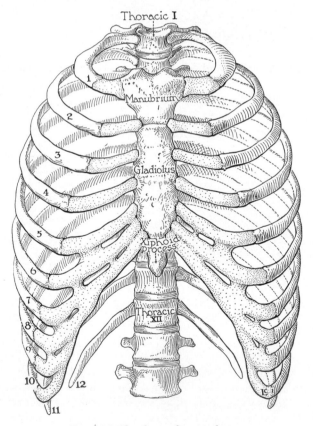

Fig. 107. The thorax from in front.

like a wedge between the halves of the pelvis. On the anterior margin of the upper surface of the body of the first sacral vertebra is an important landmark, the promontory of the sacrum.

COCCYGEAL VERTEBRAE. The *coccyx* (Fig. 119) is the terminal and most rudimentary part of the vertebral column. It is composed of four or five nodular pieces representing bodies of the vertebrae. The bone

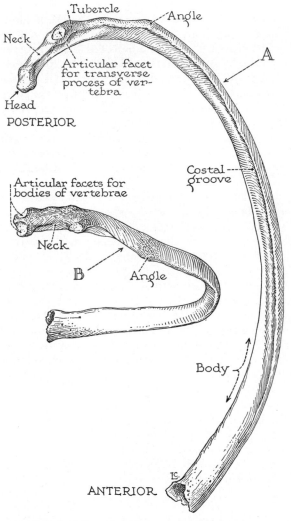

Fig. 108. A central rib of the right side. *A*, Inferior surface. *B*, Posterior view.

is triangular in shape with base above attached to the sacrum and apex below.

Bones of the Thorax. The thorax is a bony, cartilaginous cage whose walls are formed behind by thoracic vertebrae, at the sides by the ribs, and in front by the costal cartilages and the sternum (Fig. 107). It is cone-shaped, being narrow above and broad below. At birth the thorax is nearly round, but in adult life it is flattened from front to back.

The twenty-four *ribs*, placed twelve on each side of the thorax, form the greater part of its bony walls. They are long, flat bones which are curved and twisted. They are connected behind to the spine and continued forward by the costal cartilages. The first seven pairs are attached directly to the sternum through their costal cartilages and for this reason are called "true" ribs; the remaining five pairs are called "false" ribs. The cartilages of the eighth, ninth and tenth ribs each join to the lower border of the cartilage of the preceding rib. Since cartilage endings of the eleventh and twelfth ribs are unattached, they are termed "floating" ribs. Each rib slopes downward from its posterior attachment so that its anterior end is considerably lower than its posterior end.

A central rib (Fig. 108) is regarded as typical, although certain ribs show variations. The head of the rib, which is on the posterior end of the bone, is expanded, and its medial surface presents two smooth areas which articulate with the demifacets on the vertebral bodies. Below the head is the slightly constricted region, the neck, and beyond this is the body or shaft. At the junction of the neck and shaft is a tubercle which consists of an articular and a nonarticular portion. The articular portion connects with the facet on the transverse process of the vertebra; the nonarticular portion is for the attachment of ligaments. The body of the rib shows a rather sharp bend near its posterior end, which is called the angle of the rib. On the lower border of the inner surface is a groove, the costal groove, which lodges intercostal vessels and nerve. The anterior or costal end of the rib is often slightly expanded and contains a pitlike depression into which the costal cartilage sinks. The joint thus formed is called the costochondral junction. The parts are bound together by a fusion of the periosteum of the bone with the perichondrium of the cartilage.

The *sternum* or breast bone, likened to the Roman sword, is composed of the manubrium or handle, the body (gladiolus) or blade, and the xiphoid (ensiform) process.

The Appendicular Skeleton

The upper and lower extremities comprise the appendicular skeleton.

The Upper Extremity. The following divisions constitute the upper extremity:

Shoulder—scapula ⎫ shoulder girdle
           clavicle ⎭
Arm   —humerus
Forearm —ulna, radius
        ⎧ carpus (wrist)—8 small bones
Hand   —⎨ metacarpus—5 bones
        ⎩ phalanges (fingers)—14 bones

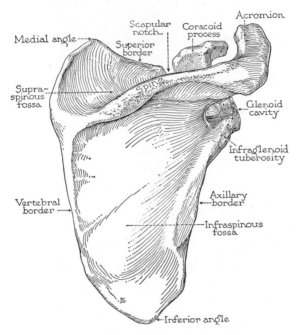

Fig. 109. Right scapula, posterior surface.

SHOULDER. The shoulder girdle is made up of the collar bone (clavicle) and the shoulder blade (scapula). The clavicle articulates with the sternum, but the scapula has no bony attachment to the axial skeleton except through the clavicle. It maintains its position through muscular attachments and is thus free and mobile. This girdle serves to attach the upper extremity to the axial skeleton.

The *scapula* (Figs. 109, 110) or shoulder blade is a triangular bone with the base upward and the apex downward. The base of the triangle forms the superior border; the medial margin, the side toward the vertebral column, the vertebral border; the lateral margin, the axillary border. The angles of the triangle are named medial, lateral and inferior. The lateral angle forms an expanded portion known as the head. On its lateral aspect is an oval, hollowed surface, the glenoid cavity, which receives the head of the humerus. The neck is the slightly constricted part which surrounds and supports the head. Above the

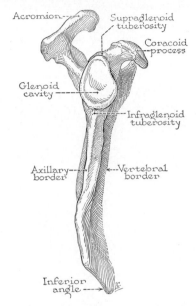

Fig. 110. Right scapula from the axillary border.

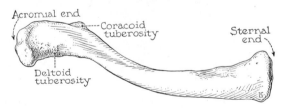

Fig. 111. Right clavicle, superior surface.

glenoid cavity is a process called the supraglenoid tuberosity; below is a prominence called the infraglenoid tuberosity. Extending across the upper part of the posterior surface is a ridge of bone, the spine, which expands laterally into a broad, flat projection, the acromion. The acromion forms the point of the shoulder and gives attachment to the clavicle. The coracoid process projects anteriorly from the upper part of the neck of the scapula.

The *clavicle* (Fig. 111) is a slender S-shaped bone which extends

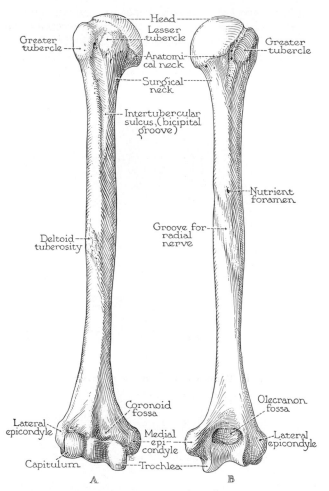

Fig. 112. *A*, Right humerus, anterior surface. *B*, Right humerus, posterior surface

horizontally across the upper part of the thorax. The medial end, since it articulates with the manubrium of the sternum, is called the sternal extremity; the lateral end, articulating with the acromion, is the acromial extremity. The bone has important muscle attachments and gives support to the shoulder joint.

ARM. The *humerus* or arm bone consists of a shaft and two enlarged extremities (Fig. 112). On the proximal extremity is the smooth, rounded head which fits into the glenoid cavity of the scapula. Just beneath the head are two rounded processes, the greater and lesser tubercles, and lying between them is the intertubercular (bicipital) groove. Between the head and the tubercles is the anatomic neck; the region below the tubercles is called the surgical neck because of its liability to fracture. The shaft exhibits on its posterior surface a groove

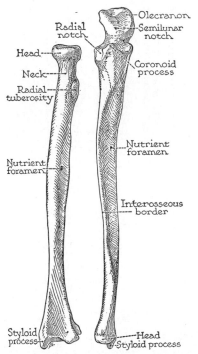

Fig. 113. Right radius and ulna, anterior view.

for the radial nerve, and, on the lateral border about midway down, a rough area, the deltoid tuberosity. The distal end of the bone has two articulating surfaces, the condyles, the lateral of which, called the capitulum, articulates with the head of the radius; the medial one, the trochlea, articulates with the ulna. Above the trochlea on the anterior surface is a depression, the coronoid fossa, and on the posterior surface the olecranon fossa, into which the corresponding processes of the ulna slip in flexion and extension, respectively. On either side just above the capitulum and trochlea are the lateral and medial epicondyles.

FOREARM.   The *radius* (Fig. 113) is the lateral bone of the forearm.

It is shorter than the ulna, but is broad below, where it forms the whole of the articulation with the wrist. The proximal end of the radius has a disc-shaped head which articulates with the humerus and with the radial notch of the ulna. Below the head on the medial side is a rough elevation, the radial tuberosity. The distal end is broad for articulation with the bones of the wrist and has a styloid process on its lateral part.

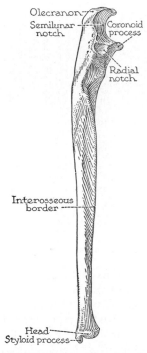

Fig. 114. Right ulna, lateral surface.

The *ulna* (Figs. 113, 114) is on the medial side of the forearm and therefore on the little finger side in relation to the hand. It forms a conspicuous part of the elbow joint and has been described as belonging to the arm, while the radius may be considered to belong to the hand. The proximal end is large, presenting on its superior and posterior aspect the olecranon, which forms the point of the elbow. The curved surface articulating with the trochlea of the humerus is the semilunar notch. Below this is a rough projection, the coronoid process. On the lateral side near the semilunar notch is a concave articular surface, the radial notch for reception of the head of the radius. The distal end is small and has a head which articulates with a disc of

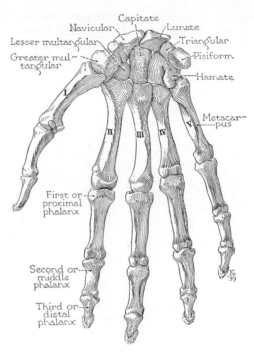

Fig. 115. Bones of right hand, palmar surface.

fibrocartilage, separating it from the bones of the wrist, and a small sharp projection, the styloid process.

HAND.   The eight *carpal* bones (Fig. 115) of the wrist are arranged in two rows of four each. Listed from lateral to medial aspects they are, in the proximal row: navicular, lunate, triangular, pisiform; in the distal row: greater multangular, lesser multangular, capitate, hamate.

The five *metacarpal* bones (Fig. 115) form the framework of the hand proper. They are numbered from one to five, beginning on the lateral or thumb side.

The *phalanges* (Fig. 115) form the framework of the fingers or digits. There are three phalanges in each finger and two in the thumb.

The Lower Extremity.   The following divisions comprise the lower extremity:

        Hip   —pelvic girdle—innominate bone
        Thigh   —femur
        Kneecap—patella
        Leg   —tibia, fibula
                        ⎧ tarsus (ankle)—7 bones
        Foot   —⎨ metatarsus—5 bones
                        ⎩ phalanges (toes)—14 bones

Hip. The hip or innominate bone constitutes the pelvic girdle. It is built for stability and is firmly united to the vertebral column. The pelvic girdle serves to attach the lower extremity to the axial skeleton.

The *innominate bone* is a large irregular bone which in youth is composed of three parts (Fig. 116). Although in the adult the parts are united into one bone, it is usual to describe the three portions. The union of the parts occurs below the center of the bone, and the location is marked by a cup-shaped cavity, the *acetabulum*. The large portion above, which is wide and flaring, is the ilium; the part passing

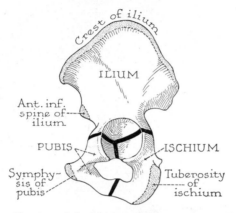

Fig. 116. Plan of ossification of the hip bone, showing union of the three parts in the acetabulum.

medially is the pubis; the downward extension is the ischium. Ilium, pubis and ischium share in the construction of the acetabulum which forms the socket for the head of the femur.

The *ilium*, broad and expanded, forms the prominence of the hip (Fig. 117). The superior border is the crest. The projection at the anterior tip of the crest forms the anterior superior spine of the ilium. This is an important anatomical landmark. The prominence just below is the anterior inferior spine. Corresponding projections on the posterior part are called posterior superior and posterior inferior iliac spines. Beneath the posterior part is the greater sciatic notch. The outer surface of the ilium is traversed by three curved or gluteal lines, the posterior gluteal line, anterior gluteal line and inferior gluteal line, all of which end near the greater sciatic notch. On the inner surface (Fig. 118) is the terminal or iliopectineal line, which begins below on the pubis and continues across the ilium to the sacrum. This line separates the lesser pelvis below from the greater pelvis above. Most of the ilium above the iliopectineal line is a smooth concavity, the iliac fossa; posteriorly, there is a rough, pitted area, the articular surface, which articulates with the sacrum in the formation of the sacroiliac joint.

The *pubic* bone (Fig. 117) comprises the anterior part of the innominate bone and, joining its fellow in the midline, forms a joint known as the *symphysis pubis.* This bone consists of a body and two

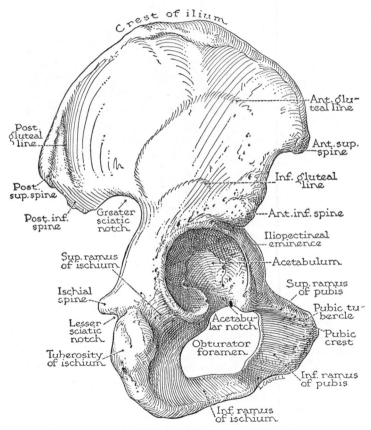

Fig. 117. Right hip bone or innominate bone, external surface.

arms or rami. The body forms about one fifth of the acetabulum. The superior ramus extends from the body to the median plane. The upper border of the superior ramus presents a rough ridge, the pubic crest. The crest ends laterally in a rounded process, the pubic tubercle. The pubic tubercle marks also the termination of the iliopectineal line. The inferior ramus passes downward and outward to meet the ischium.

The *pubic arch* is formed by the inferior rami of both pubic bones, which converge above at the symphysis.

The *ischium* (Fig. 117) forms the lower and back part of the innominate bone. It consists of a body and a ramus. The body forms

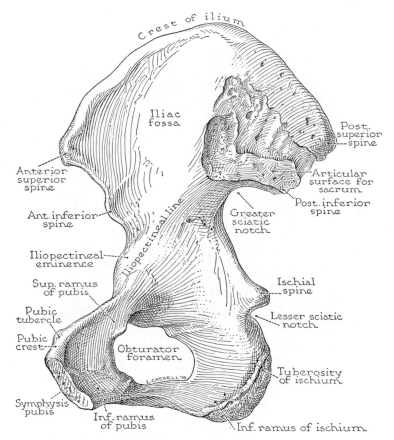

Fig. 118. Right hip bone, or innominate bone, inner surface.

a little over two fifths of the acetabulum. Below is a large, rough process, the ischial tuberosity, which supports the body in sitting position. The sharp projection above the tuberosity is the spine of the ischium. The ramus of the ischium passes upward to join the inferior ramus of the pubis. The ischium and pubis combine to close in a large aperture, the obturator foramen.

THE PELVIS. Pelvis is the Latin word meaning basin. The pelvis is formed by the right and left innominate bones, sacrum and coccyx (Fig. 119). The promontory of the sacrum and the iliopectineal line divide the pelvis into the lesser pelvis below and the greater pelvis above. The latter, bounded by the ilia and lower lumbar vertebrae, is

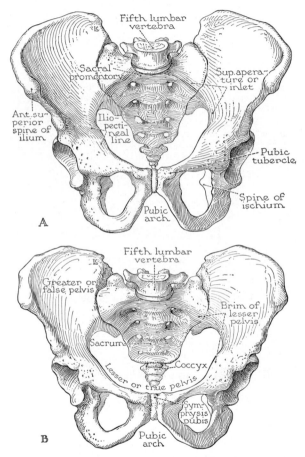

Fig. 119. A, Male pelvis, anterior view. B, Female pelvis, anterior view.

deficient in front and for this reason is referred to as the "false" pelvis. The capacious iliac fossae give support to abdominal viscera, indicating clearly that the greater pelvis really belongs to the abdomen. The lesser or true pelvis has more complete bony walls than the greater pelvis, and a well-defined inlet and outlet. The inlet or brim of the pelvis corresponds to the sacral promontory and the iliopectineal lines and marks out the circumference of the superior aperture. The lower limits of the outlet consist of the tip of the coccyx and the tuberosities and spines of the ischia.

DIFFERENCES BETWEEN MALE AND FEMALE PELVES.   The female pelvis shows adaptations related to its function as a birth canal. The

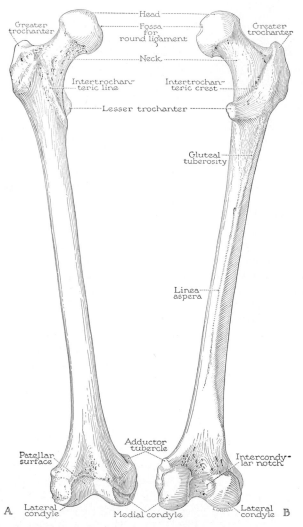

Fig. 120. *A*, Right femur, anterior view. *B*, Right femur, posterior view,

male pelvis is constructed along lines which contribute to motor power and speed. It is narrow, heavy and compact; while the female pelvis is wide, light and capacious. In the male pelvis the inlet is heart-shaped; in the female it is almost a perfect circle. The angle of the pubic arch of the male is acute; that of the female is obtuse. In the male the sacrum is narrow, long and curved; the female sacrum is broad, short and straight. Spines of the ischia are sharper and project inward farther in the male than in the female.

THIGH. The thigh bone or *femur* is the longest and strongest bone of the body (Fig. 120). It resembles the humerus in many ways. The proximal end shows a rounded head which articulates with the acetabulum, a constricted portion, the neck, and two processes, the greater and lesser *trochanters*. On the posterior surface the two trochanters are connected by a prominent ridge, the intertrochanteric crest; on the anterior surface is a more delicate ridge, the intertrochanteric line. The shaft, almost cylindrical in form, is slightly arched so that it is convex anteriorly and concave posteriorly where it is strengthened by a prominent ridge, the *linea aspera*. This is formed above by the gluteal tuberosity and spiral line; below it diverges, forming the medial and lateral supracondylar ridges. The linea aspera affords attachment for numerous muscles. The distal end of the femur widens out into two large eminences, the condyles, separated posteriorly by a deep notch, the intercondyloid fossa.

KNEECAP. The *patella* or kneecap is a sesamoid bone developed from and embedded in the tendon of the quadriceps muscle. It articulates with the femur, protecting the knee joint and affording greater leverage for the action of the muscle.

LEG. The medial bone of the leg is the *tibia* (Fig. 121). The proximal end shows flattened surfaces, the condyles, which articulate with the femur. Between the condyles is the intercondyloid eminence. In front, at the junction of head and shaft, is a prominence called the tuberosity of the tibia. The shaft is triangular, showing anterior, medial and lateral borders. The anterior border, commonly called the *shin*, is prominent. The posterior surface is traversed by the popliteal line, which runs obliquely across the upper third of the shaft. The distal end is continued downward on its medial side by a strong process, the medial malleolus. The inferior surfaces of the distal extremity and the malleolus articulate with the talus in forming the ankle joint.

The *fibula* (Fig. 121) is parallel with the tibia on its lateral aspect. It articulates with the head of the tibia, but does not enter into the knee joint. The distal end projects as the lateral malleolus and assists the tibia in boxing in the talus between the two malleoli.

ANKLE, FOOT AND TOES (Fig. 122). The bony structure of the foot corresponds roughly to that of the hands; the *tarsal* bones are the counterparts of the carpal bones, the *metatarsal* of the metacarpal bones and the *phalanges* of the toes the counterparts of the phalanges of the fingers.

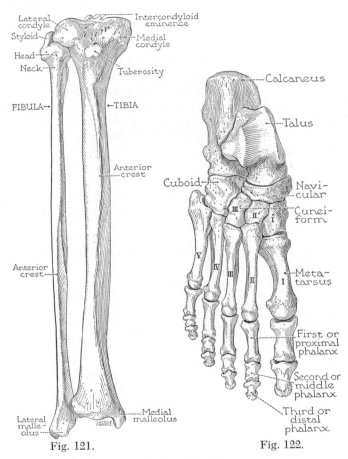

Fig. 121.   Fig. 122.

Fig. 121. Right tibia and fibula, anterior view.
Fig. 122. Bones of right foot, dorsal surface.

The *talus* occupies the uppermost and central position in the tarsus (tarsal group). The talus transmits and distributes the body weight from the tibia above to the other tarsal bones. Beneath the talus and extending posteriorly is the heel bone, the calcaneus. On its medial surface is a projecting process, the sustentaculum tali, and on its lateral surface the trochlear process, which give attachments to ligaments and may be used as bony landmarks in surface anatomy. In front of the talus on the medial side of the foot is the navicular, which in turn articulates with the three cuneiform bones distally. The cuboid bone on the lateral side of the foot lies in front of the calcaneus. Its medial border lies along the lateral borders of the navicular and the third cuneiform bones. The 1st, 2nd and 3rd metatarsals lie in front of the three cuneiform bones, and the 4th and 5th metatarsals in front of the cuboid bone. Distally, the phalanges of the toes are arranged with two in the great toe and three in each of the other toes.

The series of arches which characterize the structure of the foot provide an effective arrangement for supporting and distributing body weight. Architects have long recognized this principle and have used arches to serve the same functions. There are two longitudinal bony channels (arches) in the foot: the lateral (or cuboid) channel formed by the talus, the anterior portion of the calcaneus, the cuboid and the 4th and 5th metatarsal bones, and the medial channel formed by the medial portion of the talus, the navicular, the cuneiform bones and the 1st, 2nd and 3rd metatarsal bones. A series of transverse arches are formed by the tarsal and metatarsal bones; the arches under the posterior half of the tarsus are, however, incomplete, i.e., they form only half domes. These bony channels are bound and strengthened by ligaments.

In supporting the body, the foot may be likened to a triangular stool with one leg, the calcaneus, at the apex and five legs, the distal ends of the metatarsals, arranged along the base. The first metatarsal, which is twice as thick as the others, together with the second metatarsal, supports a quarter of the weight, the three lateral metatarsals a quarter and the heel the remaining half. The effectiveness of this arrangement may be appreciated when we realize that when we are walking or running the entire body weight is borne by one foot at a time with little or no conscious effort.

SUMMARY

The bones of the body constitute the organs of the skeletal system.

The process of bone formation begins in the fibrous membranes and hyaline cartilage of the young embryo. Bone formed in a membrane is called intramembranous bone; bone formed in cartilage is called endochondral bone.

In both types of ossification the fibroblasts become osteoblasts and lay down osseous matrix about them. In endochondral bone formation, cartilage destruction precedes bone formation. In a long bone, ossification begins in the center of the diaphysis and spreads toward each epiphysis, secondary centers developing in each epiphysis. The strip of cartilage between diaphysis and epiphysis is called the epiphyseal cartilage. It continues to grow by cell division, thus allowing for growth of the bone in length. Growth in circumference is accomplished by layers of bone formed by the periosteum.

Ossification is complete in all the bones of the body about the twenty-fifth year.

Special terms are used to describe the projections and depressions on the surfaces of the bones.

The bones of the skeleton are divided into two main groups: those comprising the axial skeleton, and those forming the appendicular skeleton. The former is made up of the bones of the skull, spine and thorax; the latter consists of the upper and lower extremities.

The skull consists of the bones of the cranium and the face.

The spine is composed of the vertebrae: seven cervical, twelve thoracic, five lumbar, five sacral and four coccygeal.

The thorax is formed by the sternum and ribs. The ribs are attached posteriorly to the thoracic vertebrae.

The upper extremity is made up of the shoulder girdle, bones of the arm, forearm, wrist, hand and fingers.

The lower extremity includes the pelvic girdle, bones of the thigh, leg, ankle, foot and toes.

QUESTIONS FOR DISCUSSION

1. Explain how a long bone grows in circumference and in length.

2. Describe and discuss the blood circulation in bone during growth and maturity.

3. In what situations do bones serve protective functions?

Chapter 11

Articulations

Classification of Articulations. The bones of the skeletal system are joined together to form the supporting framework of the body. The joints, or articulations, may be classified by the presence or absence of a joint cavity.

Table 8
Classification of Articulations

TYPE	CHARACTERISTICS	EXAMPLES
Synarthroses	Joint cavity absent; motion very limited	
Sutures (Fig. 123)	Serrated bone ends approximated by fibrous tissue	Bones of skull; teeth in mandible and maxilla
Synchondroses	Bone ends approximated by cartilage	Metaphyses; ribs and costal cartilages; acetabulum
Syndesmoses	Bone ends approximated by fibrous or elastic tissue	Laminae of vertebrae; distal extremities of tibia and fibula
Symphyses (Fig. 125)	Bone ends covered by cartilage and separated by disc of cartilage; approximated by fibrous capsule; slight cavity may be present in disc	Bodies of vertebrae; pubic bones
Diarthroses (Figs. 126, 127, 128, 129, 130, 131, 132, 133)	Joint cavity present; bone ends covered by cartilage may be separated by disc; approximated by fibrous capsule lined with synovial membrane and fluid freely movable	Extremities; vertebral column; jaw

The architecture of the synarthroses is that of a continuous union of the bones with fibrous tissue and/or cartilage. The sutures and synchondroses of the adult skeleton may change entirely into bone and become *synostoses*. There is little or no movement at the synarthroses.

The diarthrodial joints have a more elaborate structure than synarthrodial joints. The two or more bones are united by an encircling

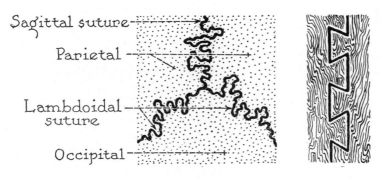

Fig. 123.   Fig. 124.

Figs. 123 and 124. Synarthrosis. Fig. 123, Serrated suture of the skull. Fig. 124, Dovetail joint in wood, showing interlocking nature of the articulation.

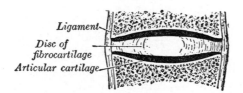

Fig. 125. Diagrammatic section of a symphysis. (Gray, Anatomy of the Human Body, Lea & Febiger.)

band of fibrous tissue called the articular or fibrous capsule. The articular capsule is lined with synovial membrane, and the opposed ends of bone are covered by a layer of hyaline cartilage, called articular cartilage. Synovial fluid, which lubricates and nourishes the joint, fills the cavity. It is a colorless, viscid material resembling white of egg. A disc of fibrous cartilage may divide the cavity of some joints, such as the temporomandibular and sternoclavicular articulations. The fibrous capsule is reinforced and strengthened by bonds or cords called ligaments, which withstand strains and serve to secure the joint.

Most of the joints of the body are diarthroses. Some are more freely movable than others; this variation in the degree of movement is determined to a large extent by the shape of the articulating surfaces forming the joint. A division into groups illustrating the association of structure and movement can be made as follows:

1. Ball and socket joints: Movement is freest in this type of joint, in which a rounded head on one bone moves in a cuplike cavity of another. Examples of ball and socket joints are the shoulder joint, formed by the head of the humerus and the glenoid cavity of the scapula, and the hip joint, formed by the head of the femur and the acetabulum of the innominate bone. Functionally, the wrist and ankle perform like ball and socket joints.

2. Saddle joints: Opposing articulating surfaces that are convex and

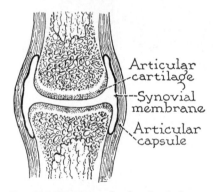

Fig. 126. Diagram of a diarthrodial joint.

concave alternately, such as the carpal-metacarpal articulation in the thumb, allowing great freedom of motion.

3. Hinge joints: Action in a hinge joint is limited to movement in one plane, usually forward or backward. The elbow, knee and ankle joints are examples of this type.

4. Pivot joints: These joints exhibit a rotary movement in which a ring rotates around a central axis as in the articulation between the first and second cervical vertebrae (atlas and epistropheus), or in which an axis turns within the ring as in the articulation between the head of the radius and the radial notch of the ulna. In this case the ring is completed by the annular ligament which encircles the head of the radius and is attached to the margins of the radial notch.

5. Irregular joints: Very little movement takes place in these joints. The articular surface of one bone slides upon that of the other to a limited extent, the form of the articulating parts often serving to restrict

the movement. The joints between the articular processes of the vertebrae and those between the carpal and tarsal bones are of this type.

Bursae.   In various places where friction occurs there are sacs filled with synovial fluid. These sacs are called bursae. They develop in fibrous tissue; in fact, some of them seem little more than exaggerations of the spaces between layers of areolar tissue. The lining bears some resemblance to synovial membrane and secretes the characteristic fluid. Prominent bursae are found at the elbow, the hip, the knee and the heel.

Movements at Joints.   *Flexion* is bending, decreasing the angle between the parts of the body. Flexion takes place at the elbow joint when the forearm is bent on the arm.

Extension is straightening or stretching out, increasing the angle between the parts of the body. It is the reverse of flexion. Extension occurs at the elbow joint when the forearm is straightened on the arm.

Abduction is movement away from the midsagittal plane. It occurs in the shoulder joint when the arm is raised.

Adduction is the opposite of abduction. The part is moved toward the median plane, as when the raised arm is brought down to the side of the body.

Abduction and adduction of fingers and toes are movements from and toward the median planes of the hand and foot; that is, middle finger for the hand and second toe for the foot. *Inversion* and *eversion* of the foot are forms of abduction and adduction (Fig. 133).

Circumduction is movement in which the end of a part describes a circle and the part itself the sides of a cone. It occurs in ball and socket joints and combines the movements of flexion, extension, abduction and adduction.

Rotation is to turn or revolve on an axis without displacement, as in rotation of the atlas on the epistropheus. Turning the palm of the hand and forearm upward in *supination* or downward in *pronation* by the rotation of the radius about the ulna serve as other examples of this movement (Fig. 130). It is a movement which is never complete, but is limited by the ligaments of the joint and the muscles which cross it.

Axes and Levers.   The movements listed for diarthrodial joints are brought about by the contraction of skeletal muscles attached to or near the bones forming the articulations. The axis of a joint is taken as an imaginary line about which movement occurs. Since the articular surfaces are not regular, as they would be in mechanical ball and socket, or hinge or pivot joints of uniform radius, there is no single center of movement. The "axis" shifts its position slightly during movement of the joint just as it would in an eccentric mechanical counter-

part in which the opposing surfaces are somewhat irregular. The ball
and socket joints of the skeletal system have many axes permitting
movement in a number of directions, but the greatest motion is around
the transverse, anteroposterior and vertical axes (Figs. 128, 130). In a

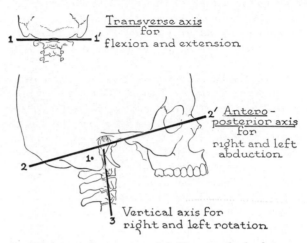

Fig. 127. Axes of movement of skull on vertebral column.

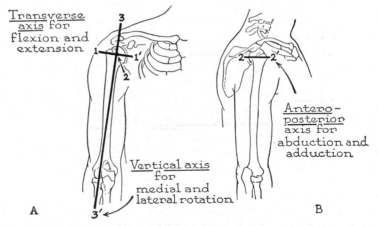

Fig. 128. Axes of movement at shoulder joint. A, Anterior view. B, Lateral view.

hinge joint only a transverse axis is present (Fig. 132), while pivot
joints have a vertical axis (Fig. 127). Flexion and extension take place
on a transverse axis. Abduction and adduction of a part are performed
around an anteroposterior axis. A vertical axis permits rotation to occur.

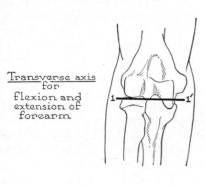

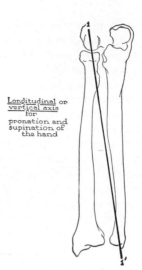

Fig. 129. Axis of movement
at elbow joint.

Fig. 130. Axis of movement
of the forearm.

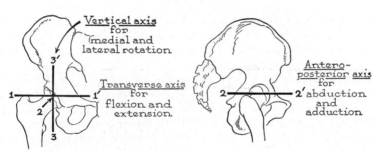

Fig. 131. Axis of movement at the hip joint.

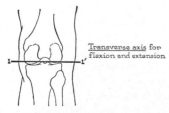

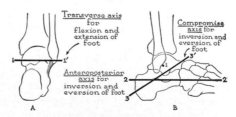

Fig. 132. Axis of movement
at the knee joint.

Fig. 133. Axes of movement
at ankle joint and foot.
A, Posterior view. B, Lateral view.

The axes represent the fulcrums in the lever systems made up by bones, their articulations and associated muscles. The body part, or the part together with the external object it is moving or supporting, constitutes the weight or resistance of the system, while the muscles supply the power for performing work. Thus the architectural structure is admirably suited to function; for *levers provide means (mechanical advantage) by which a small force can be made to overcome a large force, or the distance which a load is moved can be greatly increased over the distance through which the force acts.*

There are three general classes of levers on the basis of the relative positions of the weight (or resistance), the fulcrum and the force, but only two classes of levers are found in the body. In class I levers the fulcrum lies between the weight (or resistance) and the point at which the force or effort is applied. Such an arrangement exists where the axis of the atlanto-occipital joint acts as the fulcrum and the muscles on the back of the neck as the force in raising the head. Class III levers, in which the force is applied between the fulcrum and the weight, are the most common type found in the body. The action of the brachialis on the forearm serves as an example of this type of lever system.

SUMMARY

Joints are classified as synarthroses (containing no cavity between the bones) or diarthroses (containing a cavity between the bones).

Negligible or no movement may occur at sutures, synchondroses, symphysis and syndesmosis joints.

The structural features of a diarthrodial or true joint are the articular cartilage covering the ends of the bones entering into the joint, the articular capsule or sheath of fibrous tissue which encloses the joint, and the synovial membrane which lines the articular capsule.

Sacs of synovial fluid called bursae are found in various places where friction occurs.

Types of movement involving joints are flexion, extension, abduction, adduction, inversion, eversion, circumduction, rotation, pronation and supination.

These movements are brought about by the contraction of skeletal muscles.

The axis of a joint is taken as an imaginary line about which movement occurs. Flexion and extension take place on a transverse axis. Abduction and adduction of a part are performed around an antero-posterior axis. A vertical axis permits rotation to occur.

The axes represent the fulcrums in the lever systems, the body part constitutes the weight or resistance of the system, and the muscles supply the power for performing work.

Levers are classified on the basis of the relative positions of weight, fulcrum and force. Only two classes of levers are found in the body: class I, in which the fulcrum lies between the weight and the force, and class III, in which the force lies between the fulcrum and the weight.

QUESTIONS FOR DISCUSSION

1. Do you notice any relation between the degree of motion in a joint and its structure? How is this shown?

2. In diarthrodial joints the shape of the articulating parts of the bones may contribute to the security of the joint, preventing dislocation, may provide for a great variety of movements in the joint or, in certain instances, may serve to limit the movement between the parts. Support the claims made in this statement by citing specific examples.

3. Demonstrate the axes of movement in all the diarthrodial joints of the body.

Chapter 12

Muscular Tissue

PROPERTIES OF MUSCULAR TISSUE

Contractility, or the capacity to shorten, is the most striking characteristic of muscle tissue. In contrast to undifferentiated protoplasm, which may contract in any direction, muscle tissue contracts only in the direction corresponding to the long axis of the cells. Other characteristic properties are *viscosity,* or resistance to change in shape, and *elasticity,* or capacity to return to its resting length following contraction or stretching. The properties of *excitability* and *conductivity* are also well developed.

CLASSIFICATION OF MUSCULAR TISSUE

Muscle cells are long, protoplasmic fibers which contain parallel bundles of myofibrils. The myofibrils constitute the contractile substances of the cell. There are three types of muscle, which are characterized by their structure and function. These are:

TYPE	STRUCTURE	FUNCTION AND INNERVATION
Smooth	nonstriated	involuntary contraction; autonomic nervous system
Skeletal	striated	voluntary movement; central nervous system
Cardiac	striated	heart beat; modified by autonomic nervous system

Smooth or nonstriated muscle tissue is found in the walls of tube-like viscera such as the stomach, esophagus, intestines, trachea, bronchi, genito-urinary organs, blood vessels, some lymphatic vessels, and also in connection with certain glands, the interior of the eye and the hair follicles of the skin. The cells appear as thick spindles 40 to 100 microns* long and 3 to 8 microns broad (Fig. 134). The largest

* Micron = 1/1000 millimeter.

are in the pregnant uterus, where they may be 500 microns long and 30 microns wide. Each cell shows *myofibrils* in the semifluid cytoplasm or *sarcoplasm* and one long, rodlike nucleus near the thickened middle portion of the cell. Collagenous, elastic and reticular connective tissues support and bind these cells into the structure of which they are a part. Smooth muscle tissue is innervated by the autonomic nervous sys-

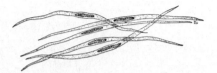

Fig. 134. Isolated smooth muscle cells.

tem. In most of its locations, the activity of the part is a result of both thoracolumbar and craniosacral autonomic nervous influence (see Table 4, Page 155—and Figure 78).

SKELETAL muscle constitutes the largest of the three classes, almost half of the total weight of the body. It includes all of the muscles attached to the skeletal system. The masses or units of tissue form discrete organs of the muscular system.

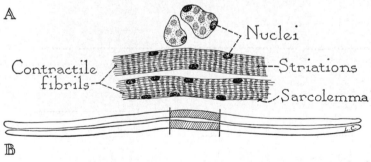

Fig. 135. A, Longitudinal and cross sections of striated muscle. Longitudinal sections are magnifications of shaded area in B. B, Diagram showing two whole muscle cells.

Cells of striated muscle tissue (Fig. 135) are like long cylinders enclosed in an elastic sheath, the *sarcolemma*, in much the same manner that a link of sausage is enclosed in its casing—isolated and yet connected to adjacent muscle cells. The protoplasm contains myofibrils embedded in sarcoplasm. Minute *myofilaments* have been demonstrated in the myofibrils. The myofibrils are marked by alternate light and dark lines, the *striations*. Variations in the density of both parts of the striations may be observed (Fig. 136). The *sarcomere*, or unit of the striation, is taken from z to z. Each cell has many nuclei which are under the sarcolemma, near the periphery of the fiber. Skeletal muscle fibers are unusually long, ranging from 4 to 12 cm. in length

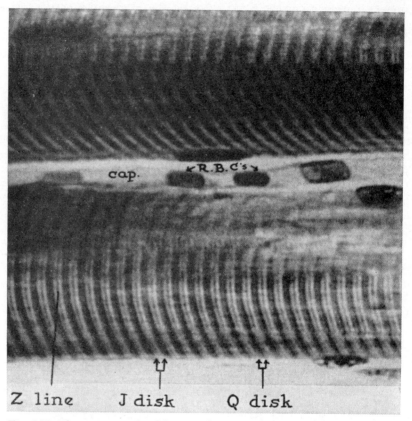

Fig. 136. Photomicrograph of human skeletal muscle. J and Q disks represent striations. Sarcomere extends from Z line to Z line. (From Ham: Histology. J. B. Lippincott Co.)

with a width of 10 to 100 microns. They are bound together in bundles or fasciculi by areolar connective tissue; the fasciculi are in turn held together in larger bundles, and the whole muscle enclosed in a fibrous membrane or *fascia* of the muscle. The fascia is continuous with attachments to the bony framework. These muscles are supplied by peripheral nerves of the central nervous system, with connections to the sensory and motor areas of cerebral cortex. Skeletal muscular action may be consciously directed, and is therefore called voluntary.

CARDIAC muscle forms the main part of the heart wall. Striated myofibrils embedded in sarcoplasm are surrounded by sarcolemma. Myofibrils pass without interruption through *intercalated discs.* The intercalated discs give a false impression of cell membranes. Round or oval nuclei are situated in the center of the fiber. Cardiac muscle has a syncytial or netlike structure showing no separate cells; the various portions of heart muscle are in a plexus of branching and anastomosing fibers (Fig. 137). Each fiber is about 100 microns in diameter.

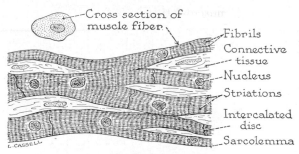

Fig. 137. Cardiac muscle.

In certain regions of the heart, there are groups of cardiac muscle fibers with different histologic characteristics from those of the adjacent fibers. These special groups constitute an *impulse-conducting system* of the heart. *Purkinje fibers* are representative of the pathways transmitting the impulses rapidly throughout the heart, engaging the many fibers to contract in an orderly coordinate heartbeat. The Purkinje fibers are characterized by fewer myofibrils, whose striations are fainter and whose increased quantity of sarcoplasm contains a large amount of glycogen. The rhythmic contractions of cardiac muscle are not dependent on nervous activity, since the heart will continue to beat after all nerves have been cut. Like smooth muscle, its normal activity is governed by a balance of nerve impulses from craniosacral vagus nerves and thoracolumbar accelerator nerves whose processes and ganglia are found in close association to the conducting system (see Fig. 227).

SUMMARY

Contractility is the most outstanding property of muscular tissue. Muscular tissue contracts only in the direction corresponding to the long axis of the cells.

Other properties of muscular tissue are irritability, conductivity, elasticity and viscosity.

Muscle tissue is grouped into three classes, smooth or nonstriated muscle, skeletal or striated muscle and cardiac or heart muscle.

Smooth muscle tissue shows a simple structure. The cells have no striations and no sarcolemma, and are usually arranged in layers or sheets. Striated muscle cells are distinct and separate units each enclosed by an investing membrane, the sarcolemma. Cardiac muscle fibers are not isolated from each other, but arranged in the form of a plexus of branching and anastomosing fibers.

QUESTION FOR DISCUSSION

1. Compare the structure of cardiac and striated muscle fibers. Which of the two fibers is more highly specialized?

Chapter
13

The Physiology
of Muscle

SOME PHYSIOLOGIC ACTIVITIES OF MUSCLE

VOLUNTARY muscle enables man to maintain erect posture and to hold his head, body and extremities in a variety of positions. Skeletal muscular contraction, resulting in movement and locomotion, enables him to secure food and shelter, to escape danger and to communicate his wishes, thoughts or reactions to his fellows by speech, facial expression, signal, or body attitude. It is essential for breathing, since muscular contractions are responsible for alterations in chest capacity which result in inspiration and expiration. Part of the energy liberated by muscular contraction is converted into heat which aids in the maintenance of body temperature. Furthermore, skeletal muscle aids in hearing, and both skeletal and involuntary muscle are used in vision.

In the digestive system, the ureters and bladder, the ducts of the reproductive glands, and in the blood vascular system, smooth muscle activity propels ingested substances, body fluids, and excretions from place to place. Cardiac muscle performs the work necessary for pumping the blood to all tissues of the body and for maintaining filtration pressures.

OBSERVATIONS ON MUSCULAR CONTRACTION

Observations of everyday activity show that there may be wide variations in the extent of muscular movement. The skeletal muscles are adapted to carry out tasks of the utmost precision, such as the delicate manipulations of a difficult surgical operation or watch repair, and they are capable of performing acts involving the application of great forces such as lifting or sustaining heavy weights. Wide variations in the speed of movement can be observed. Under conditions of rest or during delicate tasks the muscles are firm to the touch, but do not exhibit the hardness and bulging characteristic of strenuous exercise. Many other characteristics of muscular contraction are common knowledge because they are readily observable in daily activity. If we exercise vigorously, the body becomes warm and we may perspire; we breathe more rapidly; yet when in good physical condition we can run 100 yards on one breath. The heart beats more rapidly and forcefully during and after exercise. Muscular fatigue sets in if hard work is continued over an extended period, and eventually we are obliged to stop. If we work at an optimum rate, the onset of the muscular fatigue is delayed, but in maximum work it occurs in a short time. Even in a single act such as lifting a heavy weight, the work is carried out more efficiently and a heavier load can be lifted if we "ease into it" and lift slowly than if we attempt to raise it rapidly.

In order to interpret the phenomena of muscular contraction and gain an understanding of the mechanisms involved, we must isolate and study single muscles and even single muscle fibers under controlled experimental conditions. This eliminates the influence of the many factors acting upon intact muscle and allows us to observe the effects of changing one experimental condition, or *variable*, at a time. The skeletal muscles of frogs are well adapted to laboratory observations; a length of attached nerve is frequently removed with the muscle. The excised heart of the frog or turtle is particularly well adapted for studies of some phases of muscular contraction, since cardiac muscle reacts more slowly than skeletal muscle and the details of its response can be more readily observed.

Let us consider what information we could gain from experiments on these isolated tissues, first studying the more obvious reactions involving relatively simple technics, and then inquiring into the physical and chemical changes associated with contraction. These observations will prepare us for subsequent analysis of the behavior of skeletal muscles in living man, and of the heart and smooth muscles when they are discussed in the sections on Circulation and Digestion.

SOME PHENOMENA OF CONTRACTION IN ISOLATED MUSCLE

Experimental Methods. When skeletal muscle is removed from the body, artificial stimuli must be substituted for the impulses which normally pass out over the motor nerves from the central nervous system and cause contraction. The artificial stimuli may be applied directly either to the muscle or the nerve which supplies it. The nerve-muscle preparation is frequently used, since, unless special precautions are taken to block the nerve endings in the muscle by drugs or by allowing for degeneration of the nerve, the stimuli applied directly to the muscle will probably cause muscular contractions by acting on the surviving nerve tissue as well as on the muscle fibers themselves. The relation of the nerve to the muscle is important in interpreting the reactions. Each fiber of a motor nerve may innervate anywhere from several to over a hundred muscle fibers; the single fiber together with the muscle fibers it supplies is called a *motor unit*.

In experiments on cardiac muscle we can use a whole excised heart or a strip of heart muscle. If we use the heart, it will, under proper conditions, continue to beat even after all connections with the body have been severed. It displays the property of inherent rhythmicity. Artificial stimuli can, however, be applied directly to the heart at such a rate that they will control the contractions. A strip of cardiac muscle can be cut in such a way that it will respond only to direct artificial stimuli. In contrast to skeletal muscle, cardiac muscle fibers are not supplied with nerve fibers. Cardiac tissue responds to a wave of excitation which spreads through the meshwork or syncytium involving all the cardiac muscle fibers.

The electrical form of stimulus is frequently used in studying muscle, since its strength, duration and rate of change may be controlled, and, within limits, it does not injure the tissues. Electrical stimuli are normally applied by current from a battery (galvanic stimuli), from a condenser discharge, or by single (single induction) or repeated (tetanic) shocks from an induction coil.

Two principal methods are commonly utilized in studying muscular contraction. One method is to attach the muscle between two rigid supports so that it cannot shorten when it is stimulated. Contraction without shortening is known as an *isometric contraction*. This method

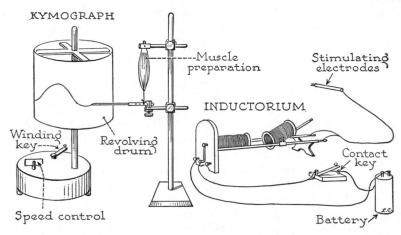

Fig. 138. Kymograph and inductorium; apparatus used in making a record of muscle contractions.

is not suitable for general laboratory work, since observations on isometric contractions require the use of delicate complex equipment such as thermocouples or a thermopile for measuring the energy which is released as heat, or optical manometers or strain gages for measuring the tension which is developed.

The second method is to allow the muscle to shorten upon stimulation. Contractions in which the muscle is allowed to shorten are called *isotonic contractions*. Isotonic contractions are studied conveniently by using a muscle lever and recording the muscular activity on smoked paper fitted to the drum of a kymograph (Fig. 138). One end of the muscle is attached to a rigid clamp, the other end to a muscle lever bearing a writing point placed against the smoked drum in such a way as to transcribe the movements of the lever. As the muscle shortens, it raises the lever and records the contraction. The lever arm amplifies the movement of the muscle so that the contractions are sufficiently large for study. The kymograph drum, when made to rotate at the desired speed, amplifies the time element by showing the contraction spread out so that the events occurring during a single contraction may make a record occupying the entire length of the smoked paper. For some studies, contractions are recorded on a stationary drum.

Responses to Single Stimuli of Constant Strength. Let us assume that, having removed the gastrocnemius muscle from the leg of a frog and arranged it for recording on a rapidly moving kymograph drum, we apply a single induction shock of sufficient intensity to the attached nerve. The details of the phases of a single contraction are now apparent on the record of the drum (Fig. 139). The lever does not start to rise for a short time after the application of the stimulus. This interval between the stimulus and the mechanical shortening of the muscle is known as the latent period. Mechanical shortening then occurs until the maximum height of contraction is reached; this is known as the

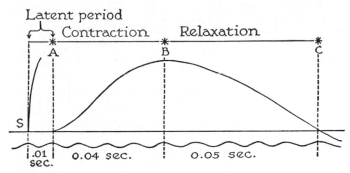

Fig. 139. Kymograph record of a single twitch of a frog muscle taken with fast moving drum. Lower tracing is time record, obtained by using a tuning fork. S indicates the moment that the stimulus is applied.

period of contraction. In the last phase, the period of relaxation, the muscle returns to its original length. The total time consumed in this single muscle twitch is about 0.1 second. In the frog muscle the latent period is 0.01 second, the period of contraction 0.04 second, and the period of relaxation 0.05 second. The phases of muscle response to stimulation may be modified by one or all of these factors: changing the load the muscle is lifting, changes in temperature and fatigue.

Continuing our experiment with the frog gastrocnemius muscle, let us now observe the effect of a series of single induction shocks to the attached nerve. Here we keep the intensity of stimulus constant and well above threshold level. With the kymograph drum moving slowly, we see that the first four or five stimuli show contractions of increasing height. This is known as *treppe* or the staircase phenomenon (Fig. 140). It represents a "warming up" process in which the muscle responds to a greater extent as the physiologic conditions change because of the gradual formation of small amounts of chemical waste products. If we continue to apply single stimuli of a constant strength, the height of the individual contractions becomes constant and remains so for a relatively large number of stimuli. Eventually, however, fatigue sets in and the contraction becomes smaller; the muscle does not relax completely after each contraction, as shown by the fact that the writing lever does not return to the base line. This condition is known as *contracture*, in which the muscle loses its ability to relax to its original resting length. The muscle finally fails to respond to further stimuli.

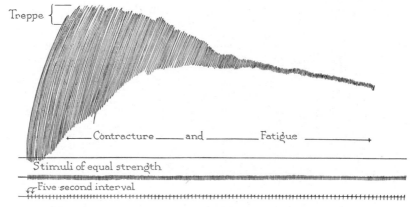

Fig. 140. Treppe, contracture and fatigue in skeletal muscle.

Responses to Single Stimuli of Varying Strength. The effect of increasing the strength of stimuli may be studied by starting with a weak stimulus, too small to cause a contraction of the muscle, and then increasing the strength of successive stimuli until the muscle shows its maximal contraction. The weak stimuli which cause no muscular contraction are known as *subthreshold stimuli;* one of just sufficient strength to cause an appreciable response of the muscle is said to be the *threshold stimulus.* As the intensity of successive stimuli is increased, the height of the contractions will increase up to a certain limit, after which no further increase in the height of the contraction occurs. This response represents the phenomena of graded response to graded stimulus. It is dependent upon the fact that, as the strength of stimulus is increased, more and more motor units, and hence more muscle fibers, enter into the response of the muscle so that greater shortening occurs. The same response is seen if the muscle is stimulated directly rather than through its nerve.

It might be thought that the individual fibers were capable of different degrees of contraction, but this is not the case. If a muscle is dissected so as to allow only a few fibers to remain intact, the number of increases in the height of the contractions corresponds to the number of fibers in the preparation. Furthermore, in heart muscle, where the architecture is such that stimulation at any point of the muscle gives a response of the entire mass of muscle, no evidence of the graded response is seen. The syncytium makes heart muscle fibers physiologically continuous, so that if it responds to a stimulus at all it responds by a maximal contraction. This behavior of single skeletal muscle fibers and of cardiac muscle provides evidence that muscle, as

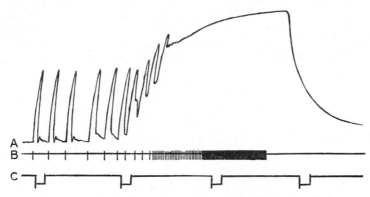

Fig. 141. Tetanus in skeletal muscle. When stimuli (B) are applied to a muscle at a gradually increasing rate of frequency, the individual muscle twitches (A) blend together so that, when the stimuli are applied in rapid succession, a smooth sustained contraction results. Ordinary muscle movements are of this tetanic nature. Note that the height of contraction is greater in tetanus than in a single twitch. Time (C) is in five-second intervals. (Carlson and Johnson, The Machinery of the Body. University of Chicago Press.)

well as nerve tissue, obeys the *all-or-none law*. The absolute degree of contraction may be modified by a number of factors such as temperature, load and fatigue.

The Effects of Rapidly Repeated Stimuli on Muscular Contraction. If a single stimulus just below threshold strength is applied to a muscle, no response occurs; but if these subminimal stimuli are repeated rapidly, the muscle responds with a contraction. This is known as summation of subminimal stimuli. The initial stimulus, though causing no contraction, results in a change in the physiologic state at the motor end plate of the muscle fiber, i.e., the junction of motor nerve endings and the muscle. If additional stimuli are given before the effects of the previous stimuli have worn off, a critical value of the local change at the end plate is reached; the disturbance is transmitted to the muscle fibers and contraction results. In order for this additive effect to be obtained, the interval between stimuli must be extremely short.

If stimuli above threshold level are used, two important phenomena of muscular response may be observed. When rapidly repeated stimuli are applied to skeletal muscle, with stimuli reaching the muscle when it is contracting in response to the previous stimuli, the muscle stays in a state of contraction. This phenomenon in which the stimuli are applied in such rapid succession that they allow for no relaxation or only partial relaxation is known as *tetanus*. When rapid stimulation causes a smooth fusion of contractions, the tetanus is said to be complete. With less rapid stimulation, when some relaxation occurs between successive stimuli, the condition is known as incomplete tetanus or *clonus*. Complete and incomplete tetanus are shown in Figure 141. Normal contractions of the skeletal muscles in the body are tetanic in

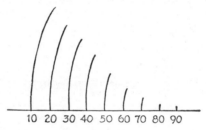

10 20 30 40 50 60 70 80 90

Fig. 142. Effect of load on simple muscle contraction. The muscle was successively loaded with 10-gm. weights.

nature. Tetanus results in the development of a greater tension or strength of contraction than is seen in the single muscle twitch. This is probably because of the longer duration of the contractile process and the influence of greater initial tension.

The *absolute refractory period* determines the maximum rate at which the muscle fibers can respond. The duration of this period differs with the type of muscle and its physiologic state. In skeletal muscle it is relatively short, as evidenced by its capability for the development of complete tetanus; in cardiac muscle it is much longer; and in smooth muscle it has the longest duration. We cannot obtain a complete fusion of contractions in cardiac muscle; a second contraction can be initiated experimentally only after relaxation has resulted in an appreciable lengthening of muscle fibers. An incomplete tetanus, or clonus, represents the most rapid series of contractions of which the heart is capable.

Work Performed by Muscle.   Muscular contraction liberates energy which is used in performing work and in giving off heat. Work of a muscle may be calculated by multiplying the weight which is raised by the height to which it is lifted. Figure 142 shows the effect of load on the height of muscle contraction. There is an optimum load for a muscle which can be determined by observing the greatest value obtained for the product of weight times the height. If too small a weight is applied to an excised muscle, it does not return it to its "resting" length; further, it allows the muscle to shorten too rapidly, and too great an amount of the energy is used in overcoming the viscosity of the muscle. This can be visualized by thinking of the comparative ease with which a bowl of molasses may be stirred slowly and the far greater amount of work that is required to stir it rapidly. The greatest strength of contraction, i.e., the greatest amount of work, results if an optimum load is applied when the fibers are at their normal resting length. In heart muscle, however, the strength of contraction increases as the initial length of fibers is increased to the physiologic maximum.

ELECTRICAL CHANGES DURING MUSCULAR CONTRACTION

Up to this time we have been concerned with the mechanical aspects of contraction. More complex recording equipment is necessary to detect and measure the electrical changes which occur in the muscle tissues when they are stimulated. By placing the electrodes of a suitable galvanometer or cathode-ray oscillograph on muscle, we can show that the bioelectric phenomena are similar to those observed in nerve. Muscle fibers, as they become active in contraction, are electrically negative to resting muscle; injury, as well as action potentials, may be demonstrated. The detailed mechanisms determining the change at the end plate, i.e., the *end plate potential* and the action or spike potential, are not definitely established. It is, however, known that they are associated with changes in the characteristics of the membranes of the muscle, the passage of ions through the membranes and redistribution of electrical charges across the membranes. These bioelectric charges have been discussed in the section on the Nerve Impulse.

CHEMICAL REACTIONS ASSOCIATED WITH MUSCULAR CONTRACTION

During the contraction of muscle, chemical energy is converted into mechanical energy, i.e., work and heat. Since a contraction, such as a simple muscle twitch, may take place in about 100 mSec., it is apparent that the chemical change must take place extremely rapidly. Further, since muscle is capable of contractions repeated rapidly for considerable periods without fatigue, it is apparent that energy stores must be available in large quantity or must be continuously renewed. Research has provided some insight into the several processes involved.

The processes for conversion of energy are set off by the splitting of phosphate from *adenosinetriphosphate* (ATP), a substance found in muscle, by the enzyme *adenosinetriphosphatase* (ATPase). Thus, the initial supply of stored energy is released without delay and the muscle contracts. The initial process may be likened to starting an automobile: a spark from the storage battery releases the chemical energy of the fuel, the engine starts and operates the generator, which not only takes over the ignition function, but recharges the battery. Once started, the conversion of chemical energy to work and heat continues as long as fuel is supplied. Two other reactions proceed and provide for the early renewal of stored energy. One is concerned with the resynthesis of ATP by the breakdown of *creatine phosphate* (CP); CP furnishes phosphate and energy for the resynthesis. The other series of reactions for the ready renewal of energy stores is the breakdown of the glycogen in the muscle. Glycogen is a long-chain polysaccharide made up of units of glucose bound together. Glycogen, in the presence of the enzyme *phosphorylase*, takes up phosphate made available through the breakdown of ATP and splits off glucose phosphate, shortening the glycogen chain by one glucose unit. Successive glucose units are broken off at corresponding points in the linkage of the glucose molecules. This process is called *phosphorolysis*. The resulting glucose phosphate undergoes a series of chemical transformations each catalyzed by its appropriate enzyme until, if no oxygen is present, it is broken down into lactic acid.

The reactions which have been described can take place even in the absence of oxygen; they constitute the anaerobic phase of the contraction cycle. In physiologic reactions within the body, it is probable that when resting muscle becomes active the initial contractions occur under conditions of low oxygen supply, since there has been insufficient time for adjustment of the circulation to the new level of activity.

Without oxygen, however, repeated contraction results in the disappearance of creatine phosphate, ATP resynthesis is finally halted and lactic acid may accumulate in the muscle. The early reactions have, however, provided for a rapid initial response and for continuation of contractions over a limited period. The anaerobic reactions may be summarized as follows:

(1) ATP $\rightleftarrows$ adenosinediphosphate (ADP) + phosphate + energy for contraction.
(2) ADP + CP $\rightleftarrows$ creatine + energy for resynthesis of ATP + ATP.
(3) Glycogen $\rightleftarrows$ intermediate stages $\rightleftarrows$ lactic acid + energy toward resynthesis of CP and ATP.

Under normal physiologic conditions, however, there is metabolic readjustment, and sufficient oxygen is soon available for the chemical reactions associated with contraction. The later reaction constitutes the aerobic phase of muscular contraction which is concerned with the oxidation of the intermediate products of the breakdown of glycogen to CO_2 and H_2O. If lactic acid has accumulated, a portion of it may be oxidized to CO_2 and H_2O plus energy for reconversion of the remaining lactic acid to glycogen. These reactions are summarized below:

(4) ⅕ lactic acid + O_2 → CO_2 + H_2O + energy for resynthesis of glycogen.
(5) ⅘ lactic acid + energy → glycogen.

In the presence of oxygen, oxidations provide energy for rebuilding the chemicals that hold the stored energy. This amounts to the reversal of the successive reactions involved in the release of chemical energy; such reversal is indicated by the arrows used in the equations to show that reactions may proceed in either direction.

The muscle employs effective mechanisms for taking up oxygen. Myohemoglobin, a substance contained in muscle, has a greater affinity for oxygen than hemoglobin of the blood so that transfer occurs even when the oxygen supply (and oxygen tension) in the blood is low. In turn, oxygen is transferred from the myohemoglobin to the muscle enzyme system, and used in the oxidative processes of the cell. These reactions provide for the continuation of muscular activity for prolonged periods.

Oxygen Debt. Oxygen is not stored in the muscle cells or their environment. The fact that muscular contraction can take place in the absence of oxygen permits muscular movements to be performed at a more rapid rate than that at which oxygen can be supplied to the tissues. This provides for the early period of contractions before the circulation is adjusted to the new level of activity. It also enables man to perform strenuous exercise, with oxygen consumption up to approximately eighteen or twenty times its resting value for brief periods.

When a man works or exercises at a moderate rate, he "goes into debt" for the oxygen required for energy to resynthesize the products of the initial anaerobic contractions. Soon, however, as the work continues, the oxygen supply meets the oxygen requirements. The glycogen is then broken down through successive steps to its final end products CO_2 and H_2O, with liberation of large amounts of energy. The oxygen debt no longer increases, but once a *steady state* condition has been established, the debt may continue at the same level throughout the work period. When the exercise stops, however, the oxygen consumption is maintained at a higher than resting level until the lactic acid has been oxidized or is resynthesized to glycogen in the liver, and the muscle glycogen has been built up again as a chain of glucose units restored to the muscle by the blood sugar.

In very strenuous exercise such as fast running, fifteen to twenty times as much oxygen may be required as during rest. For example, an athlete running a hundred-yard dash takes in only a very small part of the oxygen necessary to furnish the energy he expends; his run is performed almost without oxygen. In brief, violent exercise, man does not attain the steady state, and the oxygen debt increases very rapidly. Since there is a limit to the amount of debt a man can accumulate, the duration of very strenuous exercise or maximum work is limited.

Heat Production. In a motor driven by combustion of fuel, only part of the energy freed in combustion is converted into work, that is, into moving the parts of the machine. Most of the energy is expended as heat. This is true also for muscle. It has been estimated that only about 25 to 30 per cent of the energy is converted into mechanical work; the rest is freed as heat. This compares favorably with the efficiency of the best types of gas engines. Although the heat produced in engines is largely wasted, that produced in muscles is used to maintain body heat at a fairly uniform level.

The temperature of the human body must not fall much below 37° C. if chemical reactions are to proceed at a rate rapid enough to meet normal physiologic requirements. In this connection it is interesting to note the adaptation of the body to external cold; we exercise consciously in order to keep warm or we shiver. Shivering is a phenomenon in which muscles are activated involuntarily and heat is produced.

The heat given off in muscle contraction is divided into initial heat and recovery or delayed heat. Initial heat is produced during the course of contraction; delayed heat is produced in the recovery period. Although the delayed heat is usually only slightly greater in amount than the initial heat, it is produced much more slowly.

NORMAL ACTIVITY OF INTACT SKELETAL MUSCLES

Tonus. The firmness of skeletal muscles in man, even when he is not performing work, is explained by the fact that they are normally under slight tension. This small continuing tension is maintained by the alternate activity of different motor units within the muscle mass. The contractions of the units are isometric, and are tetanic, rather simple twitches. As the fibers of a motor unit are distributed throughout the length of the muscle, there is a smooth, uniform contraction which results in tension of the muscle as a whole. Since the motor units act asynchronously, the total number of fibers involved at any one time is not sufficient to cause movement. The degree of muscle tone, which may vary with the physiologic condition of the muscle and of the body as a whole, will depend upon the number of units acting, the frequency and duration of their response, and the tension developed by the separate groups which are contracting.

Tonus is dependent upon the integrity of the nerve connections between the muscle and the spinal cord. If the motor nerves are severed, the nerve impulses to the motor units are cut off; if the sensory nerves are severed, the afferent impulses which arise from the proprioceptor nerve endings in the muscle itself can no longer bring about reflex response of the motor units. The muscle, then, becomes atonic. Under physiologic conditions, with the nerve supply intact, tonus is determined largely by a "self regulatory" mechanism; when muscle fibers are stretched, their proprioceptor nerve endings are stimulated, afferent impulses travel to the spinal cord, where, through appropriate connections, they cause a series of impulses to be discharged over the motor nerves, and these, in turn, stimulate contraction of the muscle fibers. The proprioceptor nerve endings are themselves subject to "adjustment" by small motor nerves. These small nerve fibers appear to keep the spindles at a level of tension close to that which is favorable for firing the afferents; when the muscle is stretched so that the strain on the spindles is increased, the "small" motor nerve discharge decreases; when the strain is reduced, the small motor nerve discharge is increased and the tension on the spindles increases. Thus, muscle tone may be maintained even at low levels of activity when the "stretch" is slight. Discharge of motor impulses over the large motor nerve and changes in tone may also be initiated by activity of other parts of the central nervous system and by stimulation of other sensory nerve endings throughout the body.

Posture. The support of the body or of a body part requires an expenditure of energy sufficient to prevent movement of the affected joints. Gravity tends to cause flexion of the joints of the legs, trunk and neck; activity of the extensor or antigravity muscles resists flexion; in consequence, we are able to maintain an upright posture. If we consider the relation of the extensor muscles to the joints, it may be seen that these muscles will be stretched as the body starts to sag. This causes stimulation of the proprioceptor nerve endings in the extensors, and the resulting contraction of these muscles fixes the joints of the body. The reaction, known as the stretch or *myotatic reflex,* is of primary importance in the maintenance of normal posture. The stretch reflex can also be elicited when a muscle is stretched by the contraction of its antagonist (opposing muscle) or by applied traction, as well as by the flexion of joints. The "adjustment" of the tension of proprioceptors is a primary factor in maintaining the extent of the myotatic reflex response at an appropriate level.

Both tone and posture involve contractions which are relatively iso-metric. The energy of the contraction is converted into heat; as the muscle shortens only slightly, a small fraction of the energy appears as work (load times distance).

Static and dynamic postural reactions are discussed in greater detail in connection with the study of the labyrinth of the internal ear.

Voluntary Movement. Muscular activity which results in move-ment or work involves two sets of muscles which act, in varying degrees, in opposition to one another. The set which furnishes the power for the movement is referred to as the *agonists*. The other set, which by virtue of the tone contributes to the smooth, even movements charac-teristic of voluntary activity, is known as the *antagonists*. Normally, groups of agonists and antagonists, rather than two single opposing muscles, are engaged in voluntary movement. In movements involving flexion the flexors are the agonists and the extensors are the antago-nists. The activity of the opposing muscle groups is well coordinated in respect to the degree of tension exerted from moment to moment; as the tension in the flexors is increased, the tone of the extensors is reduced or inhibited. The central nervous system integrates the com-plex activity pattern of the muscles which carry out the movements of the body. At the beginning of contraction only relatively little movement results, since most of the initial force is spent in pulling against the joint when the extremity is fully extended. This initial phase is isometric. Further shortening causes movement, i.e., isotonic contraction. The extent of the participation of various muscle groups will depend upon the force required for the voluntary act. For example, only immediately adjacent muscles and joints would be involved in an act requiring moderate flexion. Where greater force is required, outlying groups are brought into play and the more proximal joints are steadied or fixed.

The strength of the contraction of the individual muscles, i.e., the tension developed, will depend on the number of motor units involved, their physiological state, and the frequency and duration of the volley of efferent nerve impulses.

The speed of voluntary movement depends upon the skeletal muscles which are acting, since individual muscles show great variation in the time required for contraction. The muscles which move the eyeball contract rapidly, i.e., in less than $\frac{1}{100}$ second, while muscles in the leg may require two to four times as long. Further, a limb may be moved over a considerable distance during the time it takes for a muscle to shorten; the shorter the distance between the insertion of the muscle and the joint, the greater is the extent of movement of the distal point of the extremity. Fairly precise movements over a distance of 1 to 15 inches can be carried out with the hand moving at an average speed of 2 to 3 feet per second; a maximum speed of about 4½ feet per second may be attained momentarily in a movement of this type. Even higher rates may occur in less precise movements.

SUMMARY

Important functions of the voluntary muscles are locomotion and the maintenance of posture against the force of gravity.

Other functions involving the activity of voluntary muscles are respiration, speech, vision and the maintenance of body temperature.

Observations of everyday activity show that there may be wide variations in the extent and speed of muscular contractions.

The following phenomena of contraction are observed in isolated skeletal muscle:

1. Striated muscle contracts only when stimulated.

2. With continued application of single stimuli of constant strength the height of the individual contractions increases at first during "warming up" period and then becomes constant and remains so for a relatively large number of stimuli, but eventually fatigue sets in and the contractions become smaller; finally the muscle loses its irritability and fails to respond to further stimuli.

3. When single stimuli of increasing strength are delivered to a muscle, the height of the contraction increases up to a certain limit, after which no further increase in height of contraction occurs.

This phenomenon of graded responses to graded stimuli is dependent upon the fact that as the strength of a stimulus is increased, more motor units enter into the response, so that greater shortening of the muscle occurs.

4. When a series of rapidly repeated stimuli (above threshold level) are applied to skeletal muscle with stimuli reaching the muscle when it is contracting in response to previous stimuli, the muscle remains in a state of contraction. This response to stimuli applied in such rapid succession that they allow for no relaxation or only partial relaxation is known as tetanus.

5. The work performed by a muscle may be measured by multiplying the weight which is raised by the height to which it is lifted. There is an optimum load for a muscle which can be determined by observing the greatest value obtained for the product of weight times height.

The mechanical changes of muscular contraction are accompanied by electrical changes. These can be measured with a galvanometer.

During contraction a muscle undergoes chemical changes in which the energy for the process is liberated. The immediate source of the energy for contraction is furnished by the splitting of adenosinetriphosphate by ATPase.

Because contraction is an anaerobic process, muscular movements can be performed at a more rapid rate than that at which oxygen can be supplied to the tissue.

Muscle tonus is a state of tension or partial contraction in a muscle. It is maintained by series of impulses transmitted over motor nerves, which cause a few of the motor units to contract in relays and sustain the tonus.

Maintenance of an upright posture involves the activity of extensor or antigravity muscles. The reaction known as the stretch or myotatic reflex is of primary importance in the maintenance of normal posture.

Voluntary movement involves two sets of muscles which act in opposition to one another. Agonists furnish the power for the movement; antagonists give way to the movement, but, by virtue of their tone, they effect a smooth, even performance.

QUESTIONS FOR DISCUSSION

1. How are voluntary movements, posture and muscle tone related to nervous system function?

2. Contraction in muscle tissue is an anaerobic process. Do you think this is advantageous? Give reasons for your answer.

3. Discuss the limits of the oxygen debt which can be acquired.

Chapter 14

The Skeletal Muscles

Skeletal Muscles as Organs of the Muscular System. The skeletal muscles are the organs of the muscular system. They number over 400 in the human body. Each has an arterial, venous, lymphatic and nervous supply as well as a connective tissue framework—the whole constituting an independent unit. However, muscles never act singly, but in groups. We seldom contract an individual muscle; we execute a movement, and in the performance of that movement whole groups of muscles are involved. Skeletal muscles, then, are not functionally separate and unrelated parts, but are grouped into a system which exhibits correlation and cooperation of its parts.

Attachments of Muscles. Each striated muscle consists of a body and two attachments. The body contains the muscular tissue; the attachments are composed of white fibrous tissue. The attachment of muscle to bone may be one of three types: direct to the periosteum,

239

by means of a tendon, or by means of an aponeurosis. In a direct attachment the white fibers of the connective tissue framework of the muscle fuse with the fibrous layers of the periosteum of the bone. A *tendon* is a band or cord of white fibrous tissue serving to connect a muscle to a bone. The sarcolemma and the connective tissue surrounding the muscle bundles fuse with the collagenous fibers of the tendon. An *aponeurosis* is a heavy sheet of white fibrous tissue serving to connect a muscle to a bone or in some instances to connect muscles.

The more fixed attachment of a muscle which serves as a basis of action is called the *origin*. The movable attachment where the effects of movement are produced is the *insertion*. Generally the origin is near the spinal axis of the body, while the insertion is peripheral.

Muscle Action. If the attachments of a muscle are known, its action may be determined by recalling that the insertion moves toward the origin when the muscle contracts. Muscles are arranged in opposing or antagonistic groups: flexors and extensors, adductors and abductors, internal rotators and external rotators. When the muscles flexing the forearm contract, the muscles which have the opposite effect, the extensors, are thrown into physiologic relaxation, elongating and giving way to the movement.

DESCRIPTION OF MUSCLES

The muscles described in this chapter comprise only a small part of the musculature of the body. It cannot be held that they are more important than the other muscles; they are, however, representative and serve to illustrate the principles of the mechanics of muscle. The descriptions are designed not only to provide the student with information concerning the muscles which are discussed in this text, but also to indicate a method of approach for extension of his studies to other muscles where such study is indicated by his professional requirements and interest. The muscles are arranged in opposing groups, and the description includes the origin, insertion, and principal action of each muscle. The scheme of labeling used for all the muscles is illustrated for the sternocleidomastoid muscle in Figure 145. The name of the muscle is in solid black, the origin in double stroke, the insertion in single stroke, and the related structures in upper and lower case lettering.

Muscles Which Move the Head

FLEXOR	EXTENSORS
Sternocleidomastoid	Splenius capitis
	Semispinalis capitis
	Longissimus capitis

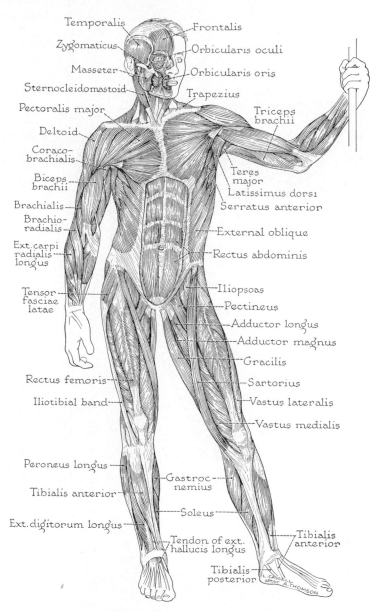

Temporalis
Zygomaticus
Masseter
Sternocleidomastoid
Pectoralis major
Deltoid
Coraco-
brachialis
Biceps
brachii
Brachialis
Brachio-
radialis
Ext. carpi
radialis
longus
Tensor
fasciae
latae

Frontalis
Orbicularis oculi
Orbicularis oris
Trapezius
Triceps
brachii
Teres
major
Latissimus dorsi
Serratus anterior
External oblique
Rectus abdominis
Iliopsoas
Pectineus
Adductor longus
Adductor magnus
Gracilis

Rectus femoris
Iliotibial band

Sartorius
Vastus lateralis
Vastus medialis

Peroneus longus
Tibialis anterior
Ext. digitorum longus

Gastroc-
nemius
Soleus
Tendon of ext.
hallucis longus
Tibialis
posterior
Tibialis
anterior

L. CASSELL
after A. THOMSON

Fig. 143. Muscles of the body, anterior view.

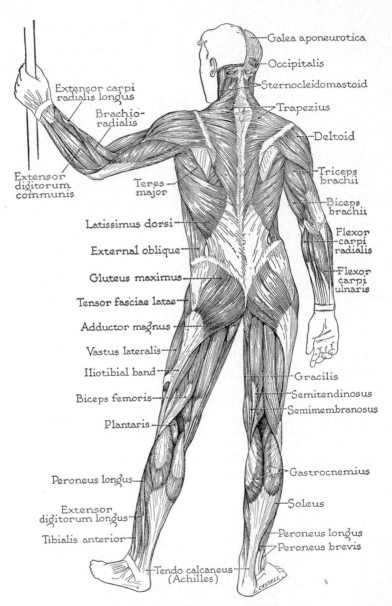

Galea aponeurotica
Occipitalis
Sternocleidomastoid
Trapezius
Deltoid
Triceps brachii
Biceps brachii
Flexor carpi radialis
Flexor carpi ulnaris
Gracilis
Semitendinosus
Semimembranosus
Gastrocnemius
Soleus
Peroneus longus
Peroneus brevis

Extensor carpi radialis longus
Brachio-radialis
Extensor digitorum communis
Teres major
Latissimus dorsi
External oblique
Gluteus maximus
Tensor fasciae latae
Adductor magnus
Vastus lateralis
Iliotibial band
Biceps femoris
Plantaris
Peroneus longus
Extensor digitorum longus
Tibialis anterior
Tendo calcaneus (Achilles)

Fig. 144. Muscles of the body, posterior view.

The joint involved in movements of flexion and extension of the head is the atlanto-occipital articulation. Here, between the condyles of the occipital bone and the superior articular surfaces of the atlas, forward and backward nodding movements take place about a transverse axis (Fig. 127, p. 214).

The **sternocleidomastoid** muscle (Fig. 145), named from its origin and insertion, passes obliquely across the side of the neck. It arises from the sternal end of the clavicle and the upper border of the manubrium of the sternum. It is inserted into the mastoid process of

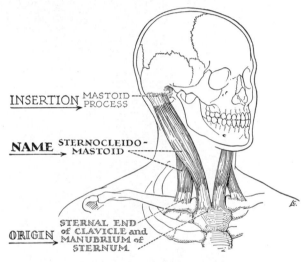

INSERTION MASTOID PROCESS

NAME STERNOCLEIDO-MASTOID

ORIGIN STERNAL END of CLAVICLE and MANUBRIUM of STERNUM

Fig. 145. Sternocleidomastoid.

the temporal bone. Both muscles acting together bend the head forward on the chest in flexion. When one muscle contracts, it draws the head and neck toward the shoulder of the same side and at the same time rotates them, pointing the chin upward and to the opposite side.

The **splenius capitis** arises from the lower part of the ligamentum nuchae (Fig. 146), the spinous processes of the seventh cervical and the upper three or four thoracic vertebrae; and is inserted into the mastoid process and lateral part of the superior nuchal line. When both muscles act, the head is pulled directly backward in extension. One muscle contracting inclines and rotates the head and neck toward the side on which the muscle is placed.

The **semispinalis capitis** (Fig. 146) takes origin from the transverse processes of the upper six thoracic vertebrae and the articular processes of the lower four cervical vertebrae. The fleshy body of the muscle fills in the hollow at the side of the cervical vertebrae and is inserted into the occipital bone between the superior and inferior nuchal lines. When both semispinalis muscles act, they pull the head backward, thus assisting the splenius muscles in extension of the head. When one muscle contracts, the head and neck are inclined and rotated toward the same side.

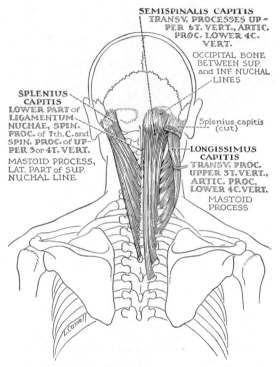

Fig. 146. Splenius capitis; semispinalis capitis; longissimus capitis.

The **longissimus capitis** (Fig. 146) may be considered an upward prolongation of the middle division of the sacrospinalis, but it is described here as a separate muscle. It is found on the lateral side of the semispinalis capitis and just beneath the splenius capitis. It arises from the transverse processes of the upper three thoracic vertebrae and articular processes of the lower four cervical vertebrae and is inserted into the mastoid process. When both muscles contract they assist the semispinalis capitis and splenius capitis in extension of the head. When one muscle acts, the head inclines to the side of the contracting muscle.

Muscles Which Move the Vertebral Column

EXTENSORS	FLEXORS
Sacrospinalis	Psoas major
Quadratus lumborum	Rectus abdominis

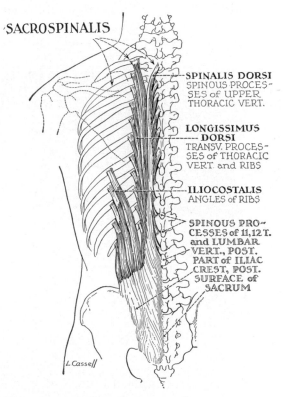

Fig. 147. Sacrospinalis.

Flexion and extension of the spine in the thoracic region are at a minimum, but in the lumbar region these movements are free, especially between the fourth and fifth lumbar vertebrae.

The **sacrospinalis** (Fig. 147) lies in the groove on the side of the vertebral column posteriorly. It arises from the posterior part of the iliac crest, the posterior surface of the sacrum, and from the spinous process of all lumbar vertebrae and the last two thoracic vertebrae. In the upper lumbar region the muscle separates into three columns: lateral or iliocostalis, middle or longissimus dorsi, and medial or spinalis dorsi. The iliocostalis is inserted into the angles of the lower five or six ribs. The longissimus dorsi is the largest and most powerful division of the sacrospinalis and has a double set of insertions on the transverse processes of the thoracic vertebrae and the backs of the ribs which give it a firm grip for extension. The spinalis dorsi is inserted into the spines of the thoracic vertebrae. The sacrospinalis, placed vertically along the vertebral column with origin below and insertion above, acts as an extensor, maintaining the spine erect against gravity.

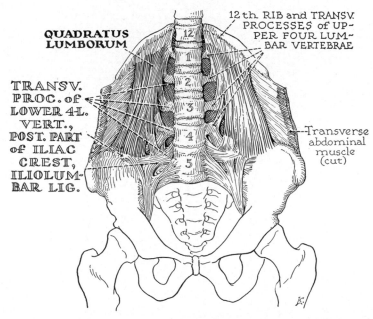

Fig. 148. Quadratus lumborum.

The **quadratus lumborum** (Fig. 148) is rectangular in shape and forms part of the posterior wall of the abdomen. Arising from the posterior part of the crest of the ilium, the iliolumbar ligament and the transverse processes of the lower four lumbar vertebrae, it is inserted into the transverse processes of the upper four lumbar vertebrae and the last rib. The two muscles acting together extend the spine at the lumbar vertebrae. Contraction of one muscle will produce lateral flexion or abduction of the vertebral column. The *rectus abdominis* muscles (description, p. 260 and Fig. 166, p. 262), together with the *psoas major* muscles (description, pp. 264-265 and Figs. 167 to 170, pp. 263-265), act synergistically to flex the spine at the lumbar region.

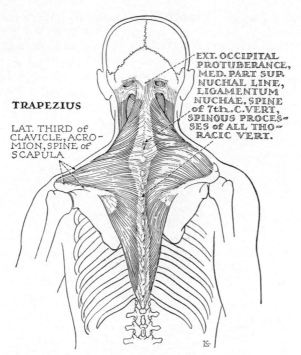

TRAPEZIUS

LAT. THIRD of CLAVICLE, ACRO-MION, SPINE of SCAPULA

EXT. OCCIPITAL PROTUBERANCE, MED. PART SUP. NUCHAL LINE, LIGAMENTUM NUCHAE, SPINE of 7th. C.VERT, SPINOUS PROCESSES of ALL THORACIC VERT.

Fig. 149. Trapezius. The right trapezius muscle is contracted, showing the scapula in adduction.

Muscles Acting on the Scapula

ADDUCTOR	ABDUCTOR
Trapezius	Serratus anterior

The **trapezius** (Fig. 149) is a flat, triangular muscle placed superficially on the posterior part of the neck and upper thorax. It arises from the external occipital protuberance and the medial part of the superior nuchal line, the ligamentum nuchae, the spine of the seventh cervical vertebra and spinous processes of all thoracic vertebrae. The fibers pass lateralward from their origin, converging around the point of the shoulder for insertion. The upper fibers are inserted in the outer third of the clavicle, the middle and lower fibers into the acromion and spine of the scapula. When the trapezius muscle contracts, it draws the scapula toward the spine (adduction) and rotates it upward, at the same time moving it outward from the chest wall. In rotation of the scapula the point of reference is the glenoid cavity; upward rotation means that the scapula is turned so that the glenoid cavity is tilted upward.

The **serratus anterior** (Fig. 150) is the physiologic antagonist of the trapezius because it moves the scapula forward, downward and inward toward the chest wall. It takes origin from the upper nine ribs by a series of fleshy digitations and is inserted the full length

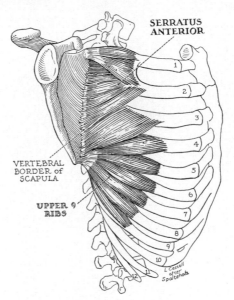

SERRATUS
ANTERIOR

VERTEBRAL
BORDER of
SCAPULA

UPPER 9
RIBS

1
2
3
4
5
6
7
8
9
10
11
12

Cassell
after
Spalteholz

Fig. 150. Serratus anterior.

of the vertebral border of the scapula. With the origin on the chest wall, the scapula is moved away from the spine (abduction). Attachment to the vertebral border keeps the scapula close to the chest wall as it is moved forward and prevents "winging."

Muscles Which Move the Humerus

ABDUCTORS	ADDUCTOR
Deltoid	Pectoralis major
Supraspinatus	

EXTERNAL ROTATORS	INTERNAL ROTATOR
Infraspinatus	Latissimus dorsi
Teres minor	

FLEXOR	EXTENSOR
Coracobrachialis	Teres major

Muscles which move the humerus act at the shoulder joint. This joint, the most freely movable one in the body, is of the ball and socket type, the head of the humerus and glenoid cavity of the scapula forming the articulating parts. There are three principal axes of movement in the shoulder joint: the anteroposterior axis for abduction and adduction, the vertical axis for rotation, and the transverse axis for flexion and extension (Fig. 128, p. 214).

The **deltoid** (Fig. 151) is a thick, triangular muscle which forms the rounded prominence of the shoulder. It arises from the lateral third of the clavicle, the lateral margin of the acromion and the spine of the scapula, and is inserted into the deltoid tuberosity of the humerus. The muscle functions as the principal abductor of the humerus. It is well developed in man, in whom it acts with speed and power in the performance of the difficult task of elevating the arm above the head when erect.

The **supraspinatus muscle** (Fig. 151) arises from the fossa above the spine of the scapula. It passes over the superior part of the shoulder joint to be inserted into the highest facet on the greater tubercle of the humerus. It assists the deltoid in abduction of the humerus.

The **pectoralis major** (Fig. 152) is a heavy, fan-shaped muscle covering the upper part of the chest in front. It arises from the medial half of the clavicle, from half of the front of the sternum and from the costal cartilages of the upper seven ribs, with the exception frequently of the first or seventh, or both, and from the aponeurosis of the external oblique. Passing lateralward, the fibers converge and the muscle inserts on the lateral margin of the intertubercular groove of the humerus. When the arm has been raised by the abductors, contraction of the pectoralis major will draw it down to the side of the body in adduction. Opposing action of abductors and adductors is shown in Figure 153.

The **infraspinatus** (Fig. 154) arises from the infraspinous fossa on the back of the scapula and is inserted into the middle facet of the greater tubercle of the humerus. The muscle rotates the humerus outward.

The **teres minor** (Fig. 154) takes its origin from the axillary border of the scapula and is inserted into the lowest facet of the greater tubercle of the humerus. It acts with the infraspinatus to turn the humerus outward.

The **latissimus dorsi,** a broad, flat muscle, arises from the spinous processes of the lower six thoracic vertebrae, from the lumbodorsal aponeurosis by which it is attached to the spinous processes of the lumbar vertebrae, the spine of the sacrum and the posterior fourth of the iliac crest, and from the outer surface of the lower four ribs by

fleshy digitations. It is inserted by a flat tendon into the floor of the
intertubercular groove of the humerus. Its action is internal rotation of
the humerus. The attachments of this muscle are shown in Figure 155.

The **coracobrachialis** (Fig. 156) lies at the upper and medial part
of the arm. It arises from the coracoid process of the scapula and is

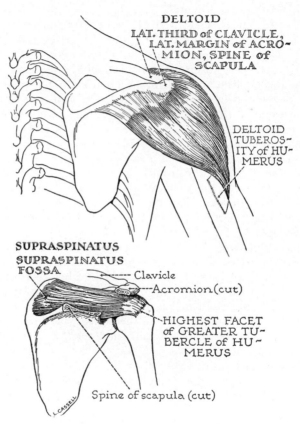

Fig. 151. Deltoid and supraspinatus muscles.

inserted into the middle of the medial surface of the humerus. It carries
the arm forward from the side of the body in flexion.

The **teres major** (Fig. 157) arises from the dorsal aspect of the
lower part of the axillary border of the scapula and is inserted into
the inner margin of the intertubercular groove of the humerus. This
muscle extends the humerus, drawing it downward and backward.

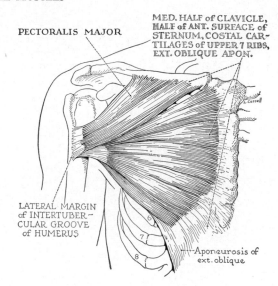

PECTORALIS MAJOR

MED. HALF of CLAVICLE, HALF of ANT. SURFACE of STERNUM, COSTAL CARTILAGES of UPPER 7 RIBS, EXT. OBLIQUE APON.

LATERAL MARGIN of INTERTUBERCULAR GROOVE of HUMERUS

Aponeurosis of ext. oblique

Fig. 152. Pectoralis major.

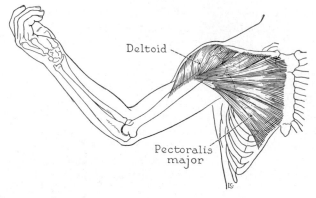

Deltoid

Pectoralis major

Fig. 153. Diagram showing opposing action of deltoid and pectoralis major muscles.

Muscles Acting on the Forearm

FLEXORS	EXTENSOR
Brachialis	Triceps brachii
Biceps brachii	

Movements of flexion and extension of the forearm take place at the elbow between the ulna and the humerus. Movement is about a transverse axis (Fig. 129, p. 215).

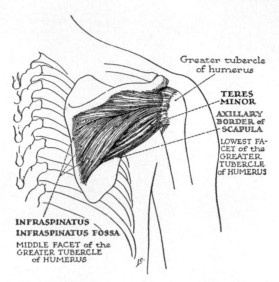

Greater tubercle
of humerus

TERES
MINOR

AXILLARY
BORDER of
SCAPULA

LOWEST FA-
CET of the
GREATER
TUBERCLE
of HUMERUS

INFRASPINATUS
INFRASPINATUS FOSSA
MIDDLE FACET of the
GREATER TUBERCLE
of HUMERUS

Fig. 154. Infraspinatus and teres minor muscles.

The **brachialis** muscle (Fig. 158) arises from the lower half of the anterior surface of the humerus and is inserted into the front of the coronoid process of the ulna. It is a strong and fleshy muscle flexing the forearm.

The **triceps brachii** (Fig. 159) is a large muscle on the posterior surface of the arm. As its name implies, it has three heads of origin: the long, the lateral, and the medial. The long head arises from the infraglenoid tuberosity of the scapula, the lateral head from the posterior surface of the humerus above the radial groove, and the medial head from the surface below the radial groove. The three heads converge in a common tendon which is inserted into the olecranon process of the ulna. It is the physiologic antagonist of the brachialis and extends the forearm (Fig. 160).

Muscles Which Move the Hand

SUPINATORS	PRONATORS
Biceps brachii	Pronator teres
Supinator	Pronator quadratus

The movement of supination and pronation of the hand takes place about the vertical or longitudinal axis of the forearm (Fig. 130, p. 215). The head of the radius turns in the radial notch of the ulna. The radius is held in place by the annular ligament, which encircles the head and is attached to the margins of the radial notch of the ulna.

The **biceps brachii** (Fig. 161) has two tendinous heads of origin, a short head from the coracoid process of the scapula and a long head from the supraglenoid tuberosity. The tendon of the long head passes through the shoulder joint and lies in the intertubercular groove of the humerus. The two heads unite to be inserted by a tendon into

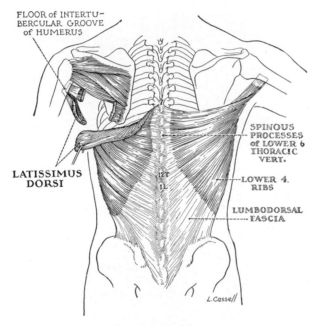

FLOOR of INTERTU-
BERCULAR GROOVE
of HUMERUS

SPINOUS
PROCESSES
of LOWER 6
THORACIC
VERT.

LATISSIMUS
DORSI

LOWER 4.
RIBS

LUMBODORSAL
FASCIA

L. Cassell

Fig. 155. Latissimus dorsi.

the tuberosity of the radius. At the bend of the elbow the tendon gives off an aponeurotic band, the lacertus fibrosus, which continues into the fascia on the ulnar side of the forearm. Contraction of the biceps rolls the radius outward, and the hand, being carried with it, is supinated. The biceps muscle also assists the brachialis in flexion of the forearm. In Figure 160 the biceps muscle is not shown; but much of the bulge that appears on the arm when the forearm is flexed is due to the biceps. It is possible to flex the forearm (brachialis) when the hand is pronated (biceps relaxed). The long head of the biceps stabilizes the shoulder joint by helping to hold the head of the humerus in the glenoid cavity of the scapula.

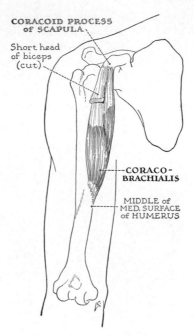

Fig. 156. Coracobrachialis.

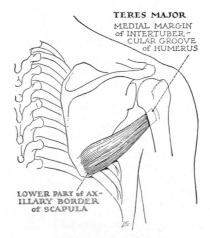

Fig. 157. Teres major.

The **supinator** *(supinator brevis)* arises from the lateral epicondyle of the humerus and ridge of the ulna and is inserted into the lateral margin of the tuberosity and oblique line of the radius (Fig. 161). It assists the biceps in supination of the hand.

The **pronator teres** (Fig. 162) is a fleshy, somewhat rounded muscle placed obliquely in the upper part of the forearm. It arises from the medial epicondyle of the humerus and is inserted into the lateral surface of the radius.

The **pronator quadratus** (Fig. 162) is a small rectangular muscle extending across the lower part of the forearm. It arises from the ulna and is inserted on the radius. The opposing action of pronators and supinators is shown in Figure 163.

Muscles of Respiration

INSPIRATION	EXPIRATION
Diaphragm	Abdominal Muscles
External intercostals	External oblique
	Internal oblique
	Transversus abdominis
	Rectus abdominis
	Internal intercostals

The respiratory movements consist of inspiration, caused by an increase in the thoracic cavity, and expiration, caused by a decrease in the cavity. In quiet inspiration the cavity is increased by the contraction of the diaphragm and the external intercostal muscles. The cavity is enlarged still further in deep or forced inspiration by the contraction of the sternocleidomastoid, sacrospinalis, trapezius, pectoralis major, serratus anterior and other muscles. The decrease in the size of the cavity in quiet expiration is largely passive; it occurs when the inspiratory muscles relax and the elastic tissues recoil. However, some muscular activity is involved in expiration; and the abdominal muscles and the internal intercostals show moderate contraction even in quiet expiration. In forced expiration the action is intensified, and the quadratus lumborum and other muscles may assist the expiratory effort. Contraction of the diaphragm and abdominal muscles in sustained inspiration will assist in micturition and defecation.

The **diaphragm** (Figs. 4, 164) is a musculofibrous partition which separates the thoracic and abdominal cavities. It is dome-shaped, the convex upper surface forming the floor of the thorax and the concave under surface the roof of the abdomen. It arises from the whole of the inner circumference of the thorax, being attached to the xiphoid process of the sternum, the costal cartilages of the lower six ribs, and

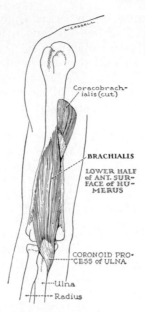

Fig. 158. Brachialis.

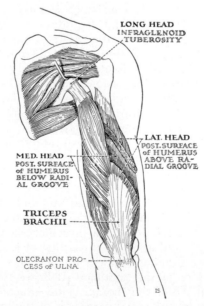

Fig. 159. Triceps brachii; posterior view of right arm.

by tendinous arches from the tip of the last rib to the transverse processes and body of the first lumbar vertebra. Posteriorly it is anchored
to the vertebral column by two muscular strips or crura, the right crus
attaching to the bodies of the upper three lumbar vertebrae and the
left to the bodies of the upper two lumbar vertebrae. From this extensive origin at the periphery, the fibers pass upward to be inserted
into the central tendon. In contraction, the dome of the diaphragm

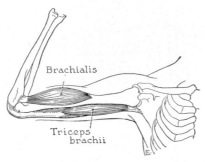

Fig. 160. Diagram showing opposing action of brachialis and triceps brachii.

descends, increasing the vertical diameter of the thorax. When this
occurs, the abdominal muscles, which are physiologic antagonists of
the diaphragm, relax and increase in length. The diaphragm has three
openings: the aortic, through which pass the aorta and thoracic duct;
the esophageal, which contains the esophagus and vagus nerves; and
on the right the caval, traversed by the inferior vena cava.

The intercostal muscles (Fig. 164) fill in the spaces between the
ribs. Both sets, internal and external, arise from the lower borders of
the upper eleven ribs and are inserted into the upper borders of the
last eleven ribs. The fibers run obliquely; those of the inner set are
directed downward and backward, those of the external set run downward and forward. The external intercostals lift the ribs and thus
increase the anteroposterior and transverse diameters of the thorax.
The internal intercostals lower the ribs and decrease the thoracic
diameters.

The *abdominal muscles* are sheets of muscle arranged in layers to
form the walls of the abdominal cavity. They act in relation to visceral
support, and their strength is greatly increased by the fact that the
fibers of the muscles run in different directions.

The **external oblique** (Fig. 165) is the largest of the abdominal
muscles. It takes its origin from the outer surfaces of the lower eight
ribs interdigitating with the fibers of origin of the serratus anterior.
It is inserted into the anterior half of the iliac crest and by means of

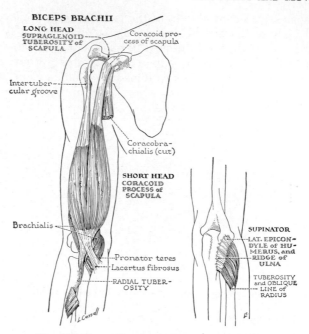

Fig. 161. Biceps brachii and supinator muscles.

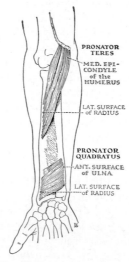

Fig. 162. Front of right forearm, showing pronator muscles.

an aponeurosis to the midline of the abdomen, where it joins with that of the opposite side in a union called the linea alba. This extends from the xiphoid process of the sternum to the crest of the pubis. The lower border of the aponeurosis extends from the anterior superior spine of the ilium to the pubic tubercle and is known as the inguinal

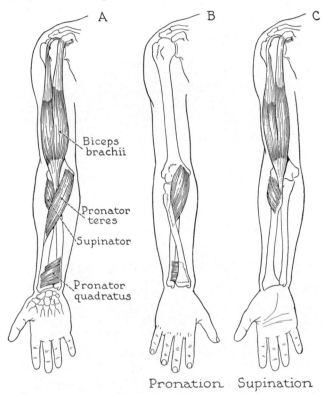

Fig. 163. Diagram showing opposing action of pronators and supinators of the hand. A, Location of the muscles. B, Pronators contracted, forearm and hand pronated. C, Supinators contracted, forearm and hand supinated.

ligament. Near the tubercle is an interval in the aponeurosis called the subcutaneous inguinal ring. The subcutaneous inguinal ring forms the external opening of the inguinal canal. The canal lies parallel to the inguinal ligament and terminates internally at an opening in the transversus abdominis muscle, called the abdominal inguinal ring. Through the abdominal inguinal ring, connection is made with the abdominal cavity. The canal contains the spermatic cord in the male and the round ligament in the female.

The **internal oblique** (Fig. 165) arises from the lateral half of the inguinal ligament, the anterior two-thirds of the iliac crest and the lumbodorsal fascia. Its fibers pass upward and medially and are inserted into the costal cartilages of the lower three ribs and the linea alba and crest of the pubis.

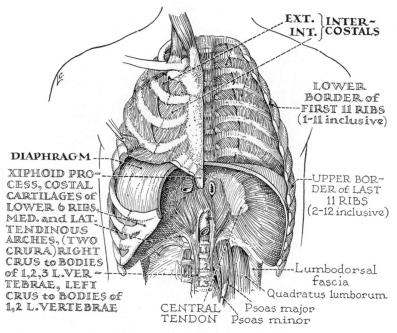

EXT. } INTER-
INT. } COSTALS

LOWER
BORDER of
FIRST 11 RIBS
(1-11 inclusive)

DIAPHRAGM

XIPHOID PRO-
CESS, COSTAL
CARTILAGES of
LOWER 6 RIBS,
MED. and LAT.
TENDINOUS
ARCHES, (TWO
CRURA) RIGHT
CRUS to BODIES
of 1,2,3 L. VER-
TEBRAE, LEFT
CRUS to BODIES of
1,2 L. VERTEBRAE

UPPER BOR-
DER of LAST
11 RIBS
(2-12 inclusive)

Lumbodorsal
fascia
Quadratus lumborum
Psoas major
Psoas minor

CENTRAL
TENDON

Fig. 164. Diaphragm and intercostal muscles.

The **transversus abdominis** (Fig. 166) lies beneath the internal oblique and is the most internal of the flat muscles of the abdomen. The origin is the outer third of the inguinal ligament, the anterior half or three-fourths of the iliac crest, the lumbodorsal fascia and the costal cartilages of the lower six ribs. It is inserted into the linea alba and crest of the pubis.

The **rectus abdominis** (Fig. 166) (right and left) lies on either side of the linea alba and extends from the sternum to the pubis. The origin of each muscle is the crest of the pubis, and the insertion is the xiphoid process of the sternum and the costal cartilages of the fifth, sixth and seventh ribs. Contraction of the rectus abdominis muscles aids in flexion of the spine at the lumbar region.

The abdominal muscles compress the abdominal contents and assist in expiration. They are the direct antagonists of the diaphragm. When the diaphragm contracts, the abdominal muscles relax and elongate to accommodate the compressed viscera; when the diaphragm relaxes, contraction of abdominal muscles replaces viscera upward against the dome of the diaphragm.

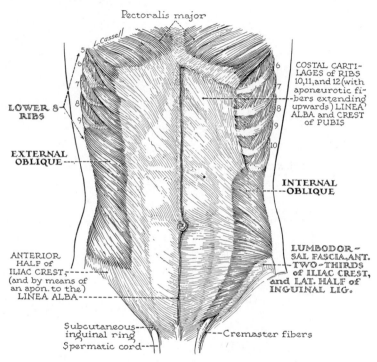

Fig. 165. External oblique and internal oblique muscles.

Muscles Which Move the Femur

FLEXORS	EXTENSOR
Iliacus	Gluteus maximus
Psoas major	

ADDUCTORS	ABDUCTORS
Adductor brevis	Gluteus medius
Adductor longus	Tensor fasciae latae
Adductor magnus	

ROTATION OUTWARDS	ROTATION INWARDS
Piriformis	Gluteus minimus

Movements of the femur are performed at the hip joint. This is a diarthrodial joint of the ball and socket type in which the head of the femur and the acetabulum of the innominate bone form the articulating parts. Movement is free in all directions, and when we consider thigh movements we assume that we are not using it for support; that

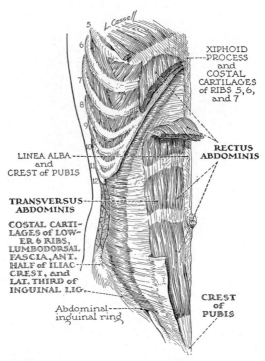

Fig. 166. Transversus abdominis and rectus abdominis muscles.

is, it is not fixed by muscles to support the weight of the body. There are three principal axes of movement in the hip joint: the transverse axis for flexion and extension, the anteroposterior axis for abduction and adduction, and the vertical axis for rotation (Fig. 131, p. 215). The muscles listed which perform these movements pass from the pelvis to the femur, with the exception of the psoas, which is attached to the lumbar spine. If, however, the femurs are fixed in support of body weight, the trunk moves and femurs become the fixed attachment or origin and the movable attachment or insertion is above. Thus origin and insertion of muscles are determined according to the free or fixed condition of the femur.

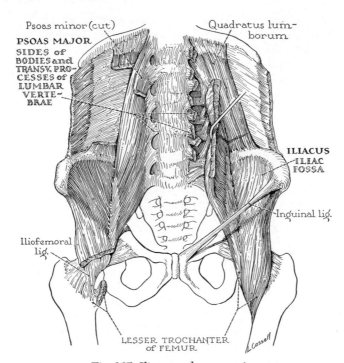

Fig. 167. Iliacus and psoas major.

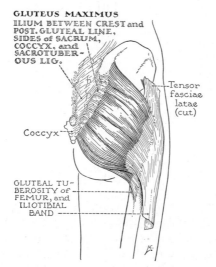

Fig. 168. Gluteus maximus.

The **iliacus** (Fig. 167) is a fan-shaped muscle which arises from the whole of the iliac fossa. It passes under the inguinal ligament to be inserted into the lesser trochanter of the femur.

The **psoas major** (Fig. 167), a long and powerful muscle, arises from the sides of the bodies and transverse processes of the lumbar vertebrae. It passes obliquely across the brim of the pelvis, beneath

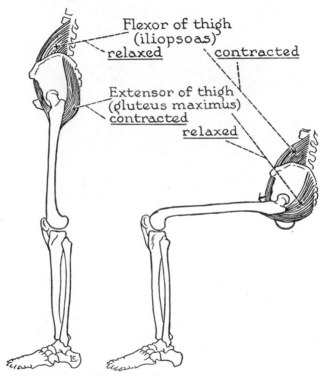

Fig. 169. Diagram showing opposing action of iliopsoas and gluteus maximus.

the inguinal ligament, where it comes into relation with the iliacus and accompanies it to the common insertion, the lesser trochanter. The iliacus and psoas major flex the femur on the trunk. Because of their close association and common insertion, the two muscles are sometimes called the *iliopsoas*. If the femur is fixed, the origin and insertion of muscles are reversed and the trunk is flexed on the thigh, as when we stoop to pick up an object from the floor (Fig. 170). Contraction of psoas major muscles, along with the rectus abdominis muscles, flexes the lumbar portion of the vertebral column.

The **gluteus maximus** (Fig. 168), physiologic antagonist of the iliopsoas, is the large and powerful muscle on the posterior aspect of the hip joint. It arises from the posterior part of the ilium between the crest and the posterior gluteal line, sides of the sacrum and coccyx

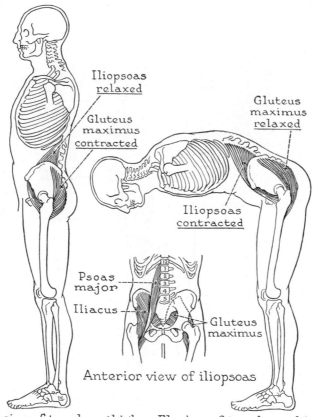

Fig. 170. Diagram showing action of iliopsoas and gluteus maximus with femurs fixed.

and the sacrotuberous ligament, which is the fibrous band from the posterior iliac crest and sacrum to the ischial tuberosity. The fibers pass downward and somewhat lateralward to be inserted into the iliotibial band (Fig. 174) and the posterior part of the femur along the gluteal tuberosity. The action is extension of the femur, bringing the thigh in line with the body. The opposing action of iliopsoas and gluteus maximus is shown in Figure 169.

Contraction of the gluteus maximus muscles, using the thighs as the fixed attachment, extends the trunk on the lower extremities. This would result in bringing the body back to the erect position after stooping to pick up an object (Fig. 170).

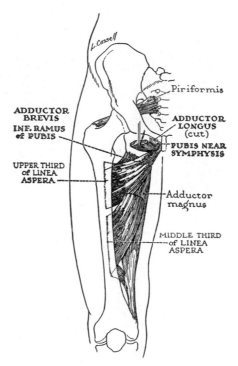

Fig. 171. Adductor brevis and adductor longus muscles.

The three adductors (Figs. 171, 172) of the femur are closely associated and may be considered together. They all arise from the innominate bone and are inserted into the linea aspera of the femur. The **adductor brevis** arises from the inferior ramus of the pubis and is inserted into the upper third of the linea aspera. The **adductor longus** arises from the pubis near the symphysis and is inserted about the middle third of the linea aspera. The **adductor magnus** arises from the tuberosity and inferior ramus of the ischium and is inserted the whole length of the linea aspera, extending below to the adductor

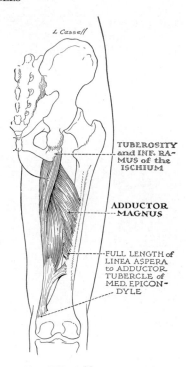

Fig. 172. Adductor magnus.

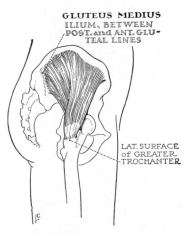

Fig. 173. Gluteus medius.

tubercle on the medial condyle. These muscles adduct the femur, bringing it in toward the midline.

The **gluteus medius** (Fig. 173), on the lateral aspect of the hip joint, arises from the outer surface of the ilium between the anterior

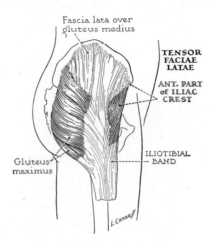

Fig. 174. Tensor fasciae latae.

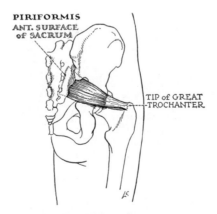

Fig. 175. Piriformis.

and the posterior gluteal lines and is inserted into the lateral part of the greater trochanter of the femur. It acts to abduct the femur.

Tensor fasciae latae (Fig. 174) arises from the anterior part of the iliac crest and is inserted into the iliotibial band. The muscles of the thigh are enveloped in a fascial sheet which is thickened on the lateral side to form the iliotibial band. The tensor fasciae latae tightens this band and assists the gluteus medius in abduction of the thigh.

The **piriformis** (Fig. 175) is a muscle which connects the axial skeleton to the lower extremity. The origin is within the pelvis on the anterior surface of the sacrum. It passes through the great sacrosciatic

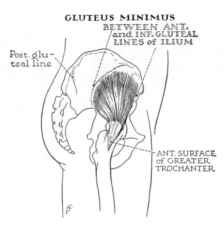

Fig. 176. Gluteus minimus.

notch and is inserted on the upper part of the greater trochanter. It is one of the external rotators of the femur.

The **gluteus minimus** (Fig. 176) opposes the piriformis and the other external rotators. This muscle arises from the surface of the ilium between the anterior and inferior gluteal lines and is inserted into the anterior surface of the greater trochanter. It acts to rotate the femur inwards.

Muscles Which Move the Leg

FLEXORS	EXTENSOR
Sartorius	Quadriceps femoris
Gracilis	Rectus femoris
Semitendinosus	Vastus lateralis
Semimembranosus	Vastus medialis
Biceps femoris	Vastus intermedius
Popliteus	

The knee joint is a modified hinge joint. The articular surfaces entering into the knee joint are the condyles and patellar surface of the femur, the upper surface of the tibia and the articular surface of the patella. The two concavities on the superior articular surface of the tibia which receive the condyles of the femur are deepened by semilunar rings of fibrocartilage, called the medial and lateral menisci. The joint is secured by many ligaments and fibrous expansions. The muscles acting on the knee joint move about a transverse axis (Fig.

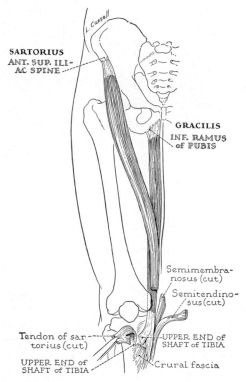

Fig. 177. Sartorius and gracilis muscles.

132, p. 215). The principal actions of the muscles listed are flexion and extension of the leg.

Sartorius (Fig. 177). This is the longest muscle in the body; it passes obliquely across the front of the thigh. It arises from the anterior superior spine of the ilium, and passes back of the medial condyle of the femur to be inserted on the inner surface of the upper end of the shaft of the tibia. The center of motion of the sartorius is the knee joint, and, since the muscle passes back of the condyle, it flexes the leg.

The **gracilis** (Fig. 177), on the inner side of the thigh, arises from the descending ramus of the pubis and is inserted with the sartorius on the inner surface of the tibia just below the head.

The three flexor muscles of the leg on the posterior aspect of the thigh are called the "*hamstrings.*" They are the **semitendinosus, semimembranosus** and **biceps femoris** (Fig. 178).

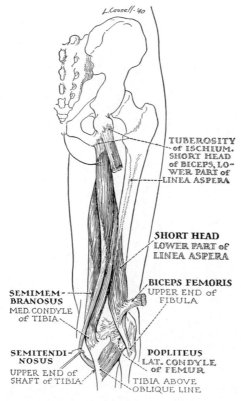

Fig. 178. Semitendinosus, semimembranosus, biceps femoris and popliteus.

The origin of the semitendinosus, semimembranosus and the long head of the biceps is from the tuberosity of the ischium. The short head of the biceps arises from the lower part of the linea aspera. The biceps muscle passes to the lateral side of the leg and is inserted on the upper end of the fibula. The semitendinosus passes to the medial side of the leg and is inserted with the sartorius and gracilis on the upper end of the shaft of the tibia. The semimembranosus inserts on the posterior part of the medial condyle of the tibia.

Popliteus (Fig. 178). This is a short muscle placed at the back of the knee joint. It arises from the lateral condyle of the femur and is inserted into the upper part of the tibia above the oblique line. The popliteus muscle aids in flexion of the leg.

The **quadriceps femoris** (Fig. 179) is a large muscle on the anterior

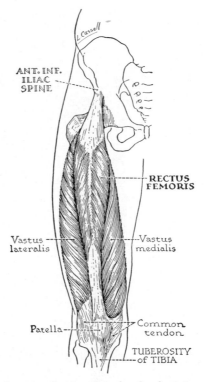

Fig. 179. Quadriceps femoris, showing three heads of origin: vastus lateralis, vastus medialis, and rectus femoris. Origin and insertion of rectus femoris are given.

part of the thigh composed of four parts: namely, *rectus femoris, vastus lateralis, vastus medialis,* and *vastus intermedius.* The rectus femoris arises from the anterior inferior spine of the ilium and by a reflected tendon around the margin of the acetabulum, the vastus lateralis (Fig. 180) arises from the lateral lip of the linea aspera, the vastus medialis (Fig. 180) from the medial lip of the linea aspera, and the intermedius (Fig. 181) from the anterior surface of the femur. All four heads meet in a common tendon which encloses the patella and passes over the knee joint to be inserted on the tuberosity of the tibia. The action of the quadriceps is one of the most powerful in the body. It extends the leg on the femur, opposing the action of the six flexors (Fig. 182). Its action is essential in standing. It also plays an important part in walking, because the leg must be extended each time in order to take the next step.

Muscles Acting on the Foot

FLEXORS	EXTENSORS
Tibialis anterior	Gastrocnemius
Peroneus tertius	Soleus
	Tibialis posterior
	Peroneus longus
	Peroneus brevis

INVERTORS	EVERTORS
Tibialis anterior with flexion	Peroneus longus with extension
Tibialis posterior with extension	Peroneus brevis with extension
	Peroneus tertius with flexion

Muscles acting on the foot produce the movements of flexion or upward movement in which the foot is bent toward the anterior part of the leg (dorsiflexion), and of extension or downward movement in which the foot is straightened on the leg (plantarflexion), as well as inversion—turning the foot in—and eversion—turning the foot out. Movements of flexion and extension take place at the ankle joint, which is a diarthrodial joint of the hinge type composed of the medial malleolus of the tibia and lateral malleolus of the fibula which box in the talus. Movement is about a transverse axis (Fig. 133, p. 215). Movements of inversion and eversion occur mainly in the tarsal articulations.

The **tibialis anterior** (Fig. 183), which arises from the outer surface of the tibia, is attached to the lateral condyle and upper two-thirds of the shaft. The tendon passes obliquely across the ankle and is inserted on the proximal end of the first metatarsal and medial cuneiform bones. It flexes the foot and turns it inward.

Peroneus tertius (Fig. 184) arises from the anterior aspect of the lower third of the fibula and inserts on the base of the fifth metatarsal bone. It flexes and everts the foot.

Peroneus brevis (Fig. 184) arises from the lower two-thirds of the lateral surface of the fibula, passes back of the lateral malleolus, and is inserted on the tubercle and dorsal surface of the fifth metatarsal. It extends and everts the foot.

The **gastrocnemius** (Fig. 185) is a superficial muscle which forms the greater part of the calf of the leg. It arises by two heads from the posterior surfaces of the medial and lateral condyles of the femur and is inserted by means of the tendo calcaneus, or tendon of Achilles, to the calcaneus. The gastrocnemius extends the foot and aids in flexing the leg.

The **soleus** (Fig. 186) lies just beneath the gastrocnemius and takes

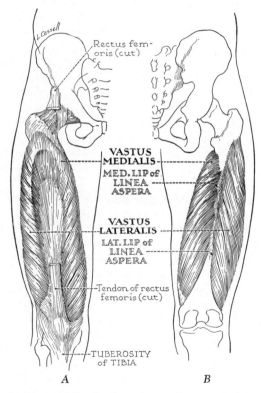

Fig. 180. Lateral and medial heads of quadriceps femoris. *A,* Anterior view. *B,* Posterior view.

its origin from the head of the fibula and popliteal line of the tibia. Like the gastrocnemius, it is inserted by means of the tendo calcaneus into the calcaneus. The soleus and gastrocnemius are powerful muscles which extend the foot; when one is standing on tiptoe, they support the weight of the body against the force of gravity. The opposing action of these extensor muscles and the flexor, tibialis anterior, is shown in Figure 187.

The **tibialis posterior** (Fig. 188) is the most deeply placed muscle on the back of the leg, arising from the adjacent surfaces of the tibia and fibula and the interosseus membrane between them. The tendon passes behind the medial malleolus to its principal insertion on the tuberosity of the navicular bone, and in addition fibrous expansions pass to the three cuneiform bones, the cuboid, the second, third and

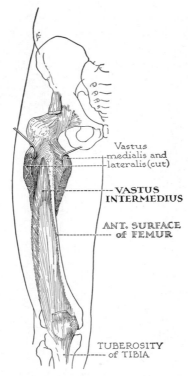

Vastus
medialis and
lateralis (cut)

**VASTUS
INTERMEDIUS**

ANT. SURFACE
of FEMUR

TUBEROSITY
of TIBIA

Fig. 181. Vastus intermedius portion of the quadriceps.

fourth metatarsals and the sustentaculum tali, giving the insertion a firm grip on the sole of the foot. This muscle extends and inverts the foot.

Peroneus longus (Fig. 189) arises from the lateral condyle of the tibia and the upper two-thirds of the lateral surface of the fibula. Its tendon passes behind the lateral malleolus along with that of peroneus brevis, running in the groove of the cuboid obliquely across the sole of the foot to be inserted into the proximal end of the first metatarsal and the medial cuneiform. Peroneus longus extends and everts the foot.

Muscles of Mastication

ELEVATE MANDIBLE	DEPRESS MANDIBLE
Temporal	External pterygoid*
Masseter	
Internal pterygoid	

The muscles of mastication, or craniomandibular muscles, pass from the skull to the lower jaw and act upon the temporomandibular joint (Fig. 190). This articulation is formed by the condyle of the mandible

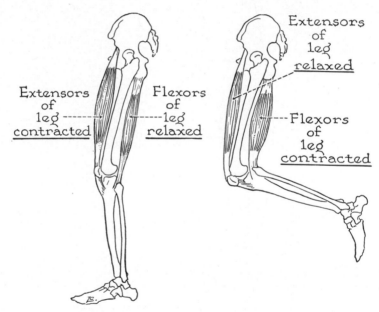

Fig. 182. Diagram showing opposing action of quadriceps femoris and the flexors of the leg.

and the mandibular fossa and articular tubercle of the temporal bone. An articular disc is interposed between and adapted to the two articular surfaces. It divides the joint cavity into an upper and a lower compartment. Hinge movements occur in the lower cavity; gliding movements in the upper cavity.

The **temporal** muscle arises from the temporal fossa and is inserted

* Other muscles not included in this discussion assist the external pterygoid in depressing the mandible.

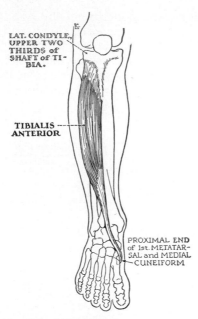

LAT. CONDYLE,
UPPER TWO
THIRDS of
SHAFT of TI-
BIA.

TIBIALIS
ANTERIOR

PROXIMAL END
of 1st. METATAR-
SAL and MEDIAL
CUNEIFORM

Fig. 183. Tibialis anterior.

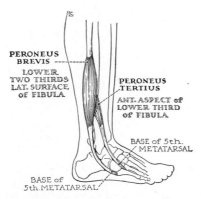

PERONEUS
BREVIS

LOWER
TWO THIRDS
LAT. SURFACE
of FIBULA

PERONEUS
TERTIUS

ANT. ASPECT of
LOWER THIRD
of FIBULA

BASE of 5th.
METATARSAL

BASE of
5th. METATARSAL

Fig. 184. Peroneus brevis and peroneus tertius muscles.

on the anterior border of the ramus and coronoid process of the mandible. It closes the jaws by elevating the mandible.

The **masseter** muscle arises from the zygomatic arch and is inserted into the lateral surface of the ramus and angle of the mandible. It assists the temporal muscle in closure of the jaws. It stands out prominently when the jaws are vigorously closed and can easily be felt just above the angle of the mandible.

The **internal pterygoid** muscle on the inner surface of the ramus of the mandible parallels the masseter muscle on the external surface, both in shape and position. It arises from the medial surface of the

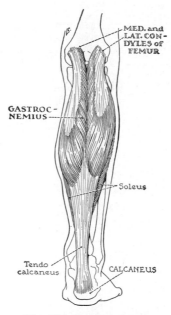

Fig. 185. Gastrocnemius.

lateral pterygoid plate, the palatine bone, and the tuberosity of the maxilla, and is inserted into the ramus and angle of the mandible.

The **external pterygoid** muscle arises from the lower part of the lateral surface of the great wing of the sphenoid, the lateral pterygoid plate, the palatine bone and tuberosity of the maxilla. It is inserted into the neck of the condyle of the mandible and the articular disc of the joint.

The internal pterygoid muscle assists in closing the jaws, while the external pterygoid opens them. Side-to-side movements such as take place in the grinding of food are produced by the pterygoid muscles on the two sides contracting alternately. Acting together, they protrude the mandible.

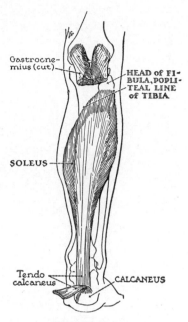

Fig. 186. Soleus.

Muscles of Facial Expression

Epicranius
Corrugator
Orbicularis oculi
Orbicularis oris
Zygomatic
Risorius
Platysma
Buccinator

The muscles of facial expression are a complex group of cutaneous muscles (Fig. 190). For the most part they arise either from fascia or from the surface of the skull and insert into the skin. They are arranged in sheets or thin bands, and the fibers of one muscle blend with those of neighboring muscles in such a way that the line of demarcation is often indistinct. Only a few of the muscles will be described.

The **epicranius**, or occipitofrontalis, consists of two muscular portions, *frontalis* and *occipitalis*, connected by a fibrous sheet, the galea aponeurotica. The occipitalis arises from the lateral part of the superior

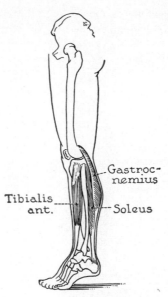

Fig. 187. Soleus and gastrocnemius opposing the action of tibialis anterior.

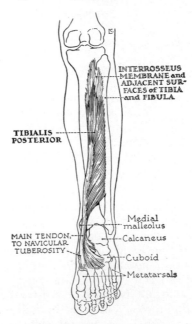

Fig. 188. Tibialis posterior.

nuchal line and the mastoid part of the temporal bone and is inserted into the aponeurosis. It draws the scalp backward. The frontalis arises from the anterior border of the galea aponeurotica and is inserted in the fibers of the orbicularis oculi and the corrugator muscles. The frontalis raises the eyebrows in the expression of surprise and at the same time draws the scalp forward, throwing the skin of the forehead into transverse wrinkles.

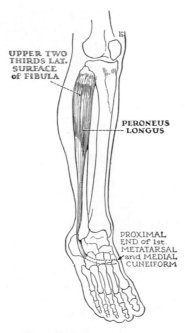

Fig. 189. Peroneus longus.

The **corrugator** muscle arises from the medial end of the superciliary arch and is inserted into the skin of the forehead, wrinkling it vertically, as in frowning.

The **orbicularis oculi** encircles the eyelids and spreads out over adjacent parts of the cheek and the forehead. It consists of three parts. The orbital part arises from the frontal bone and frontal process of the maxilla, encircles the aperture of the orbit, and inserts near its origin. The palpebral (eyelid) portion arises from the inner canthus of the eye, passes through each eyelid and is inserted into the outer canthus. The lacrimal portion arises from the lacrimal bone and passes across the lacrimal sac to join the palpebral portion. The orbicularis oculi closes the eyelids, wrinkles the skin of the forehead and compresses the lacrimal sac. The levator palpebrae superioris, described with ocular muscles on page 142, is the direct antagonist of the orbicularis oculi; it raises the upper eyelid.

The **orbicularis oris** muscle encircles the mouth. It consists of numerous layers of fibers which run between the skin and mucous membrane

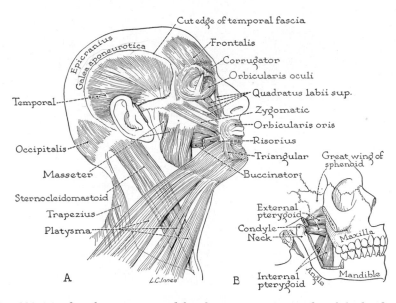

Fig. 190. Muscles of mastication and facial expression. A, Muscles of the head and neck. B, Pterygoid muscles.

of the lips and cheeks. It acts to close the lips and push them forward. Several small muscles converge upon it to draw the corners of the mouth in various directions.

The **zygomatic** muscle arises from the zygomatic bone; it descends obliquely to insert into the angle of the mouth, where it blends with the fibers of the orbicularis oris and other muscles. It draws the angles of the mouth upward and backward as in laughing.

The **risorius** arises from the fascia over the masseter and passes forward transversely to insert at the angle of the mouth, where it unites with the orbicularis oris. It draws the angle of the mouth outward and, when strongly contracted, imparts a tense and strained expression to the face.

The **platysma,** a large, thin, sheetlike muscle, arises from the fascia of the pectoralis major and deltoid muscles. Its fibers pass medialward over the side of the neck to insert into the lower border of the mandible, the skin of the lower part of the cheek and the corner of the mouth, where it fuses with the orbicularis oris. It draws down the lower lip and angle of the mouth and wrinkles the skin of the neck.

The **buccinator,** sometimes called the trumpeter's muscle, is the principal muscle of the cheek and forms the lateral wall of the oral cavity. It arises from the alveolar processes of the maxilla and mandible, and inserts by fusing with the fibers of the orbicularis oris. It compresses the cheeks and assists mastication by holding the food in contact with the teeth.

Table 9

Muscles

Muscles Which Move the Head

NAME OF MUSCLE	ORIGIN	INSERTION	ACTION
Sternocleidomastoid (Fig. 145)	Sternal end of clavicle, upper border of manubrium of sternum	Mastoid process of temporal bone	Both muscles acting flex head on chest; one muscle acting bends head to side of contracting muscle
Splenius capitis (Fig. 146)	Lower part of ligamentum nuchae, spinous processes of seventh cervical and upper three or four thoracic vertebrae	Mastoid process and lateral part of superior nuchal line	Both muscles acting extend head; one muscle contracting inclines and rotates head and neck to same side
Semispinalis capitis (Fig. 146)	Transverse processes of upper six thoracic vertebrae, articular processes of lower four cervical vertebrae	Between superior and inferior nuchal lines of occipital bone	Both muscles acting extend head; when one muscle contracts, head and neck are inclined and rotated to same side
Longissimus capitis (Fig. 146)	Transverse processes of upper three thoracic vertebrae and articular processes of lower four cervical vertebrae	Mastoid process	Both muscles acting extend head; one muscle acting inclines head to side of contracting muscle

Muscles Which Move the Vertebral Column

NAME OF MUSCLE	ORIGIN	INSERTION	ACTION
Sacrospinalis (Fig. 147)	Posterior part of iliac crest, posterior surface of sacrum, spinous processes of all lumbar vertebrae and last two thoracic vertebrae	Three divisions: 1. Iliocostalis—angles of lower five or six ribs 2. Longissimus dorsi — transverse processes of thoracic vertebrae and ribs 3. Spinalis dorsi—spinous processes of upper thoracic vertebrae	Extends vertebral column
Quadratus lumborum (Fig. 148)	Posterior part of iliac crest, iliolumbar ligament, transverse processes of lower four lumbar vertebrae	Transverse processes of upper four lumbar vertebrae, last rib	Extends spine at lumbar vertebrae
Rectus abdominis and Psoas major	See p. 289	See p. 289	Flex the vertebral column at lumbar vertebrae

Muscles Acting on the Scapula

Trapezius (Fig. 149)	External occipital protuberance, medial part of superior nuchal line, ligamentum nuchae, spine of seventh cervical vertebra, spinous processes of all thoracic vertebrae	Lateral third of clavicle, acromion and spine of scapula	Adduction and upward rotation of scapula
Serratus anterior (Fig. 150)	Upper nine ribs	Vertebral border of scapula	Abduction of scapula

Table 9 (Continued)

Muscles Which Move the Humerus

NAME OF MUSCLE	ORIGIN	INSERTION	ACTION
Deltoid (Fig. 151)	Lateral third of clavicle, lateral margin of acromion, spine of scapula	Deltoid tuberosity of humerus	Abduction of humerus
Supraspinatus (Fig. 151)	Supraspinatus fossa of scapula	Highest facet on greater tubercle of humerus	Abduction of humerus
Pectoralis major (Fig. 152)	Medial half of clavicle, half of anterior surface of sternum, costal cartilages of upper seven ribs, aponeurosis of external oblique	Lateral margin of intertubercular groove of humerus	Adduction of humerus
Infraspinatus (Fig. 154)	Infraspinatus fossa of scapula	Middle facet of greater tubercle of humerus	Outward rotation of humerus
Teres minor (Fig. 154)	Axillary border of scapula	Lowest facet of greater tubercle of humerus	Outward rotation of humerus
Latissimus dorsi (Fig. 155)	Spinous processes of lower six thoracic vertebrae, lumbodorsal aponeurosis (by which it is attached to spinous processes of lumbar vertebrae, spine of sacrum, posterior fourth of iliac crest) and lower four ribs	Floor of intertubercular groove of humerus	Internal rotation of humerus

Muscle	Origin	Insertion	Action
Coracobrachialis (Fig. 156)	Coracoid process of scapula	Middle of medial surface of humerus	Flexion of humerus
Teres major (Fig. 157)	Lower part of axillary border of scapula	Inner margin of intertubercular groove of humerus	Extension of humerus

Muscles Acting on the Forearm

Muscle	Origin	Insertion	Action
Brachialis (Fig. 158)	Lower half of anterior surface of humerus	Coronoid process of ulna	Flexion of forearm
Triceps brachii (Fig. 159)	Long head from infraglenoid tuberosity of scapula, lateral head posterior surface of humerus above radial groove, medial head from surface below radial groove	Olecranon process of ulna	Extension of forearm

Muscles Which Move the Hand

Muscle	Origin	Insertion	Action
Biceps brachii (Fig. 161)	Long head supraglenoid tuberosity of scapula, short head coracoid process of scapula	Tuberosity of radius; lacertus fibrosus, a fibrous expansion of tendon, is attached to fascia on medial side of forearm	Supinates hand and assists in flexion of forearm
Supinator (Fig. 161)	Lateral epicondyle of humerus, ridge of ulna	Lateral margin of tuberosity and oblique line of radius	Assists biceps in supination of the hand
Pronator teres (Fig. 162)	Medial epicondyle of humerus	Lateral surface of radius	Pronation, back of hand turned forward

Table 9 (Continued)

NAME OF MUSCLE	ORIGIN	INSERTION	ACTION
Pronator quadratus (Fig. 162)	Distal part of ulna	Distal part of radius	Assists pronator teres in pronation

Muscles of Respiration

NAME OF MUSCLE	ORIGIN	INSERTION	ACTION
Diaphragm (Fig. 164)	Xiphoid process of sternum, costal cartilages of lower six ribs, medial and lateral tendinous arches; (two crura) right crus to bodies of first three lumbar vertebrae, left crus to bodies of first two lumbar vertebrae	Central tendon	Increases vertical diameter of thorax
External intercostals (Fig. 164)	Lower borders of upper eleven ribs	Upper borders of last eleven ribs	Elevate ribs and increase anteroposterior and transverse diameters of thorax
Internal intercostals (Fig. 164)	Lower borders of upper eleven ribs	Upper borders of last eleven ribs	Lower ribs and decrease thoracic diameters
External oblique (Fig. 165)	Lower eight ribs	Anterior half of iliac crest, by means of an aponeurosis to linea alba	Compresses abdominal contents, assists in expiration

Muscle	Origin	Insertion	Action
Internal oblique (Fig. 165)	Lateral half of inguinal ligament, anterior two-thirds of iliac crest, lumbodorsal fascia	Costal cartilages of ribs 10, 11, 12, linea alba, crest of pubis	Compresses abdominal contents, assists in expiration
Transversus abdominis (Fig. 166)	Lateral third of inguinal ligament, anterior half of iliac crest, lumbodorsal fascia, costal cartilages of lower six ribs	Linea alba and crest of pubis	Compresses abdominal contents, assists in expiration
Rectus abdominis (Fig. 166)	Crest of pubis	Xiphoid process of sternum, costal cartilages of fifth, sixth and seventh ribs	Compresses abdominal contents, assists in expiration; flexes lumbar region of vertebral column

Muscles Which Move the Femur

Muscle	Origin	Insertion	Action
Iliacus (Figs. 167, 169, 170)	Iliac fossa	Lesser trochanter of femur	Flexes femur
Psoas major (Figs. 167, 169, 170)	Sides of bodies and transverse processes of lumbar vertebrae	Lesser trochanter of femur	Flexes femur and lumbar region of vertebral column
Gluteus maximus (Figs. 168, 169, 170)	Ilium between crest and posterior gluteal line, sides of sacrum, coccyx, sacrotuberous ligament	Gluteal tuberosity and iliotibial band	Extends femur
Adductor brevis (Fig. 171)	Inferior ramus of pubis	Upper third of linea aspera	Adducts femur
Adductor longus (Fig. 171)	Pubis near symphysis	Middle third of linea aspera	Adducts femur

Table 9 (Continued)

NAME OF MUSCLE	ORIGIN	INSERTION	ACTION
Adductor magnus (Fig. 172)	Tuberosity and inferior ramus of ischium	Linea aspera, adductor tubercle	Adducts femur
Gluteus medius (Fig. 173)	Outer surface of ilium between anterior and posterior gluteal lines	Lateral surface of greater trochanter	Abducts femur
Tensor fasciae latae (Fig. 174)	Anterior part of iliac crest	Iliotibial band	Tightens iliotibial band, assists in abduction of femur
Piriformis (Fig. 175)	Anterior surface of sacrum	Superior tip of greater trochanter	Outward rotation of femur
Gluteus minimus (Fig. 176)	Outer surface of ilium between anterior and inferior gluteal lines	Anterior surface of greater trochanter	Inward rotation of femur

Muscles Which Move the Leg

NAME OF MUSCLE	ORIGIN	INSERTION	ACTION
Sartorius (Fig. 177)	Anterior superior spine of ilium	Upper end of shaft of tibia	Flexes leg
Gracilis (Fig. 177)	Inferior ramus of pubis	With sartorius, inner surface of tibia, just below the head	Flexes leg
Semitendinosus (Fig. 178)	Tuberosity of ischium	With sartorius and gracilis, upper end of shaft of tibia	Flexes leg

Semimembranosus (Fig. 178)	Tuberosity of ischium	Medial condyle of tibia	Flexes leg
Biceps femoris (Fig. 178)	Long head, tuberosity of ischium; short head, lower part of linea aspera	Upper end of fibula	Flexes leg
Popliteus (Fig. 178)	Lateral condyle of femur	Upper part of tibia above oblique line	Assists in flexing leg
Quadriceps femoris (Figs. 179, 180, 181)	Four heads of origin: 1. Rectus femoris—anterior inferior spine of ilium, reflected tendon around margin of acetabulum 2. Vastus lateralis—lateral lip of linea aspera 3. Vastus medialis—medial lip of linea aspera 4. Vastus intermedius—anterior surface of femur	By a common tendon which encloses patella and inserts on tuberosity of tibia	Extends leg

Muscles Acting on the Foot

Tibialis anterior (Fig. 183)	Lateral condyle and upper two-thirds of shaft of tibia	Proximal end of first metatarsal and medial cuneiform	Flexes and inverts foot
Peroneus tertius (Fig. 184)	Anterior aspect of lower third of fibula	Base of fifth metatarsal	Flexes and everts foot

Table 9 (Continued)

NAME OF MUSCLE	ORIGIN	INSERTION	ACTION
Peroneus brevis (Fig. 184)	Lower two-thirds of lateral surface of fibula, passes back of lateral malleolus	Dorsal surface, base of fifth metatarsal	Extends and everts foot
Peroneus longus (Fig. 189)	Lateral condyle of tibia and upper two-thirds of lateral surface of fibula	Tendon passes back of lateral malleolus, runs in groove of cuboid across sole of foot, inserted into proximal end of first metatarsal and medial cuneiform	Extends and everts foot
Gastrocnemius (Fig. 185)	Posterior surface of medial and lateral condyles of femur	Calcaneus by means of tendo calcaneus	Extends foot
Soleus (Fig. 186)	Head of fibula, popliteal line of tibia	Calcaneus by means of tendo calcaneus	Extends foot
Tibialis posterior (Fig. 188)	Interosseus membrane and adjacent surfaces of tibia and fibula	Tuberosity of navicular bone	Extends and inverts foot

Muscles of Mastication

NAME OF MUSCLE	ORIGIN	INSERTION	ACTION
Temporal (Fig. 190)	Temporal fossa	Anterior border of ramus and coronoid process of mandible	Closes jaws

Masseter (Fig. 190)	Zygomatic arch	Lateral surface of ramus and angle of mandible	Closes jaws
Internal pterygoid (Fig. 190)	Medial surface of lateral pterygoid plate, palatine bone, tuberosity of maxilla	Medial surface of ramus and angle of mandible	Closes jaws
External pterygoid (Fig. 190)	Lateral surface of great wing of sphenoid, lateral pterygoid plate, palatine bone, tuberosity of maxilla	Neck of condyle of mandible, articular disc of joint	Opens jaws; side-to-side movements are produced by pterygoid muscles on two sides contracting alternately

Muscles of Facial Expression

Epicranius (Fig. 190) two parts { Occipitalis	Lateral part of superior nuchal line, mastoid part of temporal bone	Galea aponeurotica	Draws scalp backward
Frontalis	Anterior border of galea aponeurotica	Fibers of orbicularis oculi and corrugator	Raises eyebrows, wrinkles skin of forehead transversely
Corrugator (Fig. 190)	Medial end of superciliary arch	Skin of forehead	Wrinkles skin of forehead vertically as in frowning
Orbicularis oculi, three portions (Fig. 190):			

Table 9 (Continued)

NAME OF MUSCLE	ORIGIN	INSERTION	ACTION
1. Orbital portion 2. Palpebral portion 3. Lacrimal portion	Frontal bone, frontal process of maxilla Inner canthus Lacrimal bone	Near origin after encircling orbit Outer canthus Joins palpebral portion after crossing lacrimal sac	Closes eyelids, wrinkles skin of forehead, compresses lacrimal sac
Orbicularis oris (Fig. 190)	Many layers of fibers surrounding the mouth	Angles of mouth	Closes lips and protrudes them
Zygomatic (Fig. 190)	Zygomatic bone	Angle of mouth, fibers of orbicularis oris	Draws angles of mouth upward and backward, as in laughing
Risorius (Fig. 190)	Fascia over the masseter	Angle of mouth, fibers of orbicularis oris	Draws angle of mouth outward, gives strained expression to face
Platysma (Fig. 190)	Fascia of pectoralis major and deltoid	Lower border of mandible, skin of cheek and corner of mouth	Draws down lower lip and angle of mouth, wrinkles skin of neck
Buccinator (Fig. 190)	Alveolar processes of maxilla and mandible	Fibers of orbicularis oris at angle of mouth	Compresses cheeks, holds food in contact with teeth

SUMMARY

The skeletal muscles are the organs of the muscular system. They number more than 400 in the human body.

Each striated muscle has two attachments which are composed of white fibrous tissue. The attachment of muscle to bone may be one of three types: direct to the periosteum, by means of a tendon, or by means of an aponeurosis. The more fixed attachment of a muscle which serves as a basis of action is called the origin. The movable attachment where the effects of movement are produced is the insertion.

Muscles are arranged in opposing or antagonistic groups. When muscles flexing a part are contracted, those opposing the action, the extensors, are in a state of physiologic relaxation, in which they elongate and give way to the movement.

The following groups of muscles are described:

1. Muscles which move the head.

   The joint involved is the atlanto-occipital articulation, in which forward and backward nodding movements take place. The muscles consist of one flexor and three extensors.

2. Muscles which move the vertebral column.

   The joints involved are the articulations between the lumbar vertebrae, particularly the fourth and fifth lumbar vertebrae. Here the movements of flexion and extension of the spine occur.

3. Muscles acting on the scapula.

   The scapula has no articulation with the axial skeleton, but is joined with it indirectly through the clavicle. Its position is maintained largely through muscular attachments. The trapezius muscle carries it toward the spine in adduction, and the serratus anterior moves it away from it in abduction.

4. Muscles moving the humerus.

   These muscles act at the shoulder joint. This joint, the most freely movable one in the body, is of the ball and socket type. The movements are adduction, abduction, external rotation, internal rotation and flexion and extension.

5. Muscles acting on the forearm.

   Movements of flexion and extension of the forearm take place at the elbow between the ulna and the humerus.

6. Muscles which move the hand.

   These movements of the hand consist of pronation and supination, and the joint involved is the radio-ulnar articulation.

7. Muscles of respiration.

   These muscles fall into two groups: those concerned with inspiration which produce an increase in chest diameters, and those concerned with expiration.

8. Muscles which move the femur.
   Movements of the femur are performed at the hip joint. This is a diarthrodial joint of the ball and socket type. The movements are flexion, extension, abduction, adduction, and outward and inward rotation.

9. Muscles which move the leg.
   The articulation involved is the knee joint, which is formed by the condyles of the femur and the upper surface of the tibia. The movements are flexion and extension.

10. Muscles acting on the foot.
    These muscles produce the movements of flexion or upward movement, extension or downward movement, inversion and eversion of the foot.

11. Muscles acting on the mandible.
    These are the muscles of mastication which open and close the jaws by depressing and elevating the mandible.

12. Muscles of facial expression.
    These are cutaneous muscles which produce the characteristic facial expressions.

QUESTIONS FOR DISCUSSION

1. Compare the relative size and position of the flexor and extensor groups of muscle and explain the differences.

2. How are the skeletal muscles related to the axes of the articulatory system?

Unit
4

MAINTAINING THE METABOLISM OF THE BODY

IN UNICELLULAR forms such as the ameba, the physicochemical structure in the organism is maintained within the limits necessary for life by direct exchange with an external fluid environment. Constancy in the cells of man is maintained by exchange between the cells and the fluids which surround and bathe the tissues, and so constitute an internal, rather than an external, liquid environment. So effective are the mechanisms which serve to maintain the physiologic range of constancy that man can enjoy the freedom of living under a wide variety of conditions involving extremes of environmental temperature, levels and types of activity and differences in the chemical composition of ingested substances. Claude Bernard, a great physiologist of the last century, pointed out that freedom and independence of existence is possible only because of the liquid environment or "milieu interieur," i.e., the lymph or plasma, which "is diffused through the tissues and forms the ensemble of intercellular liquids, and is the basis of all local nutrition and the common factor of all elementary exchanges." It is the purpose of this unit to provide some understanding of how each of the various mechanisms of circulation, respiration, digestion, metabolism, excretion and hormone production contributes to the continual readjustments or reactions preserving the constant physicochemical conditions necessary for life.

297

Chapter
15

Blood

FUNCTIONS OF THE BLOOD VASCULAR SYSTEM

In maintaining the cellular environment constant, the blood vascular system carries out a number of functions. These include:

Respiratory—Conveying oxygen from the lungs to the cells and carbon dioxide from the cells to the lungs.

Nutritive—Carrying glucose, amino acids, fats, minerals and vitamins from the digestive tract to the cells.

Excretory—Transporting waste products of nitrogenous metabolism to the organs of excretion.

Regulatory—Distributing hormones of the ductless glands, such as the thyroid and suprarenals, to the cells which they affect.

Transporting water and other substances to excretory organs with the result that their concentrations are held relatively constant.

Equalizing body temperature and giving off heat from the superficial blood vessels.

Protective—Aiding in the defense of the body against injurious agents by means of the antibodies and white blood cells which it contains.

DESCRIPTION OF THE BLOOD

Blood is a tissue which makes up about one-thirteenth of the total body weight. A man of average size, weighing 65 to 75 kilograms, would thus have 5 to 6 liters of blood. Direct observation of its gross characteristics may be carried out by withdrawing a sample of blood from a vessel and placing it in a test tube with a small amount of oxalate to prevent clotting. The color of a specimen may vary between the brilliant red of arterial blood and the dark red of venous blood, depending upon the amount of oxygen it contains. Determination of its specific gravity shows it to be about 1.05 to 1.06, with viscosity 5 to 6 times greater than water. Blood is slightly alkaline with a pH 7.37 to 7.44.*

If the specimen is centrifuged or allowed to stand for a sufficient length of time, the components of the blood separate so that either

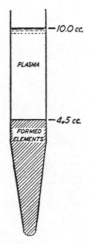

Fig. 191. Separation of the formed elements (cells) of blood from the liquid portion by gravity. (Carlson and Johnson, The Machinery of the Body, University of Chicago Press.)

two or three distinct layers may be seen. At the top of the tube there will be a layer of clear straw-colored liquid, the plasma. If a graduated centrifuge tube is used, it may be seen that the plasma layer constitutes 50 to 60 per cent of the volume of whole blood (Fig. 191). The formed elements, that is, the red and white blood cells and the blood platelets, settle out below the plasma. It is frequently possible to observe a thin layer of the white blood cells, or leukocytes, just below the layer of plasma. The red blood cells, or erythrocytes, and the blood platelets form the bottom layer, which makes up approximately 40 to 50 per cent of the blood volume.

* pH is a means used to express hydrogen ion concentration, i.e., the acidity (or alkalinity) of a solution. A pH of 7.0 is neutral; those more than 7.0 are alkaline and less than 7.0 acid.

THE BLOOD CELLS, OR CORPUSCLES

Erythrocytes. The erythrocytes (Figs. 192, 193) are biconcave discs which show a dumbbell outline when viewed edgewise. The disc has no nucleus. The average diameter is about 7.7 microns. In the embryo the red corpuscles are formed in the liver and in the bone marrow, but in the adult they are formed only in the red bone marrow. Red bone marrow in the adult is found in the sternum, ribs, vertebrae, diploë of cranial bones and proximal epiphyses of femur and humerus.

The erythrocyte develops from the common stem cell of the red

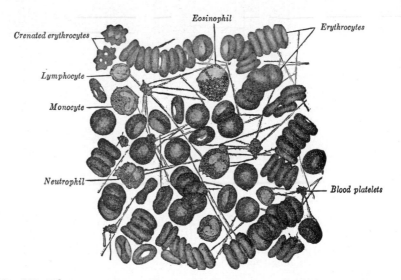

Fig. 192. Fibrin preparation of human blood. Note strands of fibrin. High magnification. (Maximow and Bloom.)

bone marrow, the hemocytoblast. The cell in its immature stages has a nucleus but no hemoglobin. Later it becomes smaller and is colored with hemoglobin. After mitotic divisions cease, the nucleus is extruded and the cell is transformed into an erythrocyte which consists mainly of hemoglobin and the supporting framework, called the stroma. The top row of cells in Figure 194 shows different stages in development.

Fig. 194. Various stages in the development of the cells of human bone marrow stained with Wright's stain. The common stem cell, the hemocytoblast, is not shown. The top row shows stages in the development of an erythrocyte. *Prbl*, a proerythroblast, is the youngest generation; that is, it is closest to the stem cell. *Mybl*, the myeloblasts, are the young forms from which neutrophile, eosinophile and basophile granulocytes develop. (Bailey, Textbook of Histology, Williams & Wilkins Co.)

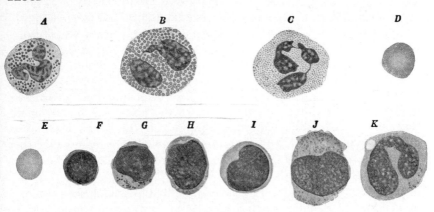

Fig. 193. Blood corpuscles of various types. A, Basophile leukocyte. B, Eosinophile leukocyte. C, Neutrophile leukocyte. D, E, Erythrocytes, F, G, H, I, Lymphocytes. J, K, Monocytes. (Maximow and Bloom.)

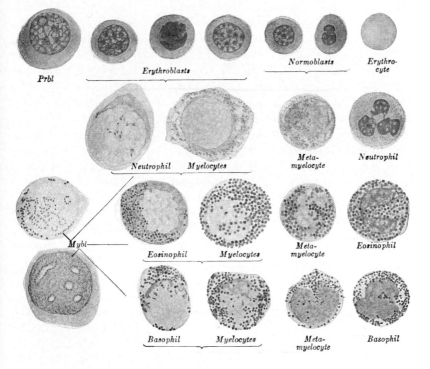

Fig. 194.

Hemoglobin is a conjugated protein composed of an iron-containing compound and a protein. It is believed that the presence of small amounts of copper and cobalt are necessary to act as catalysts in some phase of hemoglobin production. The protein globin is responsible for the oxygenation of hemoglobin to form oxyhemoglobin.

The red cells lead a short but active life. Their functions are to carry oxygen from the lungs to other cells of the body and to aid in the transport of carbon dioxide from those cells to the lungs. Their absolute life span has not been determined, but it is estimated that they survive for eight to 120 days. They are destroyed mainly by the histiocytes of the liver and spleen.

The cell-forming and cell-destroying activities, which proceed at a tremendous rate and in such widely separated organs, appear to be remarkably well correlated, since under normal conditions the number of red cells in each cubic millimeter of circulating blood remains almost constant, between 4.5 to 5.0 million for women and 5.0 to 5.5 million for men. Daily variations, within these limits, of one half million cells are normal and greater transient increases may occur during stress. Our knowledge of the mechanisms by which this physiologic equilibrium is maintained is incomplete. It is known that *hemopoiesis*, i.e., the formation of blood, may be stimulated by a decrease of oxygen in the blood and by an *antianemic principle* present in the liver. The antianemic principle is formed in the stomach and intestine by the interaction of an extrinsic factor from food and an intrinsic factor from gastric juice. It is absorbed through the small intestine, stored in the liver and acts on the bone marrow to bring about the formation of normal erythrocytes (Fig. 195). The interrelationship between the several substances which play a part in normal red blood cell formation is not yet clear. We know that vitamin B_{12} and a protein of mucin (mucoprotein) of gastric juice is effective in the treatment of pernicious anemia. Another vitamin, one of those in the B complex, known as folic or pteroylglutamic acid when injected into the body also stimulates the formation of normal red cells. It is probable that some type of action takes place in the body which converts the folic acid to an active hemopoietic substance.

Leukocytes. The white blood corpuscles, or leukocytes (Fig. 193), are always nucleated and are capable of ameboid movement. The leukocytes are less numerous than the erythrocytes, a cubic millimeter of blood averaging between 5000 and 9000 of these cells. There are several varieties of white blood cells, but they may be divided into

Table 10

The Leukocytes

TYPE	PER CENT OF TOTAL LEUKOCYTE COUNT	DISTINGUISHING CHARACTERISTIC
Granular Leukocytes		
Eosinophils	2–5	About 12 microns in diameter; nucleus consists of two oval lobes; granules stain bright red with Wright's stain
Basophils	0.5	About 10 microns; nucleus irregular in shape, often bent in form of an **S**; granules large, staining dark purplish blue with Wright's stain
Neutrophils	65–75	About 10–12 microns; nucleus has three to five lobes; fine granules give light orchid hue to cytoplasm
Nongranular Leukocytes		
Lymphocytes	20–25	About 8 microns; large nucleus, indented on one side, stains bright purple with Wright's stain; the thin layer of cytoplasm surrounding the nucleus stains robin-egg blue
Monocytes	3–8	Usually about 15 microns (range 12–20); nucleus lobulated, deeply indented or horseshoe shape, stains less densely with Wright's stain than lymphocyte; wide zone of cytoplasm about nucleus stains a grayish-blue color

two main groups: the nongranular leukocytes, or *agranulocytes,* which have no granules in their cytoplasm, and the granular leukocytes, or *granulocytes,* which have distinguishing granules in their cytoplasm.

The granulocytes have lobulated nuclei which show great diversity of form. The polymorphous nature of the nuclei is responsible for another name, *polymorphonuclear* leukocytes, often applied to this group. The granulocytes are classified in three groups according to the type of granules in the cytoplasm: eosinophil, basophil and neutrophil. The nongranular leukocytes are the lymphocytes and monocytes.

The granulocytes function chiefly to protect the body against bacterial invasion. They can change their shape and move about, passing through the wall of the blood vessel and migrating into the tissues. Here they act as phagocytes, engulfing and digesting bacteria, cell fragments and foreign particles.

The granular leukocytes are formed in the red bone marrow from stem cells, the hemocytoblasts, and destroyed by liver histiocytes and by migration into the lumen of the intestines.

The lymphocytes are formed in the lymphoid tissues, including that of the bone marrow. It is thought that the lymphocytes play a role in the repair of tissues. In tissue culture, lymphocytes become transformed into fibrous connective tissue. It is suggested that possibly the lymphocytes undergo the same changes in the body and contribute to the repair of wounds by connective tissue formation. They are fre-

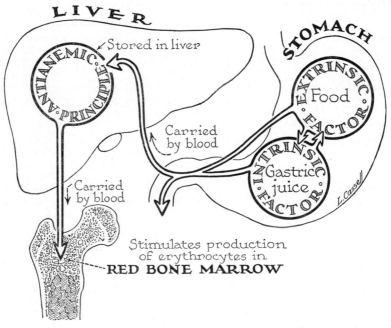

Extrinsic factor + Intrinsic factor = Antianemic principle

Fig. 195. Diagram to illustrate one factor responsible for normal erythrocyte formation.

quently seen in large numbers where healing is taking place or in regions where tissue destruction and repair are going on at the same time.

The monocytes are the largest cells of the blood. There is no general agreement among investigators concerning their origin. They probably develop from the lymphocytes; that is, they are hemocytoblasts that have developed phagocytic properties.

It is currently thought that the life span of leukocytes does not exceed one to two days in circulation.

Platelets. The platelets are small, non-nucleated, disc-shaped bodies. They are formed from the megakaryocytes of the bone marrow. There are about 250,000 in each cubic millimeter of blood and are probably replaced every two to four days. They play an important part in the coagulation of the blood.

PLASMA

The composition of the plasma may be considered from two standpoints: first, it is a part of the vascular *tissue* and therefore contains constituents common to all protoplasm; second, it is a vehicle of transportation and consequently contains materials in transit.

The high water content of the plasma provides the aqueous medium necessary for physiologic processes.

Table 11

Composition of Plasma

ORGANIC CONSTITUENTS—9%		INORGANIC CONSTITUENTS—0.9%		SPECIAL SUBSTANCES—90%	
	Gm. %		*mEq./L.*		*vol. %*
Proteins	7–9	Sodium	150	Water	90
Albumin	4–7	Potassium	4	Blood gases	
Globulin	2–3	Calcium	5	Nitrogen	1
Fibrinogen	0–0.5	Magnesium	2	Oxygen	2.5
		Chlorides	111	Carbon Dioxide	50–60
Nonprotein nitrogenous		Phosphates	3	Antibodies ⎤	
bodies		Sulfates	1	Enzymes ⎬ Variable	
	mg. %	Bicarbonates	28	Hormones ⎪ quantities	
Urea	10–15	Iron ⎤		Vitamins ⎦	
Uric acid	3–4	Copper ⎬	Small		
Creatinine	0–1	Iodine ⎦	amounts		
Creatine	0–4				
Ammonium					
salts	0.1–0.2				
Nutrients					
	mg. %				
Glucose	80–120				
Fatty acid	350				
Cholesterol	120–230				
Cerebroside	15				
Amino acid	4–7				
Phospholipids	180–200				

The *plasma proteins*—fibrinogen, albumin and globulin—make up 7 to 9 per cent of the plasma. They are formed chiefly in the liver.

Small quantities of globulins are produced by lymphocytes and the closely related plasma cells from reticular tissues in the spleen, lymph glands and bone marrow. Antibody chemicals from the globulins will aid in the protection of the body from foreign protein essentially of bacterial origin. Fibrinogen is important in blood coagulation. All of the proteins help to maintain pH, viscosity and osmotic pressure of the blood.

The *inorganic salts* comprise 0.9 per cent of the plasma. They represent a basic constituent of protoplasm found in all cells and necessary for life. They aid in maintaining the osmotic pressure of the blood, in transporting carbon dioxide to the lungs and in keeping the blood slightly alkaline. They consist chiefly of the chlorides, carbonates, bicarbonates, sulfates, phosphates and iodides of sodium, potassium, calcium, magnesium and iron. Sodium chloride (common table salt) constitutes over half of the inorganic salts.

About 20 to 25 milligrams of *nonprotein nitrogenous* bodies are important constituents of the plasma. Urea, uric acid, creatine, creatinine and ammonium salts are breakdown products of protein metabolism. They are waste materials which the blood carries to the kidneys for excretion. The amino acids, on the other hand, are food materials in transport to be used as building stones for new proteins; excess amounts are excreted by the kidneys.

The principal *non-nitrogenous bodies* are sugar and lipids. Glucose, or blood sugar, averages about 0.1 per cent. It is customary to express the amount in terms of the number of milligrams present in 100 cc. of blood: thus 0.1 per cent is expressed as 100 mg. of glucose in 100 cc. of blood. Glucose remains remarkably constant even during all but the final stages of starvation. The value does rise, however, after each meal when carbohydrates are eaten. The excesses are transformed into glycogen and stored in the liver and muscles. As glucose is used up, the stored glycogen is reconverted into glucose. Lipids, consisting of fatty acids, cholesterol, phospholipids, and cerebrosides, are food and building materials in transit to cells or for storage in fat depots. Cholesterol is an essential constituent of the tissue cells and fluids, especially bile. Large quantities of cholesterol are present in nerve tissue and adrenal glands. Cholesterol is related to the formation of vitamin D and the sex hormones. The amount of cholesterol ranges from 120 to 230 mg. in 100 cc. of blood.

The blood gases—oxygen, carbon dioxide and nitrogen—are slightly soluble in water and are therefore carried in small amounts dissolved in the plasma. Larger amounts of carbon dioxide are carried in chemical combination with the bases.

Special substances carried by the blood are enzymes, vitamins, hormones and antibodies.

COAGULATION OF THE BLOOD

The clotting of the blood is an adaptive mechanism necessary to the preservation of life. When a vessel is ruptured, the clot plugs the opening and prevents undue loss of blood. Minute hemorrhages with subsequent clot formation are continually occurring throughout the body.

When blood from a blood vessel is collected in a tube, it is soon changed into a semisolid gelatinous mass, the clot. When examined under the microscope the clot is seen to consist of an interlacing network of fine threads of fibrin, in which blood cells and some fluid are trapped. In a short time the fibrin threads contract; the clot shrinks and solidifies; and a thin straw-colored fluid, the serum, is squeezed out (Fig. 196). Serum, then, is blood plasma minus the fibrin.

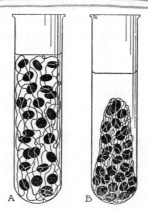

Fig. 196. A, Coagulated blood; the fresh clot, which consists of fibrin strands, corpuscles and serum. B, Coagulated blood after standing some time; clot has contracted and separated from the serum. (Highly diagrammatic.)

Advances in our knowledge of coagulation have shown that a number of our previous concepts are no longer tenable, but have not as yet provided us with a clear picture of what does occur. On certain points there is general agreement. All theories include the transformation of the soluble blood protein, *fibrinogen*, into insoluble *fibrin*. This is brought about by a substance called *thrombin*.

Soluble fibrinogen + thrombin → insoluble fibrin

Thrombin as such is not present in significant amounts in unshed blood; if it were, it would be difficult to explain why clotting does not occur in normal circulating blood. It is thought that this substance exists in the form of a globulin, *prothrombin*. Prothrombin in shed blood is converted into thrombin by the action of calcium salts and *thromboplastin*. There appears to be more than one thromboplastic substance. They are fat-protein compounds of the phospholipid class such as cephalin and the lipoproteins (see page 466). Injured fixed tissues are an excellent source of thromboplastic substance, so that favorable conditions for clotting exist in wounds and in blood vessels in which the endothelium has been damaged. Thus:

$$\text{Prothrombin} + \text{Ca}^{++} + \text{thromboplastin} \rightarrow \text{thrombin}$$

It is thought that the reactions involved in thrombin formation are hastened by accelerator substances in the plasma and the blood platelets. The platelets also appear to influence retraction of the clot once it has been formed.

Blood will clot if it is drawn from a blood vessel even without coming into contact with injured tissue or without the addition of a tissue extract, but clotting under these conditions is a much slower process. Even though the blood contains all the essentials for the formation of thromboplastin, and the accelerators, calcium ions, prothrombin (or its precursor) and fibrinogen, it is common experience that it does not clot in undamaged blood vessels under normal conditions. This may be explained by the fact that (*a*) little, if any, thrombin exists in the blood where there is no destruction of fixed tissues or of the components of the blood itself, and (*b*) such small amounts of thrombin as are formed react with a substance, *antithrombin,* to form an inactive compound *metathrombin*.

Several measures are used in clinical tests to evaluate the coagulating properties of blood. *Bleeding time* is measured by puncturing the skin with a needle or a small lancet, and observing the time for a drop of blood to clot over the wound; normal bleeding time is approximately two and a half minutes. *Coagulation time* is the interval elapsing between the drawing of the blood into a capillary tube or test tube and the formation of the clot. It varies from three to ten minutes in normal persons. *Prothrombin time,* as its name denotes, is the time required for the coagulation of oxalated plasma upon the addition of thromboplastin and calcium chloride; normal clotting times are between twenty-five and thirty seconds.

Clotting of the blood is hastened by contact with injured tissue, contact with foreign surfaces, warming, and by stirring the blood. It can also be hastened by adding certain coagulants such as calcium; thromboplastins from extracts of brain, other tissues, platelets or from some diluted snake venoms; and thrombin from serum, extracts of clotted blood and certain snake venoms. Clotting can be prevented or retarded by cooling, by dilution, and by the addition of oxalates and citrates, heparin, Dicumarol from clover, or hirudin from the head of a leech. Cooling reduces destruction of platelets; oxalates and citrates unite with calcium; heparin acts, probably in combination with antithrombin, to prevent thrombin from reacting with fibrinogen, and possibly in reducing the formation of thrombin from prothrombin; Dicumarol action may be due to a reduction in prothrombin and perhaps interference with one of the accelerator substances; hirudin also is an antithrombin, inactivating thrombin.

Certain hemorrhagic diseases are associated with deficiency of vitamin K in the blood stream. The formation of prothrombin in the liver depends upon the presence of vitamin K. Deficiency of the vitamin results from lack of bile salts in the intestinal tract which are required for the absorption of the vitamin, rather than an absence of vitamin K from the diet. Low levels of prothrombin, in turn, prolong the coagulation time of the blood.

BLOOD TYPING AND Rh FACTOR

A small amount of blood mixed with two testing sera will quickly show the individual's blood type, as indicated in Figure 197. The clumping or agglutination of red blood cells follows a definite pattern based upon inherited blood characteristics. Combination of the *agglutinogens* of the red blood cell with appropriate *agglutinins* of the plasma or serum will cause the red blood cells to adhere to one another in clumps. This pattern of characteristics is grouped as follows:

Group AB serum contains no agglutinins and will not agglutinate other erythrocytes. The cells, however, have A and B agglutinogens.

Group A serum contains *b* agglutinins and cells A agglutinogens.

Group B serum contains *a* agglutinins and B agglutinogens, which are in the erythrocytes.

Group O serum has *a* and *b* agglutinins which will agglutinate erythrocytes of the first three types, while its own cells have no agglutinogens.

Type or group O blood may be used as *universal donor* for blood transfusion to individuals with other blood groups (AB, A, B) since the erythrocytes do not carry agglutinogens, and hence would not be expected to cause agglutination when injected into a recipient. While it might be expected that some reaction could result because of the presence of the *a* and *b* agglutinins, the rapid dilution of the serum ameliorates this effect. Type AB individuals may receive blood transfusions from all other groups since their serum does not contain agglutinins and hence would not be expected to agglutinate the cells of blood from donors of groups A, B, and O. *Crossmatching*, i.e., mixing a drop of donor and recipient blood, will rapidly indicate incompatibility other than these type reactions through additional agglutination.

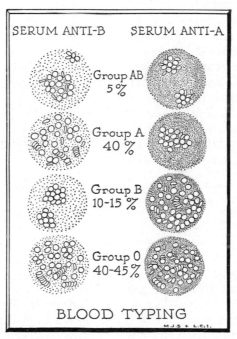

Fig. 197. Blood typing; erythrocytes of groups AB and B carry B agglutinogens and are agglutinated with serum anti-B containing *b* agglutinins. Erythrocytes of group AB and A carry A agglutinogens and are agglutinated by serum anti-A containing *a* agglutinins.

There are other blood groups which can be determined by similar agglutination reactions. Most important of these is the Rh type. In the Caucasian population about 85 per cent of individuals possess this factor, while the remaining 15 per cent do not. However, if a contact occurs between the blood of an Rh positive and an Rh negative individual, the latter will build up agglutinins or *antibodies* in response to the agglutinogens or foreign protein *antigenic* character of the Rh positive blood cells. In subsequent contacts of the two different blood types, agglutination and destruction of erythrocytes may occur.

SUMMARY

In maintaining a constant composition in the internal environment the blood vascular system carries out a number of functions which may be classified as respiratory, nutritive, excretory, regulatory and protective.

Blood makes up about one-thirteenth of the total body weight.

Blood consists of cells and plasma. The cells form 40 to 50 per cent of the volume of whole blood.

The cells of the blood are the erythrocytes or red blood corpuscles, the leukocytes, or white corpuscles, and the platelets.

The erythrocytes are nonmotile, non-nucleated biconcave discs containing hemoglobin. The number in each cubic millimeter of blood is between 4.0 and 5.5 million.

The leukocytes are motile, nucleated cells. The number in each cubic millimeter of blood averages between 5000 and 9000. The two main groups are the granulocytes and agranulocytes.

The platelets are small, non-nucleated bodies, numbering about 250,000 in each cubic millimeter of blood.

The constituents of the plasma may be divided into two groups: those which are common to all protoplasm, and those which represent substances in transit. Ninety per cent of the plasma is composed of water, 7 to 9 per cent of serum proteins, and about 0.9 per cent of inorganic salts.

The clotting of blood is an adaptive mechanism necessary to the preservation of life. The basic principle underlying all theories of coagulation is that a soluble substance, fibrinogen, is changed to an insoluble substance, fibrin, by thrombin.

Clinical tests made to evaluate the coagulating properties of the blood include the determination of bleeding time, coagulation time, and prothrombin time.

Blood typing, crossmatching and Rh determinations may be ascertained by various agglutination reactions.

QUESTIONS FOR DISCUSSION

1. What factors are responsible for maintaining the formed elements of the blood?

2. How are the constituents of plasma maintained at relatively constant values?

3. How is blood typing related to antigen-antibody reactions?

Chapter 16

The Circulatory System: The Heart

ROLE OF THE HEART IN MAINTAINING CIRCULATION OF BLOOD

THE CIRCULATORY system provides for the metabolic requirements of all the tissues of the body over a wide range of activity. In the body at rest this burden is at a physiologic minimum. Increased activity of any cell, tissue or organ results in utilization of more oxygen and nutrient material, and in the formation of greater quantities of carbon dioxide and waste products. The circulatory system meets these additional burdens, and maintains the internal environment within physiologic limits, by increased blood flow to the local area of greater activity or by widespread increase in the blood flow if the body as a whole is involved.

The heart furnishes the power to maintain the circulation of the blood. It expels blood at a pressure sufficient to drive it through the vascular circuit. Part of the energy of the heart beat is used in moving the mass of blood through the circulatory bed, part is used in overcoming the resistance to flow or the friction offered by the blood vessels, and part is expended as filtration pressure in the formation of tissue fluids of the body and of the glomerular filtrate in the process of urine secretion. The amount of blood pumped by the human heart can be determined by several indirect methods, i.e., without actually collecting and measuring the blood. The results of one such study on thirteen men at rest show an average cardiac output of 84 cc. per beat with a *standard deviation* of 17 cc.;[*] the range of values reported for cardiac output in several studies on resting men, using different methods of measurement, is 38 to 108 cc. per beat. When circulatory requirements are increased, the heart responds to the nervous and chemical stimuli which result from greater activity by performing more work. This can be done by increasing either the heart rate or the volume of blood expelled at each heart beat, or by both heart rate and output per beat.

If we assume that when a man is at rest his heart is pumping 70 cc. of blood per beat and his heart rate is 60 per minute, the cardiac output is 70 cc. times 60, or 4200 cc., i.e., 4.2 liters per minute. The output per beat may increase with heart rates up to 80 per minute. If, in a given period of exercise, the heart rate rises to 80 per minute and the output per beat to 200 cc., the resulting cardiac output is 16 liters per minute. At faster rates the output per beat decreases, but since there are a greater number of beats per minute, the cardiac output may continue to increase. Trained athletes may exhibit outputs of 35 or more liters per minute during periods of maximum exertion. At very fast heart rates the minute output starts to decrease, since there is too little time for effective filling of the heart until a condition is reached at which the blood flow can no longer keep up with the demands of the body.

The blood vessels are capable of changing their size in response to appropriate stimuli, so that the circulation through any area may be increased or decreased in proportion to its activity or to the activity of the body as a whole.

The architecture and mechanisms of the circulatory system whereby it performs its role as the "obedient servant" of the body are of great importance to the student of physiology. A summary of some of the factors controlling circulation begins on page 378; reference to this summary should be of assistance to the student in correlating this material during his reading of the following sections on the circulatory system.

[*] The notation, *standard deviation*, is a statistical description of the variation of the individual subjects above and below the average. It means that 68 per cent of the subjects would be expected to have cardiac outputs between 67 cc. (84 cc. — 17 cc. = 67 cc.) and 108 cc. (84 cc. + 17 cc. = 101 cc.) if the results are normally distributed. Averages, to be meaningful, should be accompanied by a notation giving the standard deviation.

ANATOMY

Location of the Heart (Fig. 198).   The heart lies obliquely in the chest behind the sternum and the costal cartilages. Approximately two-thirds of the heart lies to the left of the median plane; the base is directed upward and to the right, the apex downward and to the left. The apex of the heart moves toward the anterior chest wall during contraction, and its beats may be felt in the fifth intercostal space just inside the nipple line about 8 cm. to the left of the midsternal

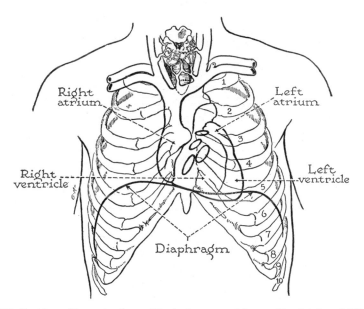

Fig. 198. Position of heart in chest. (Eycleshymer and Jones. Hand Atlas of Clinical Anatomy, Lea & Febiger.)

plane. The heart is situated between the lungs; below it is the diaphragm, and above it are the great vessels.

Pericardium (Fig. 199).   The heart is enclosed in a double-walled membranous sac. Its relations may be visualized by thinking of a ball pushed into a completely closed bag or slightly distended balloon. The layer which is next to the heart and adherent to it is the visceral pericardium, or epicardium. The layer forming the outer wall of the bag is the parietal pericardium. This is reinforced and strengthened on the outside by a layer of white fibrous tissue which is continuous with the fibers of the central tendon of the diaphragm. The heart and the beginnings of the great vessels completely fill the pericardial cavity, and under normal conditions the visceral pericardium is in contact with the parietal layer. The smooth serous surfaces are kept moist and are lubricated by a small amount of serum.

Structure of the Heart. The heart is a hollow muscular organ, roughly cone-shaped, about the size of the fist. It is completely divided by a partition into right and left halves. Physiologically, it functions

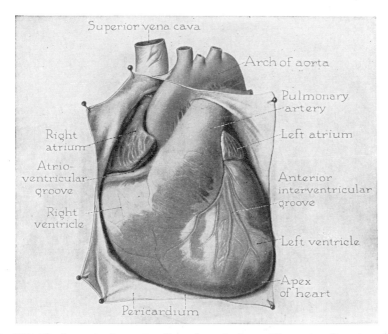

Fig. 199. The heart in the pericardium, from in front. The pericardium is opened from in front. (Sobotta and McMurrich.)

as two pumps, the right side forcing blood through the pulmonary circulation for exchange of gases in the lungs, while the more muscular left side pumps blood through the systemic circulation. Each half of the heart is divided into an upper chamber, the *atrium*, and a lower chamber, the *ventricle*. The division of the heart into four chambers is indicated on the external surface by grooves or sulci. The atria are separated from the ventricles by an encircling constriction, the coronary (atrioventricular) sulcus. The ventricles are separated by two grooves, the anterior and posterior longitudinal (anterior and inferior interventricular) sulci. Internally, the atria are separated by the interatrial wall, which is marked by a depression, the fossa ovalis (see Fetal Circulation, page 356). The right and left ventricles are separated by the interventricular septum (Fig. 200).

The walls of the heart in both atria and ventricles consist of three layers, an inner, the endocardium, a middle, the myocardium, and an outer, the epicardium or visceral pericardium.

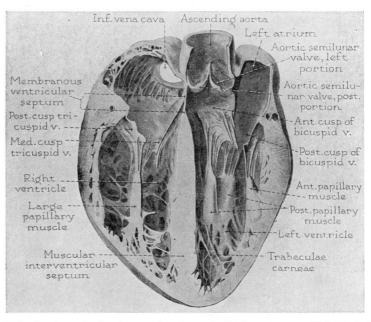

Fig. 200. Section of the heart, showing ventricular septum. (Modified from Spalteholz.)

The *endocardium* is an epithelial lining of the chambers of the heart completely covering the tissues in contact with the blood. It is continuous with the endothelial linings of the blood vessels entering and leaving the heart.

The *myocardium* consists of layers or bands of heart muscle which form complex patterns in the atria and ventricles. These muscular layers are relatively thin in the atria, but thick in the ventricles. Such an architectural arrangement is well adapted to function, since the burden of pumping the blood falls upon the ventricles. The walls of the left ventricle, which is responsible for forcing blood through the systemic circulation at high pressure and against considerable resistance, are three times the thickness of the right ventricular walls (Fig. 200). The right ventricle maintains the circulation of blood through the pulmonary circuit at a relatively low pressure. The myocardium of the atria is separated from that of the ventricles by yellow fibrous tissue except at one point where a specialized muscle band, the atrio-ventricular bundle of His, connects the atria with the ventricles.

The epicardium or visceral pericardium consists of a single layer of mesothelial cells supported by a small amount of connective tissue.

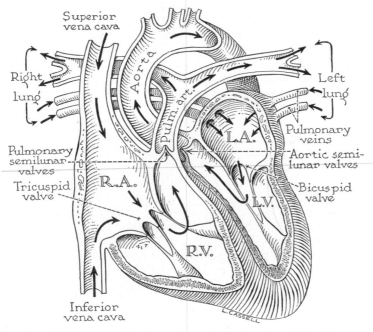

Fig. 201. Diagram of the heart, showing the direction of blood flow.

THE OPENINGS OF THE HEART CHAMBERS AND THE HEART VALVES (Fig. 201). There are openings in the heart for the great veins, the aorta and the pulmonary artery, and between the right atrium and right ventricle, and left atrium and left ventricle. The orifices between the atria and ventricles and between the ventricles and aorta and pulmonary artery are guarded by heart valves which permit the passage of blood in one direction only. If the heart is to function effectively as a pump, valves are necessary at these points, or energy will be wasted in pumping blood in the wrong direction. The valves consist

Valves) are composed

of membranous leaflets which are opened or closed by the pressure of the blood.

The right atrium shows four openings, two for the venae cavae, and one for the coronary sinus, which return the blood from the systemic circulation to the heart, and a fourth, the atrioventricular orifice. The superior vena cava, carrying venous blood from the head, thorax, and upper extremities, enters the posterior wall from above. The inferior vena cava, which drains the trunk and lower extremities, enters the posterior wall from below. These orifices are without valves, but, since the pressure developed in the atrium is low, the amount of blood forced back into the veins during cardiac contraction is slight. The atrioventricular orifice leading to the right ventricle is guarded by the tricuspid valve. This valve has three leaflets which open down into the ventricle when it is relaxed, and the pressure within the ventricle is less than that within the atrium. When the ventricle becomes filled with blood and starts to contract, these leaflets are floated into position and forced shut by the increased pressure. The valve is prevented from turning back into the atrium by tendinous chords, the *chordae tendinae,* which pass from the edges of the leaflets to muscular pillars, the *papillary muscles,* which project from the wall of the ventricle.

The right ventricle has, in addition to the atrioventricular orifice, a second opening, the pulmonary orifice, located more superficially and near the base of the heart. The pulmonary semilunar valves have three pocket-like leaflets which permit blood to flow from the ventricle into the pulmonary artery during ventricular contraction. When the ventricle relaxes and the pressure falls below that in the pulmonary artery, the leaflets are floated shut and closed tightly by back flow of blood from the pulmonary artery into the pocket-like depressions on the arterial side of the valve.

The left atrium has four openings for the pulmonary veins which return oxygenated blood from the lungs. On the floor of the atrium lies the left atrioventricular orifice; this is guarded by the bicuspid or mitral valve, which has two cusps. It permits blood to flow from atrium to ventricle, but prevents regurgitation of blood into the atrium during ventricular contraction. As is the tricuspid valve, the bicuspid valve is reinforced by chordae tendinae and the papillary muscles.

The left ventricle has the atrioventricular and aortic orifices. Semilunar valves lie at the aortic opening. They are similar to the pulmonary semilunar valves in structure and in action.

The following diagram shows the course of the blood through the heart and indicates the relationship of heart chambers, valves and vessels (Fig. 201).

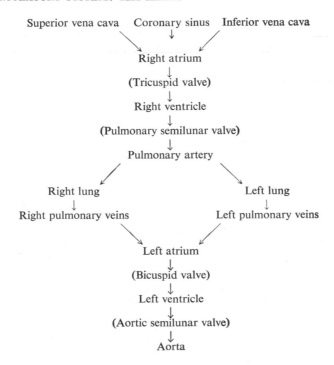

Superior vena cava   Coronary sinus   Inferior vena cava

Right atrium

(Tricuspid valve)

Right ventricle

(Pulmonary semilunar valve)

Pulmonary artery

Right lung   Left lung

Right pulmonary veins   Left pulmonary veins

Left atrium

(Bicuspid valve)

Left ventricle

(Aortic semilunar valve)

Aorta

THE HEART BEAT

Origin and Propagation of the Heart Beat. Cardiac muscle has, in addition to the properties common to all types of muscle, the property of inherent rhythmicity. Hearts which have been severed from all nervous connections or even removed completely from the body will continue to beat for some time if cared for properly. The hearts of cold-blooded animals continue to beat for relatively long periods of time with little or no attention; they serve well for studies of the properties of the heart.

The turtle heart, which is structurally different from the mammalian heart, has a sinus venosus, two atria and a single ventricle. If these three parts are divided into two parts by cutting between the sinus and the atria, both portions will begin to beat after a short period. The sinus will beat first, and then after a short period the atria and ventricle will start. The sinus beats at a faster rate than the lower portions of the heart. If a second cut is now made between the atria and the ventricle, the atria continue to beat and usually the ventricle recovers its rhythmic contractions, but at a slower rate than that of the atria. From this experiment it may be seen that the property of inherent rhythmicity is common to all chambers of the heart, but that the rate of contraction is highest for the sinus, slower for the atria and slowest for the ventricle. In the intact turtle heart the sinus is called the pacemaker of the heart, since, because it shows the most rapid rhythm, it sets the pace for the atria and ventricle.

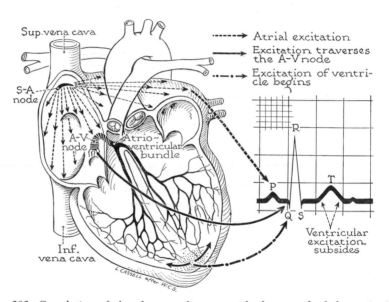

Fig. 202. Correlation of the electrocardiogram with the spread of the excitation wave.

Sinu—Atrial node = pacemaker of heart he

In the mammalian heart there is a small mass of specialized tissue, the sinu-atrial (S-A) node, located in the right atrium near the superior vena cava; this area serves as the pacemaker under normal conditions. The same gradient of rhythmicity between pacemaker, atria and ventricles is evident in the mammalian heart. The mechanism underlying rhythmicity is still obscure, but it is well established that the heart beat originates at or in the immediate vicinity of the sinu-atrial node.

The wave of excitation (Fig. 202) spreads throughout the right and left atria, the impulse traveling in the muscular tissue of their walls and causing the contraction of these chambers. On the lower part of the inner wall of the right atrium there is a second mass of specialized tissue, the *atrioventricular* (A-V) *node.* Continuing from the atrio-ventricular node, a bundle of conducting fibers, the bundle of His, passes down to the upper border of the interventricular septum, where it divides into a right and left branch. Each of these divisions passes to the corresponding ventricle, giving off numerous branches which form an interlacing network beneath the endocardium and ending in the papillary muscles and the ventricular tissue generally. The atrio-ventricular node acts as a relay station which picks up impulses that pass from the region of the sinu-atrial node, and after a brief delay transmits them to the ventricles through the atrioventricular bundle of His. Impulses reach both ventricles at approximately the same time and cause them to contract. To summarize: the wave of contraction in the mammalian heart is initiated at or close to the sinu-atrial node, radiates throughout the muscular wall of the atria, perhaps preferen-tially through an intra-atrial band between the atria, and by the most direct route to the atrioventricular node; impulses excite the atrio-ventricular nodal tissue and after a slight delay are transmitted to the ventricles through the bundle of His.

In certain abnormal conditions the region of the sinu-atrial node does not act as a pacemaker. If this occurs, the beat may originate in the center having the next highest rate of rhythmic discharge. Thus either the atrioventricular node or the atria may act as pacemaker, or, when conduction is blocked, the ventricles may beat at their own inherent rhythm.

The rate of discharge of the pacemaker which determines heart rate is normally modified by changes in its chemical environment, by temperature and by influence of the cardiac nerves. The control of heart rate is discussed in Chapter 19.

Sequence of Events in a Cardiac Cycle. In a single beat of the heart the atria and ventricles go through a succession of events which are repeated at each beat. The sequence of events during one heart beat is spoken of as a "cardiac cycle." During a cardiac cycle the term *systole* is given to the contraction phase and *diastole* to the relaxa-tion phase. We use the terms "atrial systole" and "diastole," "ventricular systole" and "diastole" to indicate the state of activity of the heart chambers.

In a single cardiac cycle atrial systole is followed closely by ven-tricular systole. Atrial systole is completed and the atria enter the diastolic phase as ventricular systole begins. Ventricular systole is followed by diastole of the ventricles. For a short time the entire mass of cardiac tissue is relaxed, since a part of the diastolic phases of the atria and ventricles overlaps. Atrial systole is again initiated as a second cardiac cycle begins.

The absolute duration of the phases of the cardiac cycle varies with the heart rate, the length of both the diastolic and systolic phases shortening as the heart rate increases. With a fast heart rate the diastolic phase shortens proportionately more than the systolic phase. When the heart is beating at a rate of 70 per minute, the duration of a cardiac cycle is about 0.8 second. Atrial systole lasts 0.1 second, atrial diastole 0.7 second; ventricular systole 0.3 second, diastole 0.5 second. The relationship of atrial and ventricular cycles is shown in Figure 203. The diastolic periods of the two chambers overlap for 0.4 second, during which brief period the entire heart is quiescent.

Some events of the cardiac cycle may be reviewed by following the course of blood through the heart (Fig. 201) and systemic and pulmonary circulations:

SYSTEMIC CIRCULATION

Oxygenated blood from the pulmonary circulation enters the left atrium from the pulmonary veins during atrial diastole. As the left ventricle relaxes and the intraventricular pressure falls, the mitral (bicuspid) valve opens and the blood enters the left ventricle. Blood flowing from the pulmonary veins, through the atrium into the left ventricle, accomplishes the greater part of ventricular filling.

Left atrial systole begins and completes ventricular filling. The contractions of the atria aid, but are not the chief factor, in filling the ventricles.

As the left ventricle fills and atrial systole continues, the two leaflets of the mitral valve are floated into position.

During the latter part of atrial systole, ventricular systole is initiated and the pressure in the ventricle rises, closing the mitral valve.

After a period of isometric contraction, with the ventricular chamber closed off, the intraventricular pressure rises above aortic pressure and the aortic semilunar valves open.

PULMONARY CIRCULATION

Venous blood from the systemic circulation is returned to the right atrium by the superior and inferior venae cavae during atrial diastole. As the right ventricle relaxes and the intraventricular pressure falls, the tricuspid valve opens and the blood enters the right ventricle. Blood flowing from the venae cavae through the atrium and into the right ventricle accomplishes the greater part of ventricular filling.

Atrial systole begins; it completes ventricular filling.

As the right ventricle fills and atrial systole continues, the leaflets of the tricuspid valve are floated into position.

Ventricular systole is initiated and the pressure in the right ventricle rises, closing the tricuspid valve.

Intraventricular pressure rises during isometric contraction until it exceeds the pressure in the pulmonary artery, and the semilunar valves open.

SYSTEMIC CIRCULATION

The left ventricle is contracting at the same time as the right ventricle. Blood passes through the aortic semilunar valves into the aorta, where it is distributed through branches which ramify to all parts of the body. Blood travels from these branches into capillaries which supply all the tissues. The capillaries unite to form veins; the blood from the veins of the lower part of the body is collected into the inferior vena cava, while that of the upper extremities and head region drains into the superior vena cava. Finally the superior and inferior venae cavae return blood to the right atrium to complete the systemic circuit.

About the time the semilunar valves open and the ventricles begin to empty their contents into the aorta, left atrial diastole begins.

As the emptying of the ventricles continues, the left intraventricular pressure falls below that of the aorta, and blood starts to flow back toward the heart and closes the semilunar valves.

The bicuspid (mitral) valve opens and filling of the left ventricle begins.

PULMONARY CIRCULATION

The pulmonary artery divides into right and left branches and carries blood to the lungs, where it passes through an intricate network of capillaries lying in close relation to the air sacs of the lungs. Here the blood takes up oxygen and gives off carbon dioxide. The coalescence of the capillaries gives rise to the pulmonary veins, two coming from each lung to enter the left atrium. This brings oxygenated blood to the left side of the heart and completes what is known as the pulmonary circuit.

Right atrial diastole begins.

As right intraventricular pressure falls below that of the pulmonary artery, a momentary reversal of blood flow closes the pulmonary semilunar valves.

As diastolic intraventricular pressure falls below atrial pressure, the tricuspid valves open and a new cardiac cycle begins.

From the foregoing account it follows:

1. That the heart plays the role of a compound pump placed between and connecting the two circulations.
2. That the right side of the heart contains only venous blood which is deficient in oxygen and laden with carbon dioxide; the left side of the heart contains only oxygenated blood.
3. That the right side of the heart is related to the pulmonary circulation and the left side to the systemic circulation.
4. That the atria are the receiving chambers; that is, vessels entering the heart come into the atria, and that the ventricles are the discharging chambers; vessels leaving the heart emerge from the ventricles.

Simultaneous Events in the Cardiac Cycle.   It is possible to arrange a series of records showing the changes in the ventricular volume and ventricular pressure, atrial pressure, aortic pressure, heart sounds and an electrocardiogram, so that simultaneous events in the cardiac cycle

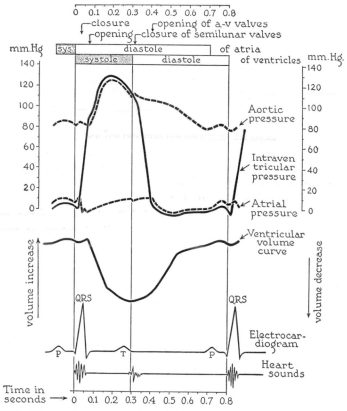

Fig. 203. Curves showing simultaneous changes in the ventricular volume and ventricular pressure, atrial pressure, aortic pressure, heart sound and electrocardiogram.

become apparent. The pressure changes are discussed in Chapter 19; the electrocardiogram and heart sounds are dealt with in the following paragraphs. It has been necessary to redraw the records to a common scale so that the characteristic tracing of events in each record can be compared at any moment in the cardiac cycle. The phases of the cardiac cycle and valve action are indicated on the diagram. Diligent analysis and study of the simultaneous curves in Figure 203 will well repay the student for his effort, for such a chart unfolds the story of related circulatory events.

Electrocardiograms. Electrical changes occur in the heart during contraction. Like all tissues, active cardiac muscle fibers are electrically negative to resting fibers. By the use of an electrocardiograph, a type of recording galvanometer, the electrical differences which occur from moment to moment in the various regions of the heart can be led off from the surface of the body by electrodes placed on the extremities, and on the chest. By using the three standard leads the manifest potential differences, i.e., the potential differences in the heart as recorded at the body surface, are taken between the following points:

Lead   I—between right arm and left arm
Lead II—between right arm and left leg
Lead III—between left arm and left leg

Other leads between the chest and an arm or leg, or between a common terminal carrying leads I, II, III, and the chest, are used for further detailed study of heart action.

The records obtained are called electrocardiograms (Figs. 202, 203). The electrocardiogram shows a series of deflections separated by segments of the record showing no deflections. Contraction of the atria causes an initial deflection, the P wave, followed by an *isoelectric* end-of-P to R segment, during which all atrial tissue is in a homogeneous and active state, so that there are no potential differences between the various areas of the atria (see p. 320). Ventricular systole is signaled by the QRS wave; this is followed by the isoelectric S-T segment, during which all the ventricular muscle fibers are contracting; as some of the ventricular fibers start to relax, another deflection, the T wave, occurs. The segment from the end of the T to the beginning of the P wave indicates the period when both the atria and ventricles are in a homogeneous, inactive state.

The electrocardiogram shows vertical white lines indicating time intervals (0.04 and 0.20 second), so that it is possible to determine the duration of any deflection or iso-electric segment, or interval, corresponding to the events of the cardiac cycle. The records are important physiologically and clinically, because they not only indicate normal activity, but also reveal abnormalities in the sequence of events in the cardiac cycle, in heart rhythm, in conduction or spread of impulses, and in the condition of the muscle fibers. For example, if the intervals between successive QRS waves are equal, we know that the heart is beating regularly; if the interval between the beginning of the P wave and the beginning of the QRS wave is normal, we know that conduction between the sinu-atrial node and the ventricles is unimpaired; where the deflections show their characteristic shapes, and the segments between the deflections are neither above nor below the isoelectric line, the spread of excitation and relaxation is proceeding normally; if the amplitudes of the waves are within normal limits, the active muscle fibers are in a normal physiologic condition. Deviations from these well-defined characteristics of normal electrocardiograms reveal abnormal cardiac conditions.

The Heart Sounds. Two audible sounds occur during each heart beat. They may be detected by placing the ear against the chest wall or by listening with a stethoscope. The sounds can be described by the syllables *lubb-dupp*. The first sound is low-pitched and of relatively long duration. This sound is best distinguished at the left fifth interspace of the ribs at the apex region of the heart. It is caused by closure of the atrioventricular valves and the contraction of the ventricular muscle. The main vibrations of the first sound occur about the same time as the QRS wave of the electrocardiogram (Fig. 203). The second sound is short, sharp, high-pitched and audible at right or left sternal borders and the second interspace of the ribs. It is produced by the closure of the semilunar valves at the beginning of ventricular diastole and would thus coincide roughly with end of the T wave of the electrocardiogram (Fig. 203).

Variations in the duration or in the character of the heart sounds are of great value in detecting certain clinical cardiac abnormalities.

SUMMARY

The heart furnishes the power to maintain the circulation of the blood.

The heart lies obliquely in the chest behind the sternum and costal cartilages, approximately two-thirds of it to the left of the median plane, with the apex directed downward and to the left.

The heart lies between the lungs; below it is the diaphragm, and above it are the great vessels.

The heart is enclosed in a double-walled membranous sac, the pericardium.

There are four chambers in the heart: two upper chambers, the atria, and two lower chambers, the ventricles.

The walls of the heart are composed of three layers: an inner epithelial layer, the endocardium, a middle muscular layer, the myocardium and an outer serous layer, the epicardium or visceral pericardium.

The wave of contraction in mammalian hearts is initiated in the sinu-atrial node, radiates throughout the muscular walls of atria, is picked up at the atrioventricular node and transmitted to the ventricles through the bundle of His.

The sequence of events during one heart beat is spoken of as the cardiac cycle. When the heart is beating at a rate of 70 per minute, the duration of a cardiac cycle is about 0.8 second. Atrial systole lasts 0.1 second, atrial diastole 0.7 second; ventricular systole 0.3 second, diastole 0.5 second. The diastolic period of the two chambers overlaps for 0.4 second, during which brief period the entire heart is quiescent.

Tracing the course of the blood through the heart reveals the following important points.

1. The heart plays the role of a compound pump placed between and connecting the two circulations.
2. The right side of the heart contains only venous blood, which is deficient in oxygen and laden with carbon dioxide; the left side contains only oxygenated blood.
3. The right side of the heart is related to the pulmonary circulation and the left side to the systemic circulation.
4. The atria are the receiving chambers; that is, vessels entering the heart come into the atria. The ventricles are the discharging chambers; vessels leaving the heart emerge from the ventricles.

Records of the changes in ventricular volume, ventricular pressure, atrial pressure, aortic pressure, heart sounds and the electrocardiogram, are arranged to show the relations of the events of the cardiac cycle.

The electrocardiogram is a magnified photographic record of the deflections of the galvanometer string produced by the electric currents given off by the heart during contraction.

The sounds of the heart are described by the syllables *lubb-dupp*. The first sound is caused by the closure of the atrioventricular valves and the contraction of ventricular muscle. The second sound is produced by the closure of the semilunar valves at the beginning of ventricular diastole.

QUESTIONS FOR DISCUSSION

1. How does the heart function in providing for oxygenation of the blood?

2. In the electrocardiogram what conditions of cardiac muscle are indicated by an isoelectric line? How are the P, QRS, and T waves associated with the action of the heart?

3. How does the activity of the heart compare with that of skeletal muscle?

Chapter
17

The Circulatory System: The Blood Vessels and Circulation

ORGANIZATION AND STRUCTURE OF THE BLOOD VESSELS

THE BLOOD vessels of the body fall into three principal classes, each of which is characterized by both functional and structural differences. There is the high pressure distributing system made up of the arteries and smaller branches, the arterioles, which carry oxygenated blood from the heart to all regions of the body. Then there is a system of minute vessels through which substances are exchanged between the blood and the tissues. Finally, there is a low pressure collecting system, made up of venules and veins, which return the blood to the heart.

Arteries. The largest vessel of the arterial system, the aorta, is about 25 mm. (1 inch) in diameter in man. It gives off branches of various sizes, which in turn divide and subdivide into smaller and smaller vessels. Where major arteries divide into two equal branches, the angles at the bifurcations are such that they cause a minimum interference with blood flow; lesser arteries arising more centrally from major vessels are given off at nearly right angles. This architectural arrangement favors equalization of pressure in corresponding

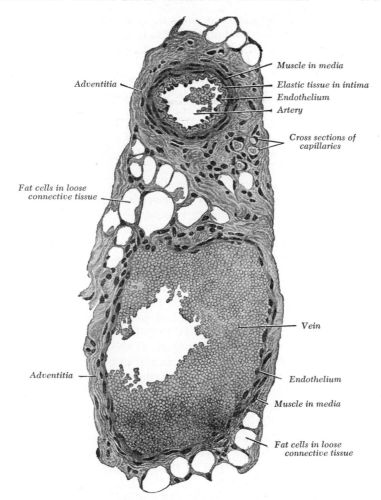

Fig. 204. Cross section through a small artery and its accompanying vein from the submucosa of a human intestine. (Maximow and Bloom.)

parts of the arterial system; the pressure within the smaller arteries is approximately the same whether they arise centrally from an artery of large caliber or peripherally as the result of numerous subdivisions.

Three layers can be distinguished in the walls of every artery (Fig. 204): (1) the inner coat, the tunica intima, (2) the intermediate coat, or tunica media, and (3) the external coat, or tunica adventitia. The structural detail of each of the three layers varies somewhat with the size of the artery.

The *tunica intima* is composed of a smooth layer of endothelial cells and a conspicuous band of elastic tissue. In the larger vessels there is a fine network of connective tissue between the endothelial and elastic layers.

The *tunica media* consists mainly of smooth muscle and elastic tissue. The elastic tissue predominates in the larger arteries, and the smooth muscle in the small arteries.

The *tunica adventitia* is made up of a loose arrangement of collagenous and elastic tissues. In small and medium sized arteries the adventitia is as thick as or thicker than the media, but in large arteries the external coat is very thin.

The Minute Vessels of the Capillary Bed. The distal portions of the arterial tree are made up of arterioles which lead into a system of minute vessels. These minute vessels, which display several types of structural design, are spoken of collectively as capillaries and the system of vessels as capillary beds. They constitute the functional units of the circulatory system for distribution and exchange of substances between the blood stream and the tissue fluid and body cells. They form the anatomical units connecting the arterial and the venous systems. Blood flows along rapidly in the arteries and veins, but in the tremendously expanded vascular bed provided by the capillary areas where it flows into a multitude of minute tubes, it is slowed down so that the stream passes leisurely through the network of vessels. This allows time for the exchange of material to occur.

Considerable variation in the detailed arrangement of the minute vessels has been observed. One view currently held is that the greatest differences in architectural pattern are between those units supplying tissues in which the nutritional requirements change markedly with functional activity, and those providing for tissues in which metabolic activities remain relatively constant. It is probable that there is a wide variety of patterns, differing in detailed arrangements, intermediate between the two extremes.

In skeletal muscle, and in the gastrointestinal tract, where the level of activity is subject to wide variations, many of the units of minute blood vessels follow the same general architectural organization. There are two more or less parallel routes, one direct and one indirect, between the most distal portions of the distributing system and the collecting system. The direct route, formed by a continuation of the arteriole, is the preferential or *thoroughfare channel;* the proximal portion of this thoroughfare channel is called a *metarteriole.* The less direct route consists of a precapillary sphincteric offshoot, called a *precapillary,* which may branch either directly from an arteriole or from a metarteriole, to lead into an interanastomosing network of *true capillaries;* a *postcapillary,* which collects the blood from the network of true capillaries, may connect with either the venous end of the thoroughfare channel or directly with a *venule.*

The thoroughfare channels, in the units supplying skeletal muscle and the gastrointestinal tract, may be structurally differentiated only in the region of the metarteriole, or throughout their length. They show a distinct though not well developed muscular element, the muscular coat of the arterial portion being more prominent. The precapillaries are characterized by sphincteric muscular elements. The true capillaries are formed by a single layer of pavement-like endothelial cells bound together by an intercellular cement substance; they have a noncellular endocapillary lining, formed, perhaps, by absorption of blood protein, and a pericapillary sheath made up of fine supporting fibrils. The musculature of the arterioles, metarterioles and precapillaries allows for adjustment and progressive restriction of blood flow through the minute vessels of the vascular bed. When the tissues are relatively inactive, the blood flow may be directed chiefly to the thoroughfare channels. As activity is increased, more frequent relaxation of the precapillaries will increase the flow through the network of true capillaries, thus providing for a greatly increased area and a greater rate of metabolic exchange. Continuation of flow through the thoroughfare channels, even when the blood flow through the true capillaries is greatly increased, may be an important factor in maintaining the pressure relations, or pressure gradient, between the arterial and venous sides of the circulatory system.

In tissues which maintain a relatively constant level of activity the organization of units of the minute vessels is less well defined; in fact, there appears to be no discernible pattern. There may be no apparent structural differentiation between what appears to be thoroughfare channels and the true capillaries, although muscular precapillaries may be seen leading to the capillary network, which average about 8 microns. When viewed through the microscope, the red cells may be seen through the transparent walls of the vessels. Frequently they may be seen passing in single file.

Blood leaving the distributing system, then, may pass through either the thoroughfare channel or the capillary network. The size of the minute vessels varies, but is closely related to that of the red blood corpuscles. Ample time for exchange is allowed by relatively slow blood flow through this vascular bed.

ARTERIOVENOUS SHUNTS.   There is still another alternative route for the blood in some areas of the body; these are *arteriovenous shunts* which provide direct, noncapillary communications between the terminal arterioles and the distal venous vessels. They are relatively numerous in the skin covering the fingers, toes, nose, lips and ears. They play a role in the regulation of temperature of tissues in these regions which are intimately exposed to variations in environmental temperature.

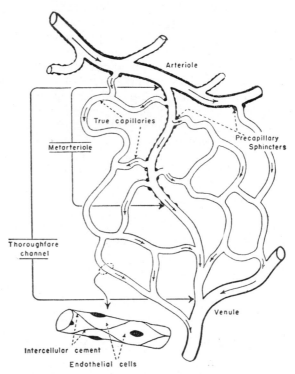

Fig. 205. Schematic diagram of ideal capillary bed according to Chambers and Zweifach. Distribution of muscle is indicated by the heavier wall thickness. Note limited distribution along thoroughfare channel and precapillary sphincters. Insert is a highly magnified portion of true capillary wall. There is reason to believe that most exchange of solutes takes place through the small area of intercellular cement rather than through the endothelial cells. (Sketch by Thomas E. Nelson, Jr.; from Fulton: Textbook of Physiology, Ed. 17.)

Veins. The veins comprise a system of vessels which collect the blood from the capillaries and return it to the heart. The structure of veins (Fig. 204) resembles that of the arteries, and usually the three layers, intima, media and adventitia, can be distinguished. The veins, however, have thinner walls than the arteries and are less elastic, owing to the poorly developed middle layer, which is thin and contains little smooth muscle and elastic tissue.

In general, veins which are greater than about 1 mm. in diameter are equipped with valves (Fig. 206). These appear as semilunar pockets, or intimal folds, on the inner surface of the vein, with their free edges lying centrally in the direction of the blood flow. This arrangement affords little interference with blood flow toward the heart, but is effective in preventing a reversal of the direction of flow. Valves are most numerous in the veins of the lower extremities. They are absent in the venae cavae and in the veins of the intestine.

DESCRIPTION OF THE SYSTEMIC ARTERIES AND VEINS

Divisions and Branches of the Aorta. The *aorta* and its branches constitute the entire arterial supply of all parts of the body (Fig. 207). The aorta arises from the left ventricle. Arching backward and to the left, it descends along the vertebral column to the level of the fourth lumbar vertebra, where it ends by dividing into the right and left common iliac arteries. For purposes of description it may be divided into ascending aorta, arch of the aorta, thoracic aorta and abdominal aorta. The main *branches of the aorta* are as follows:

Ascending aorta   Coronary arteries

Arch of aorta
- Innominate { Right common carotid / Right subclavian
- Left common carotid
- Left subclavian

Thoracic aorta
- Intercostal
- Superior phrenic
- Esophageal
- Bronchial

Abdominal aorta
- Inferior phrenic
- Celiac artery
- Superior mesenteric
- Inferior mesenteric
- Suprarenal
- Renal
- Spermatic or ovarian
- Lumbar
- Common iliac (terminal branches)
- Middle sacral

ASCENDING AORTA.   The only branches from the short ascending portion of the aorta are the right and left *coronary arteries* (Fig. 208), which supply the heart with blood.

THE ARCH OF THE AORTA.   The *innominate artery* is a short artery of large diameter which arises as the first branch from the aortic arch.

It passes upward and to the right for a short distance and then divides into right subclavian and right common carotid arteries.

The left *common carotid* arises directly from the aorta. The common carotid arteries, right and left, pass upward in the neck under cover of the sternocleidomastoid muscles. At the upper border of the thyroid cartilage each artery divides into external and internal carotid arteries. At this point of bifurcation of the common carotid there is a small sinus or dilated portion of the vessel known as the carotid sinus.

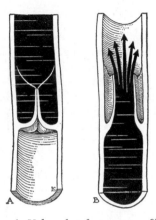

Fig. 206. Valves of a vein. *A,* Valve closed, cusps are filled with blood. *B,* Valve open, blood is passing through.

The *external carotid* artery (Fig. 209) passes upward in the neck to the angle of the jaw, where it enters the substance of the parotid gland. It continues upward in that structure to just below the zygomatic arch, where it ends by dividing into terminal branches. It gives off numerous branches to the neck, face and scalp. From below upward the principal branches are superior thyroid, lingual, external maxillary, occipital, and the terminal branches, internal maxillary and superficial temporal. The names of the vessels indicate in a general way the parts they supply. The external maxillary curves upward over the body of the mandible and passes obliquely across the face to the side of the nose. The internal maxillary, under cover of the ramus of the mandible, passes forward to the deep structures of the face and the coverings of the brain. The superficial temporal, apparently a direct continuation of the external carotid, passes up the side of the head in front of the ear and gives branches to the face and scalp.

The *internal carotid* artery (Fig. 209) passes up almost vertically in the neck in front of the transverse processes of the upper three

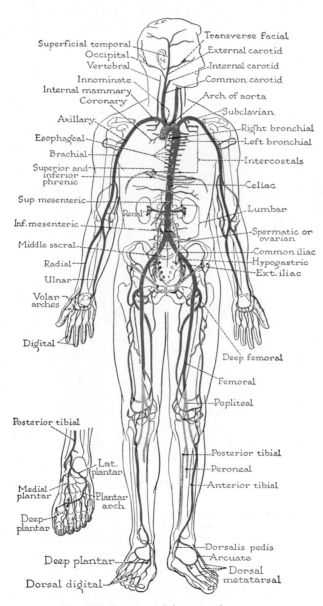

Superficial temporal
Occipital
Vertebral
Innominate
Internal mammary
Coronary
Axillary
Esophageal
Brachial
Superior and inferior phrenic
Sup. mesenteric
Inf. mesenteric
Middle sacral
Radial
Ulnar
Volar arches
Digital
Posterior tibial
Medial plantar
Deep plantar
Deep plantar
Dorsal digital

Transverse facial
External carotid
Internal carotid
Common carotid
Arch of aorta
Subclavian
Right bronchial
Left bronchial
Intercostals
Celiac
Renal
Lumbar
Spermatic or ovarian
Common iliac
Hypogastric
Ext. iliac
Deep femoral
Femoral
Popliteal
Posterior tibial
Peroneal
Anterior tibial
Lat. plantar
Plantar arch
Dorsalis pedis
Arcuate
Dorsal metatarsal

Fig. 207. Diagram of the arterial system.

cervical vertebrae and enters the cranium through the carotid canal in the petrous portion of the temporal bone. Passing forward, it makes a sigmoid curve along the body of the sphenoid bone, gives off ophthalmic and posterior communicating arteries, and ends by dividing into terminal branches, anterior cerebral and middle cerebral.

The *subclavian* arteries, right and left, arise differently on the two

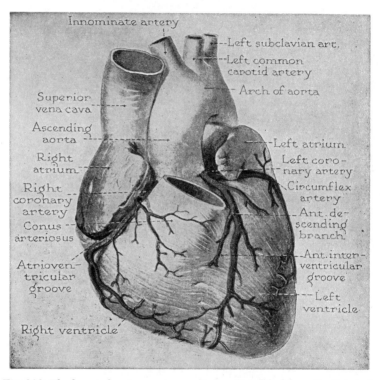

Fig. 208. The heart, showing coronary arteries. (Modified from Spalteholz.)

sides of the body. (Figs. 207, 213). The right subclavian artery is a branch of the innominate; the left arises as the third branch of the aortic arch. Each vessel arches in the neck slightly above the clavicle and passes outward toward the axilla, giving off numerous branches. An important branch, the *vertebral* artery (Fig. 209), passes upward through the foramen in the transverse processes of the cervical vertebrae and, curving around the atlas, enters the cranial cavity through the foramen magnum. A short distance above the foramen the anterior and posterior spinal branches are given off. They pass downward in the vertebral canal to supply the spinal cord. At the upper border of the medulla the vertebral artery unites with its fellow of the opposite side to form the basilar artery, which continues along the midline of the pons to its anterior border, where it ends by dividing into posterior cerebral arteries. The *posterior cerebral* arteries join posterior communicating branches from the internal carotid artery to form the

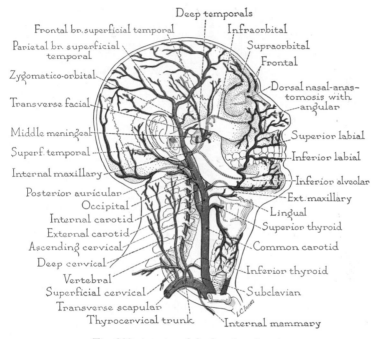

Fig. 209. Arteries of the head and neck.

arterial circle, the circle of Willis (Figs. 210, 211), at the base of the brain. Branches from the circle are distributed to parts of the brain.

Posteriorly, the circle is formed by the posterior cerebral arteries, at the sides by the posterior communicating arteries, and in front by the first portions of the anterior cerebral arteries. Anteriorly, the circle is completed by the anterior communicating artery which unites the two anterior cerebral arteries.

Another major branch of the subclavian, the *internal mammary* artery (Fig. 207), passes downward on the inner surface of the chest wall close to the sternum. It gives off branches which supply muscles of the chest wall and abdomen, the diaphragm, mammary glands, pericardium, pleura, trachea, bronchi and thymus gland.

The continuation of the subclavian artery through the axillary space is called the *axillary artery;* in the arm it is known as the *brachial artery.* A little below the bend of the elbow the brachial divides into *radial* and *ulnar* branches (Fig. 212). The ulnar ends in the super-

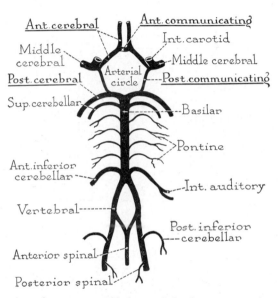

Fig. 210. Diagram of arteries at the base of the brain. Arterial circle (circle of Willis). Labels of the arteries forming the circle are underlined.

ficial volar arch; the radial terminates in the deep volar arch. The arches anastomose and give off the digital branches to supply the hand.

THE THORACIC AORTA (Figs. 207, 213). The branches of the thoracic aorta fall naturally into two groups: the parietal branches, which supply the walls of the cavity, and the visceral branches, which supply the organs within.

The parietal branches are the intercostal and superior phrenic arteries. The intercostal arteries arise in pairs, and pass laterally in the intercostal spaces to supply the intercostal muscles, chest muscles, mammary glands and pleura. They anastomose near the sternum with branches of the internal mammary artery. The superior phrenic arteries supply the posterior and superior surfaces of the diaphragm.

The visceral branches are the bronchial and esophageal arteries. The bronchial arteries, right and left, are the nutrient arteries of the lungs; they are distributed chiefly along the bronchi. The esophageal arteries, usually four or five in number, arise from the front of the aorta to form a network of vessels over the esophagus.

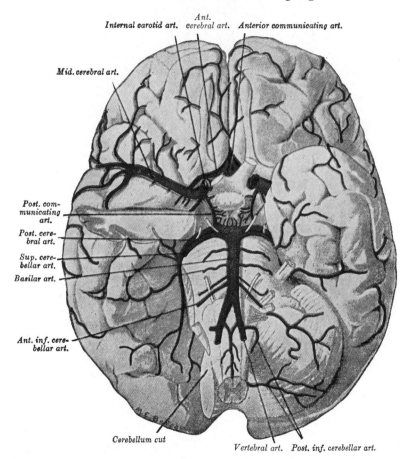

Fig. 211. Arteries at the base of the brain; circle of Willis. (Ranson, The Anatomy of the Nervous System.)

THE ABDOMINAL AORTA (Figs. 207, 213). The branches of the abdominal aorta, like those of the thoracic aorta, may be divided into parietal and visceral groups.

The parietal branches are the inferior phrenic, the lumbar, and middle sacral arteries. The inferior phrenic arteries supply the inferior

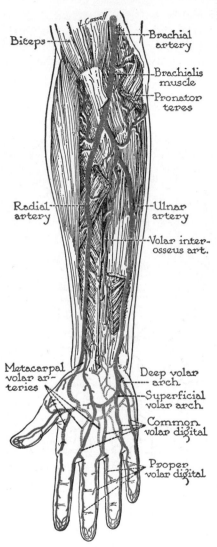

Fig. 212. Arteries of the forearm and hand. (Modified from Cunningham.)

surface of the diaphragm. The lumbar arteries, four pairs of vessels corresponding to the intercostal arteries, supply the posterior and lateral walls of the abdomen. The middle sacral artery arises from the back of the aorta a little above its bifurcation. It descends in the

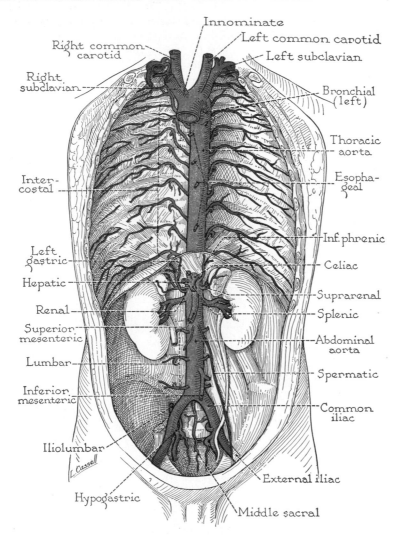

Fig. 213. The aorta and its branches. (After Spalteholz, modified and redrawn.)

midline anterior to the fourth and fifth lumbar vertebrae, the sacrum and the coccyx to supply the pelvic wall.

The visceral branches include the celiac, superior mesenteric, suprarenal, renal, ovarian or spermatic, and inferior mesenteric arteries.

The *celiac* artery is a short thick trunk arising from the front of the aorta just below the diaphragm. It divides into three large branches, the hepatic, left gastric, and splenic arteries. The *hepatic* artery is the nutrient artery of the liver and, in addition, supplies part of the stomach, head of the pancreas, duodenum and gallbladder. The *left gastric* supplies part of the stomach and esophagus. The *splenic artery,* the largest branch of the celiac artery, supplies the spleen, part of the pancreas, and part of the stomach.

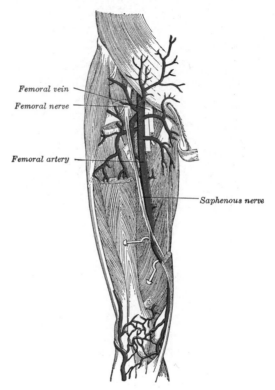

Fig. 214. The femoral artery. (After Gerrish.)

The *superior mesenteric* artery arises from the anterior surface of the aorta just below the celiac artery. It supplies all of the small intestine with the exception of the first part of the duodenum. It is distributed also to the cecum, ascending and part of the transverse colon.

The *inferior mesenteric* artery arises from the aorta just above its bifurcation. It supplies part of the transverse colon, the descending colon, sigmoid colon and greater part of the rectum.

The *suprarenal* arteries arise one from either side of the aorta just below the celiac artery. These arteries, together with similar branches from the inferior phrenic and renal arteries, supply the suprarenal glands (Figs. 213, 298).

The *renal* arteries are two short wide vessels arising from the sides of the aorta. They pass laterally to the kidneys.

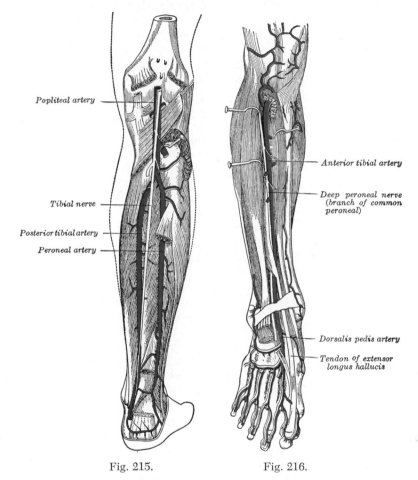

Poppliteal artery

Tibial nerve

Posterior tibial artery

Peroneal artery

Anterior tibial artery

Deep peroneal nerve
(branch of common
peroneal)

Dorsalis pedis artery

Tendon of extensor
longus hallucis

Fig. 215.   Fig. 216.

Fig. 215. Arteries of leg and foot, posterior. (After Gerrish.)
Fig. 216. Arteries of leg and foot, anterior. (After Gerrish.)

The *ovarian* arteries of the female are two long but slender vessels which arise from the aorta just below the renal vessels. They descend into the pelvis to supply the ovaries and terminate by joining the uterine artery.

The *spermatic* arteries of the male correspond to the ovarian of the female. They supply the testes.

The *common iliac* arteries are the terminal branches of the aorta. Arising opposite the fourth lumbar vertebra, they pass downward and laterally to end at the lumbosacral junction by dividing into hypogastric and external iliac arteries.

The *hypogastric* arteries descend into the pelvis and give off branches which supply pelvic viscera (Fig. 213). The branch supplying the uterus is the uterine artery. The inferior vesical and posterior hemorrhoidal branches supply the prostate gland. Posterior branches pass backward to supply muscles of the buttocks.

The *external iliac* artery passes along the brim of the pelvis; after giving off branches to the walls of the abdomen and pelvis, it slips under the inguinal ligament. From this point on, like the subclavian, it receives different names along its course: in the thigh from the inguinal ligament to the knee, it is called the femoral artery (Fig. 214); behind the knee, the popliteal artery; and in the leg, the anterior and posterior tibial arteries (Figs. 215, 216).

The *femoral artery* supplies the skin and muscles of the thigh, the lower part of the anterior abdominal wall, the external genitalia and the hip joint.

The *anterior tibial* supplies the front part of the leg and terminates in the *dorsalis pedis* artery, which supplies the dorsal aspect of the foot and toes.

The *posterior tibial* artery is the direct continuation of the popliteal artery. One large branch, the peroneal, supplies structures on the lateral side of the leg. In the foot the posterior tibial passes below the medial malleolus, where it divides into the medial and lateral plantar arteries, which supply the sole of the foot. The plantar arch is formed by the anastomosis of the lateral plantar artery with the deep plantar branch of the dorsalis pedis.

The Systemic Veins (Fig. 217). In general, the veins accompany the arteries, but certain points of difference are to be noted: First, the veins are distributed in two sets, superficial and deep veins. Second, within the skull, channels in the dura mater called venous sinuses connect the veins of the brain with the internal jugular vein. Third, the blood from the digestive tract is returned by a special system of vessels, the portal system.

For purposes of description, it is simpler to start with the veins entering the heart and proceed peripherally to describe the vessels which join together to form them. This method is used for each of the successive peripheral branches which form the next most central vein.

Three veins return the blood of the systemic system to the heart.

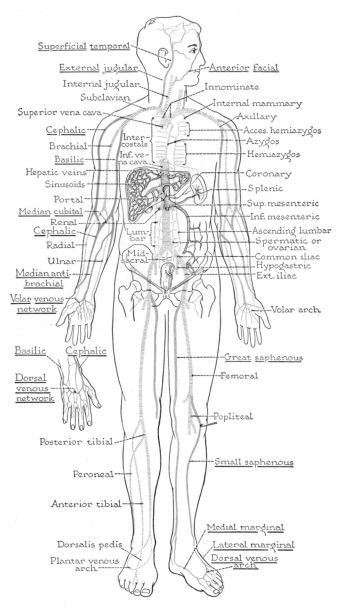

Fig. 217. Diagram of the venous system. Deep veins are cut across, superficial veins are in solid blue. The labels of the superficial veins are underlined. Vessels of the portal system are in black.

They are the coronary sinus, the superior vena cava and the inferior vena cava.

THE CORONARY SINUS.   The coronary sinus is a wide venous channel on the posterior surface of the heart. It receives most of the veins of the heart and opens directly into the right atrium.

THE SUPERIOR VENA CAVA.   The superior vena cava is formed by the union of the two innominate veins and drains the head, neck, thorax and upper extremities. It receives one important tributary, the *azygos* vein; this vessel begins in the abdomen as a continuation of

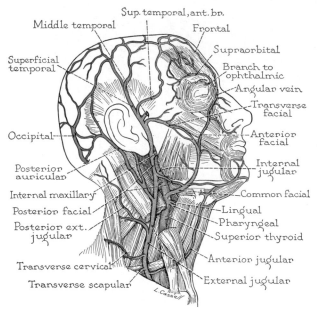

Fig. 218. Superficial veins of the head and neck.

the ascending lumbar, a tributary of the inferior vena cava. The azygos vein receives the hemiazygos veins, the right intercostal veins, several esophageal and pericardial veins and, near its termination, the right bronchial vein. Briefly, then, the azygos vein and its tributaries comprise a system of vessels for the return of blood from the thorax to the superior vena cava. The azygos vein also forms a connecting link, through the ascending lumbar, between the venae cavae returning blood from above and below the heart.

The right and left *innominate* veins are formed by the union of the internal jugular with the subclavian veins.

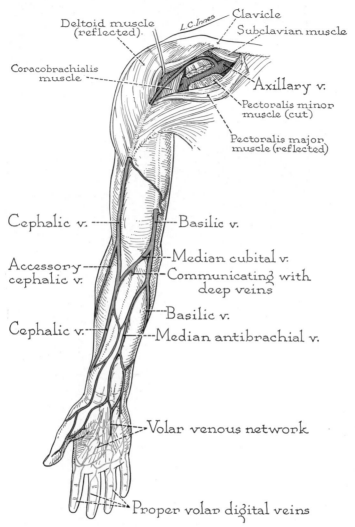

Deltoid muscle (reflected).

L.C.Innes

Clavicle

Subclavian muscle

Coracobrachialis muscle

Axillary v.

Pectoralis minor muscle (cut)

Pectoralis major muscle (reflected)

Cephalic v.

Basilic v.

Median cubital v.

Accessory cephalic v.

Communicating with deep veins

Basilic v.

Cephalic v.

Median antibrachial v.

Volar venous network

Proper volar digital veins

Fig. 219. Superficial veins of the anterior surface of the upper extremity.

The head and neck regions are drained by two large veins, the external and internal jugular veins (Fig. 218). The *external jugular* vein receives blood mainly from the face, scalp, and neck; the regions supplied by the external carotid artery. The *internal jugular* vein receives blood from the brain through the venous sinuses and from the veins of the face and neck. The veins of the upper extremity drain

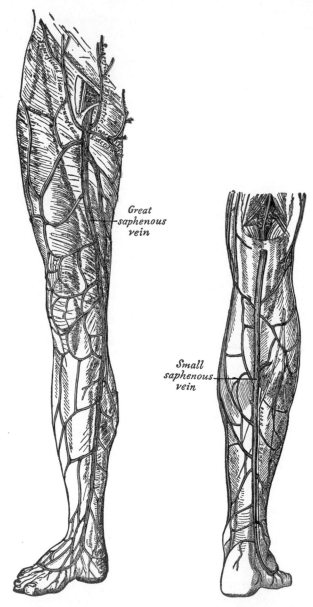

Fig. 220. The great saphenous vein and its tributaries. (Gray, Anatomy of the Human Body, Lea & Febiger.)

Fig. 221. The small saphenous vein. (Gray, Anatomy of the Human Body, Lea & Febiger.)

into the subclavian veins. The external jugular vein flows into the subclavian just before the latter unites with the internal jugular to form the innominate.

The deep veins of the upper extremity accompany the arteries and have the same names: axillary, brachial, radial and ulnar. There are two large superficial veins, the *cephalic* and *basilic* (Fig. 219). Both arise from the dorsal venous network of the hand. The cephalic begins on the radial side of the venous network, follows the lateral surface of the arm, and empties into the axillary vein. The basilic begins on the

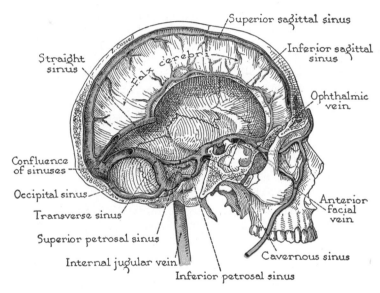

Fig. 222. Venous sinuses of the dura mater.

ulnar side of the network and joins with the brachial to form the axillary. The *median cubital* vein is an oblique connection from cephalic to basilic at the antecubital fossa. The *median antibrachial* vein, also a tributary of the basilic, begins in the volar network of the hand.

THE INFERIOR VENA CAVA. This vessel begins at the level of the fifth lumbar vertebra, where it is formed by the union of the right and left common iliac veins. It accompanies the aorta in its course along the posterior abdominal wall and receives parietal and visceral branches. The parietal branches are the lumbar, the midsacral and inferior phrenic veins. Important visceral tributaries are the suprarenal, the renal, the ovarian or spermatic, and the hepatic veins. The left spermatic in the male or ovarian in the female and the left suprarenal vein empty into the left renal vein. The blood from the portal system is returned to the inferior vena cava through the *hepatic* veins.

The deep veins of the lower extremity, as in the upper extremity, follow the same course as the arteries. The two main superficial veins of the lower extremity are the *great saphenous* and the *small saphenous* (Figs. 220, 221). The great saphenous begins at the medial end of the dorsal venous arch of the foot and passes upward along the medial side of the leg and thigh to open into the femoral. The small saphenous begins at the lateral end of the dorsal venous arch of the foot and ends in the popliteal.

VENOUS SINUSES. The venous sinuses are channels which lie between two layers of the dura mater. They receive the cerebral veins and are drained by the internal jugular veins. The location of the principal sinuses is shown in Figure 222. The blood from the superior sagittal sinus flows (usually) into the right transverse sinus, through which it passes to the right internal jugular vein. The blood from the inferior sagittal sinus flows into the straight sinus, which opens usually into the left transverse sinus, which in turn passes into the left internal jugular vein. The confluence of sinuses, opposite the internal occipital protuberance, is the point at which several sinuses meet. The cavernous sinus connects with the veins of the face, and it drains into the transverse sinuses.

SYSTEMIC CIRCULATION

Having completed the description of the systemic arteries and veins, we shall now trace the circulation to various parts of the body and follow the main systemic arteries through which the blood courses to reach each part and the principal systemic veins by which it is returned to the heart.

This description of circulation includes the following: (1) the coronary circulation, (2) circulation in the right upper extremity, (3) circulation in the lower extremity, and (4) circulation in the organs of the digestive system.

Coronary Circulation. The heart muscle is supplied from the right and left coronary arteries. These two vessels arise directly from the aorta just distal to the aortic semilunar valves and pass outward to circle the base of the heart like a crown. The left coronary artery supplies the left ventricle and may supply either the anterior half or the entire intraventricular septum; in some persons it may also serve parts of the right ventricle adjoining the septum. The right coronary artery supplies the right ventricle and may supply the posterior part of the intraventricular septum and part of the posterior region of the left ventricle.

The left coronary artery divides into two branches, the *circumflex artery* and the *anterior descending branch*. The circumflex artery runs

in the atrioventricular groove toward the left and around to the posterior aspect of the heart, where it turns downward toward the apex.
The anterior descending branch runs along the interventricular groove
toward the anterior aspect of the apex. The right coronary artery runs
in the atrioventricular groove toward the right and ends in several
descending branches on the posterior surface of the right ventricle.

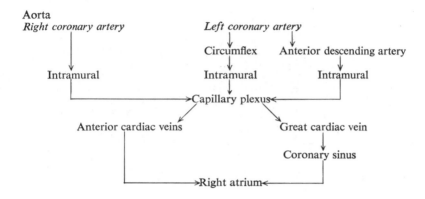

Intramural branches leave the main coronary vessels to pass inward
toward the heart chambers, and break up into extensive capillary
plexuses. There are extensive anastomoses between the terminal vessels
of the arteriolar tree, between the branches of the right and left coronary arteries and between branches of the same artery, but it appears
unlikely that they are functional in normal healthy hearts; they do,
however, supply potential alternate routes if interference with the
circulation in one area or another develops gradually. The arteries and
arterioles also give off vessels which connect directly with the heart
chambers; these are the arterioluminal vessels, which are arteriolar
in structure, and the arteriosinusoidal vessels, which break up into
sinusoids between the muscle bundles.

If we follow the blood through the capillary plexuses, we find that
the capillaries, as in other parts of the body, coalesce to form cardiac
veins which in general correspond to the arteries. Blood is returned
to the heart through the great cardiac vein, by way of the *coronary
sinus,* which opens into the right atrium, and by numerous anterior
cardiac veins, each of which has its own opening directly into the right
atrium. There are also potential alternate venous routes, the Thebesian
vessels, which run between either the capillaries or the veins and the
ventricular cavities, but it has not been demonstrated that these are
functional in the normally beating heart of man.

The simplified diagram of the coronary circulation should be studied with the knowledge that some alternate routes or potential alternate routes exist.

Circulation in the Right Upper Extremity.   The blood, on its way to the right arm, leaves the left ventricle of the heart through the ascending portion of the aorta and is returned to the right atrium by the superior vena cava. Figures 207 and 217 show the vessels through which the blood passes. They are as follows:

Ascending aorta
Aortic arch
Innominate artery
Subclavian artery
Axillary artery
Brachial artery

Radial and Ulnar arteries

Superficial and deep volar arches
Digital arteries
Arterioles
Capillaries
Venules
Digital veins

Superficial and deep volar venous arches

Radial and Ulnar veins

Brachial vein
Axillary vein
Subclavian vein
Innominate vein
Superior vena cava
Right atrium

Superficial Veins

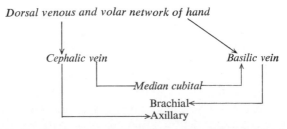

Dorsal venous and volar network of hand

Cephalic vein   *Basilic vein*

←*Median cubital*

Brachial←
→Axillary

Circulation in the Lower Extremity.   The blood which passes to the lower extremity leaves the left ventricle of the heart through the aorta and is returned to the right atrium by the inferior vena cava.

Its course may be traced on Figures 207 and 217. The vessels through which the blood passes are as follows:

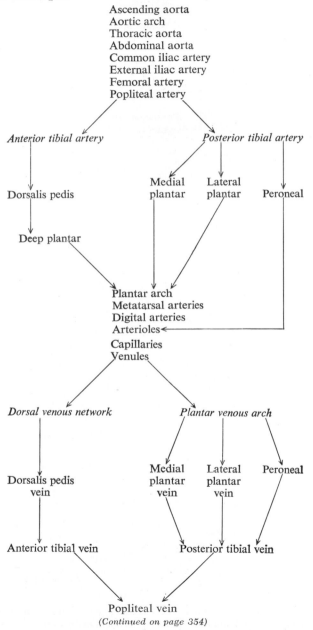

Ascending aorta
Aortic arch
Thoracic aorta
Abdominal aorta
Common iliac artery
External iliac artery
Femoral artery
Popliteal artery

Anterior tibial artery   *Posterior tibial artery*

Dorsalis pedis   Medial   Lateral
                              plantar   plantar   Peroneal

Deep plantar

                    Plantar arch
                    Metatarsal arteries
                    Digital arteries
                    Arterioles ←
                    Capillaries
                    Venules

Dorsal venous network   *Plantar venous arch*

Dorsalis pedis   Medial   Lateral   Peroneal
vein   plantar   plantar
                            vein   vein

Anterior tibial vein   Posterior tibial vein

                    Popliteal vein
                    (Continued on page 354)

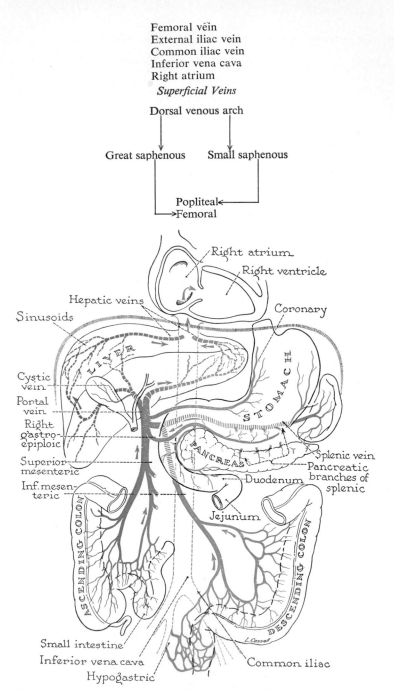

Femoral vein
External iliac vein
Common iliac vein
Inferior vena cava
Right atrium
Superficial Veins

Dorsal venous arch

Great saphenous   Small saphenous

Popliteal
Femoral

Right atrium
Right ventricle

Hepatic veins   Coronary
Sinusoids
LIVER
STOMACH
Cystic vein
Portal vein
Right gastro-epiploic
PANCREAS
Splenic vein
Superior mesenteric
Pancreatic branches of splenic
Inf. mesenteric
Duodenum
ASCENDING COLON
Jejunum
DESCENDING COLON
Small intestine
Inferior vena cava
Common iliac
Hypogastric

Fig. 223. The portal system of veins. The transverse colon and small intestine have been partially removed and the organs separated in order to show the vessels.

Circulation in the Organs of the Digestive System. The organs of the digestive system below the diaphragm are supplied by the celiac, superior mesenteric and inferior mesenteric arteries. The corresponding veins which return the blood from the digestive organs make up the portal system. The unique feature of the portal system is that the blood is detoured through the liver instead of being returned directly to the inferior vena cava. The cells of the liver effect many changes in the blood in order to prepare it for entrance to the general circulation. The vessels of this circuit (shown in Figs. 207, 217, and 223) are as follows:

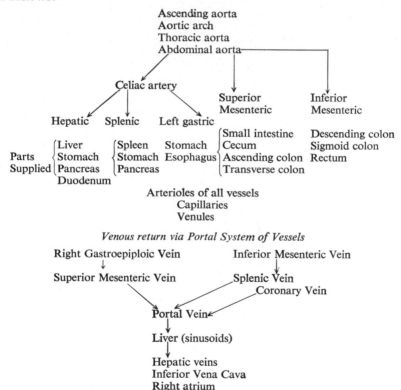

Ascending aorta
Aortic arch
Thoracic aorta
Abdominal aorta

Celiac artery

Superior Mesenteric

Inferior Mesenteric

Hepatic   Splenic   Left gastric

Parts Supplied

{ Liver
Stomach
Pancreas
Duodenum

{ Spleen
Stomach
Pancreas

Stomach   Esophagus

{ Small intestine
Cecum
Ascending colon
Transverse colon

Descending colon
Sigmoid colon
Rectum

Arterioles of all vessels
Capillaries
Venules

Venous return via Portal System of Vessels

Right Gastroepiploic Vein   Inferior Mesenteric Vein

Superior Mesenteric Vein   Splenic Vein
                                                              Coronary Vein

Portal Vein

Liver (sinusoids)

Hepatic veins
Inferior Vena Cava
Right atrium

FETAL CIRCULATION

The growth of the embryo is dependent upon nutrition. In oviparous animals the yolk of the egg supplies food for growth. In viviparous animals such as man, which develop the embryo within the body of the mother, the yolk material of the egg is small and the struggle for food begins early. In such forms the feeding layer, the trophoblast (later the chorion), eats its way into the tissues of the uterus. The digestion of these tissues stimulates the uterus to form a protective wall, and from a combination of chorion and uterus the placenta is constructed.

The oxygenated blood from the placenta is carried to the embryo by the *umbilical vein*. The blood from the embryo is returned to the placenta by two *umbilical arteries*. The general circulatory plan of the fetus may be shown by tracing the course of the blood through the umbilical vein until it returns by way of the umbilical arteries. The umbilical vein traverses the umbilical cord from placenta to umbilicus and, on entering the body of the embryo, passes upward along the free margin of the peritoneum to the inferior surface of the liver to join the portal vein. The blood in the umbilical vein empties into the portal vein and is taken to the liver. The liver is not able to accommodate the blood coming to it from both portal vein and umbilical vein, and relief is afforded by the development of a short but wide vessel, the *ductus venosus*, by which most of the blood is shunted into the inferior vena cava. On entering the inferior vena cava the oxygenated blood mixes with the blood returned from the lower extremities and passes into the right atrium of the heart. From the right atrium the blood passes through the *foramen ovale* to the left atrium. Only a small amount of blood enters the left atrium from the pulmonary veins. This joins with the blood which has entered through the foramen ovale and passes into the left ventricle. On contraction of the ventricle the blood is sent into the aorta and through its branches is distributed to all parts of the body except the lungs. The blood returning through the superior vena cava enters the right atrium and, passing by the stream from the inferior vena cava, enters the right ventricle. At ventricular systole, blood is forced into the pulmonary artery and on to the lungs. However, since the lungs of the fetus are not inflated and can use only small amounts of blood, the greater portion passes from the pulmonary artery into the aorta through a short connecting vessel, the ductus arteriosus.

By means of the *ductus arteriosus* the blood returned from the head and upper extremities enters the aorta and is carried to abdominal

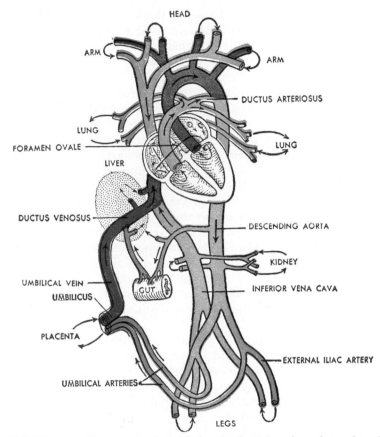

Fig. 224. Diagram of human circulation before birth. Colors show the quality of the blood, and arrows indicate its direction of flow. (Arey, partly after Dodds.)

organs and the lower extremities. On reaching the point of division of the common iliac arteries, the blood stream separates; the main portion goes into the umbilical arteries and is carried to the placenta.

During fetal life the oxygenation of the blood is carried on by the placenta; at birth this function is taken over by the lungs. Although placental circulation ceases quickly, there is no sudden overloading of the previously inactive parts of the vascular system. The heart and great vessels develop in a manner that keeps the pumping load on the different parts of the heart balanced at all times during intra-uterine life. Certain structures present in the fetal heart, the ductus arteriosus and the foramen ovale, provide channels by means of which the volume of blood in the right and left halves of the heart is equalized.

When the lungs begin to function, some of the fetal vessels and passages fall into disuse. The old channels are abandoned suddenly, but the structural occlusion is a gradual process of fibrosis which proceeds slowly in the months after birth.

With the first few breaths of the newborn infant, the ductus arteriosus closes and the blood previously shunted to the aorta now goes to the active lungs. The increase in the flow of blood to the lungs augments the volume of blood returned to the left atrium by the pulmonary veins. With increase in the pulmonary return, the compensating flow through the foramen ovale decreases and finally ceases altogether. Closure of the foramen ovale then follows as the atrial intakes are equalized. The ligation of the umbilical cord stops the flow of blood in the umbilical vessels, which are gradually obliterated by fibrous invasion. The proximal portion of the umbilical arteries remains as the functional hypogastric arteries; the distal or obliterated portions form the umbilical ligaments, extending from the bladder to the umbilicus beneath the peritoneum. The course of the umbilical vein is represented by a fibrous cord and is called the round ligament (Fig. 266, p. 436) of the liver. The remains of the ductus venosus appear as a fibrous band on the inferior surface of the liver.

In summarizing, it may be pointed out (1) that the placenta serves as a respiratory, nutritive and excretory mechanism for the fetus; (2) that the liver receives blood directly from the placenta by way of the umbilical vein—hence the large size of this organ during fetal life and at birth; and (3) that blood distributed to the head and upper extremities is less contaminated than that passing to the lower half of the body.

SUMMARY

The walls of every artery consist of three layers: the inner coat, or tunica intima, the middle coat, or tunica media, and the external coat, or tunica adventitia.

The intima is composed of epithelial tissue and a band of elastic tissue.

The tunica media consists mainly of smooth muscle and elastic tissue.

The adventitia is made up of collagenous and elastic fibers in loose arrangement.

The veins have thinner walls, but show the three layers described for the arteries. The media is poorly developed. Some veins have valves.

The capillaries are extremely fine, thin tubes. The walls consist of a single layer of squamous cells.

Blood may pass by several pathways from arterial to venous side of circulation. Arteriovenous shunts by-pass the capillary bed. Metarterioles connect arterioles to venules in a thoroughfare channel, or the blood may pass slowly through the true capillaries. The extensive networks of minute vessels provide a structurally advantageous arrangement for exchange of fluids, gases, nutrient and waste materials; they provide too for adjustment of the blood supply to a level consistent with the degree of activity of the tissue, or to changes in the internal environment.

The systemic circulation consists of all the arteries, veins and capillaries of the body except those of the lungs.

The arterial system is composed of the aorta and its branches. The aorta is divided for convenience of description into ascending, arch, thoracic and abdominal portions.

The venous system is composed of the superior and inferior vena cava and their tributaries. In general, the veins accompany the arteries and have the same names. The points of difference to be noted are:

1. Two sets of veins, superficial and deep.
2. Venous sinuses of dura mater.
3. The portal system, which returns blood from the digestive tract.

The description of the systemic circulation includes the coronary circulation, circulation in the upper and lower extremities and circulation in the digestive system.

The fetal circulation involves an arrangement by which an exchange of materials is effected between the blood of the embryo and that of the mother. The oxygenated blood from the placenta is carried to the embryo by the umbilical vein; the blood from the embryo is returned to the placenta by two umbilical arteries.

QUESTIONS FOR DISCUSSION

1. How does the arterial side of the systemic circulation compare to the venous side of the circuit in structure and function?

2. Of what value are the arrangements found in the (a) minute vessels, (b) circle of Willis, (c) portal circuit, (d) foramen ovale, (e) superficial and deep veins and (f) coronary circuit?

Chapter
18

Some Physical Aspects
of the Circulation:
Measurement
of
Blood Pressure

Observations on Blood Pressure. If a small artery is cut, blood will spurt from the point of injury to a considerable height. The column of blood will rise and fall, reaching its maximum height during cardiac systole and the minimum during diastole. This demonstrates that the blood within the arteries is under pressure and that the pressure varies with the phase of the cardiac cycle. The peak, which occurs during ventricular systole, is called systolic pressure; the minimum value, which occurs during ventricular diastole, is known as diastolic pressure. The arithmetic difference between systolic and diastolic pressures is called the pulse pressure. Blood pressure is measured in terms of the height of the column of mercury which it is capable of supporting. The values for systolic and diastolic pressure are customarily given as systolic pressure/diastolic pressure or

$$\frac{\text{systolic pressure}}{\text{diastolic pressure}}, \text{ e.g., } 120/80 \text{ or } \frac{120}{80}.$$

In young adults, under conditions of rest, the *systolic blood pressure* is about 120 mm. of mercury (Hg) and the *diastolic pressure* is 80 mm. of mercury. The significance of these values may perhaps be more readily grasped if the pressures be translated into the height to which they would raise a column of water. Let us visualize an experiment in which an artery is connected to a vertical glass tube which extends 5 feet above the level of the heart; during systole the blood would flow over at the top of the tube (120 mm. of mercury = 1.56 meters of water = 5 feet 1½ inches), and during diastole it would form a column nearly 3 feet 5 inches high within the tube.

Blood pressure is the result of the pumping action of the heart which empties blood into a closed system of elastic vessels. The volume capacity of this system does not remain constant. It is changed through the elastic stretch of the vessels and by variations in the caliber of the vessels in response to nervous and chemical stimuli. Since, during ventricular systole, blood is forced into the highly elastic arterial system faster than it can escape into the capillaries and veins, the arteries are stretched to greater capacity. As blood is continually leaving the arterial system and passing into the capillaries and then to the veins, the blood pressure starts to fall at the end of ventricular systole when the inflow into the arteries stops. The elastic recoil of the arterial walls presses upon the blood within and forces it onward through the vessels at a constantly decreasing pressure until the arteries regain the presystolic caliber. The energy which was stored up during the stretching of the elastic tissue is expended between heart beats. As a result the flow of blood through the broad bed of the capillary system and the veins is continuous rather than pulsatile.

It has been pointed out that the force of the heart beat is expended in overcoming the friction of the smaller vessels and in energy of flow (and in the capillaries, in supplying filtration pressure). That part of the energy utilized in overcoming friction is transformed into heat. The energy of flow is used in performing the work necessary for moving the blood throughout the circulatory system. Blood pressure measured at any point in the circulatory system represents the amount of energy which remains to force the blood through the vessels.

In the passage of blood through the larger arteries relatively little energy is lost as heat, so that in general the blood pressure in these arteries would be nearly the same as that in the proximal aorta. However, as the blood flows into the smaller arteries and arterioles, resistance becomes an important factor and considerable quantities of energy are used up in overcoming friction, so that energy which remains to move the blood along decreases rapidly. This results in a rapid fall in pressure as the blood passes through the arterioles into the capillaries. The capillaries are extremely small and might be expected to offer a high resistance to flow of blood with a consequent rapid fall of pressure in the capillary system. However, the frictional resistance is to some extent minimized by the low velocity and the lesser viscosity of the blood in the capillaries. Still, a significant pressure drop does occur in the capillaries, since work is expended in the transport of blood through this system. Further decreases in pressure result from the passage of blood through the venules and the veins, so that venous pressures measured at the level of the heart may show zero or even subatmospheric pressure.

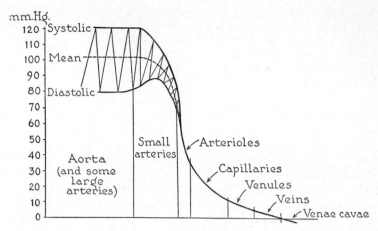

Fig. 225. Diagram showing pressure gradients in different divisions of the circulatory system.

The gradation of pressure from the mean arterial pressure of about 100 mm. of mercury to the arteriolar pressures of 70 to 30 mm. of mercury, the capillary pressures of 30 to 12 mm. and the venous pressure of 12 to less than zero mm. of mercury is called the *pressure gradient* of the circulatory system. Figure 225 illustrates pressure gradients in different divisions of the system.

Velocity of Blood Flow.   Blood flows rapidly through the arterial system, slows down as it passes through the capillaries, and speeds up again as it passes into the veins. The variations in velocity are related to the difference in the cross-section areas of the vascular bed, blood velocity decreasing as the cross-section area increases.

Approximate values for velocity and relative values for cross-section area in the various divisions of the circulatory system are shown as follows. The values are only illustrative, since wide variations exist.

DIVISION	RELATIVE AREA OF CROSS SECTION	BLOOD VELOCITY
Arterial (aorta)	1	22 cm. per sec.
Venous (venae cavae)............	2	11 cm. per sec.
Capillaries	600–800	0.1 to 0.05 cm. per sec.

The velocities in the circulatory bed may be illustrated by the more familiar example of a stream passing from a narrow channel into a pond which is drained by another relatively narrow stream. It must be borne in mind that in any given time the same amount of water passes each section along the way. When the stream bed is narrow, the water flows rapidly; in the pond the same quantity of water per unit time will pass any point on the shore, but because of the increased width of the channel the velocity of flow is reduced. Occasionally measurements are made of the time it would take a particular portion or drop of blood to be transmitted from one point in circulation to another; these are known as *circulation times*. A number of factors including differences in form and length of blood vessels, pulse rate and size of the individual will cause variations of the values. Circulation time from a vein of the arm to the tongue would be from nine to sixteen seconds.

Arterial Pulse. If we place a fingertip over a superficial artery, we feel an impact or pulse which appears to coincide closely with the beat of the heart. If we were equipped to make sufficiently precise observations of the time relations, we would find that the pulse occurred shortly after the beginning of systolic ejection and that the interval between these two events was greater in the more peripheral arteries such as the radial and femoral arteries than in the more central vessels such as the subclavian and carotid arteries.

The pulse is the result of the sudden pressure variations which occur as blood is forced out of the heart against the column of blood already filling the arterial system at a time when the vessels are only moderately stretched and are capable of considerable further elastic expansion. The expansion and the elastic recoil of the arteries set up vibrations in the arterial wall which are transmitted peripherally. These vibrations in the arterial wall will travel faster than the column of blood which has been ejected from the heart. The pulse may travel at a rate of 6 to 9 meters a second, while the blood travels only about 0.2 to 0.6 meter per second.

The pulse may be taken wherever an artery approaches the surface of the body. It is felt in the radial artery at the wrist, the common carotid artery in the neck, the superficial temporal artery in front of the ear over the zygomatic arch, the popliteal artery under the knee and the dorsalis pedis in the foot.

Palpation of the pulse is a convenient way of determining heart rate; it is of value in detecting abnormal cardiac rhythms and variations in pulse pressure. The character of the pulse may differ with variations in the factors which affect and maintain blood pressure (see outline on page 378).

Measurement of Blood Pressure: Direct Methods. Direct methods of measuring pressure in arteries, veins or capillaries are usually limited to experimental animals since they involve a certain amount of operative procedure. A method used for determining *venous pressure* in man can illustrate the principles involved. A small glass tube or needle called a cannula is inserted into the median basilic vein. Sterile saline solution is allowed to enter from a manometer or measuring device in the direction opposite to blood flow. The phlebomanometer is calibrated to show the number of millimeters of water required to collapse the vein, indicated by a cessation of inflow of saline. Pressure varies in the median basilic vein from 40 to 140 mm. of water pressure. Venous pressure is elevated when the heart does not contract efficiently to maintain pulmonary circulation.

Arterial pressure is commonly measured with a mercury manometer; it may even be recorded on a moving cylinder by having the column of mercury in one arm of a U-tube carrying a small float and writing point. This type of manometer is satisfactory for measurement of mean blood pressure (the average of systolic and diastolic values), but, because of its inertia, does not record systolic and diastolic pressures accurately.

The optical manometer, which is a far better instrument to use for recording, consists essentially of a short segment of metal tubing which is covered by a suitable rubber membrane on which a mirror is mounted. When the metal tube is connected to an artery through a cannula and tubing, the pulse moves the membrane and the mirror reflects a moving spot of light onto a recording camera. This device is used to obtain accurate records of pressure curves from the various parts of the circulatory system for study and comparison.

The contours of the arterial pressure curve will vary somewhat, depending upon the artery selected. A record taken from the aorta or a proximal artery usually shows (a) an abrupt rise of pressure corresponding with the beginning of ejection of blood from the ventricles, (b) a fall in pressure as the ejection of blood falls off, (c) the dicrotic notch, which signals the closure of the aortic semilunar valves, and (d) a gradual drop in pressure during diastole (Fig. 203).

Measurement of Arterial Blood Pressure in Man (Fig. 226). Clinically, blood pressure is measured with a sphygmomanometer by an indirect method. The principle of the method is to balance the pressures in the artery with an externally applied air pressure and to observe the air pressure by means of a mercury or aneroid (air-pressure gauge type) manometer.

The sphygmomanometer consists of (1) a rubber bag covered with an unyielding material which extends to a length convenient for wrapping the bag around the arm, (2) a hand bulb for inflating the cuff connected to the cavity of the bag by a rubber tube, (3) an escape valve (usually made as part of inflating bulb) which permits release of air at various rates, and (4) a manometer connected to the pressure bag by a length of rubber tubing.

The *brachial artery* is usually chosen as the site of measurement. Pressure is applied over the artery at a value (*a*) which just permits the passage of blood under the cuff at the systolic peak—this value is taken as systolic—or at a value (*b*) which permits the passage of blood under the cuff through the entire cardiac cycle—diastolic pres-

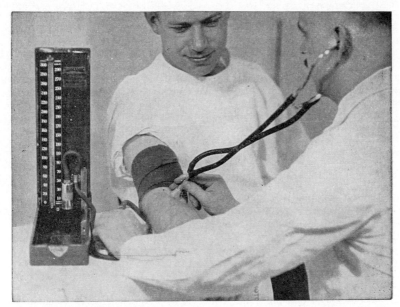

Fig. 226. Determining the blood pressure by the auscultatory method, using a mercury type of sphygmomanometer. (Crandall, Introduction to Human Physiology.)

sure. In determination of systolic pressure the passage of blood under the cuff is noted by the auscultatory method, in which the observer listens for characteristic sounds with a stethoscope placed over the artery, or the palpatory method, in which the observer feels the radial pulse.

"The Standardization of Blood Pressure Readings," as recommended by the American Heart Association and the Cardiac Society of Great Britain and Ireland, is quoted here:

1. BLOOD PRESSURE EQUIPMENT. The blood pressure equipment to be used, whether mercurial or aneroid, should be in good condition and calibrated at yearly intervals—more often if defects are suspected. (Mercurial preferred—British Committee.)

2. THE PATIENT. The patient should be comfortably seated (or lying—British

Committee), with the arms slightly flexed and the whole forearm supported at heart level on a smooth surface. If readings are taken in any other position, a notation of that fact should be made. The patient should be allowed time to recover from any recent exercise or excitement. There should be no constriction of the arm by clothes.

3. POSITION AND METHOD OF APPLICATION OF THE CUFF.   A standard-sized cuff containing a rubber bag 12 to 13 cm. in width should be used. A completely deflated cuff should be applied snugly and evenly around the arm with the lower edge about 1 inch above the antecubital space and with the rubber bag applied over the inner aspect of the arm. The cuff should be of such a type and applied in such a manner that inflation causes neither bulging nor displacement.

4. SIGNIFICANCE OF PALPATORY AND AUSCULTATORY LEVELS.   In all cases palpation should be used as a check on auscultatory readings. The pressure in the cuff should be quickly increased in steps of 10 mm. of mercury until the radial pulse disappears, and then allowed to fall rapidly. If the radial pulse returns at a higher level than that at which the first sound is heard, the palpatory reading should be accepted as the systolic pressure; otherwise the auscultatory reading should be accepted.

5. POSITION AND METHOD OF APPLICATION OF STETHOSCOPE.   The stethoscope should be placed over the previously palpated brachial artery in the antecubital space, not in contact with the cuff. There should be no opening between the lip of the stethoscope and the skin; this should be accomplished with the minimum pressure possible. The hand may be pronated or supinated, depending on which position yields the clearest brachial pulse sounds.

6. DETERMINATION OF THE SYSTOLIC PRESSURE.   The cuff should be rapidly inflated to a pressure about 30 mm. above the level at which the radial pulse can be palpated. The cuff should then be deflated at a rate of 2 to 3 mm. of mercury per second. The level at which the first sound regularly appears should be considered the systolic pressure unless the palpatory level is higher, in which event the palpatory level should be accepted. This should be noted.

7. DETERMINATION OF THE DIASTOLIC PRESSURE AND THE PULSE PRESSURE. With continued deflation of the cuff, the point at which the sounds suddenly become dull and muffled should be known as the diastolic pressure. If there is a difference between that point and the level at which the sounds completely disappear, the American Committee recommends that the latter reading should be regarded also as the diastolic pressure. This should then be recorded in the following form: RT* (or LT†) 140/80–70, or 140/70–0. If these two levels are identical, the blood pressure should be recorded as follows: 140–70–70. The cuff should be completely deflated before any further determinations are made.

Normal Values.   Blood pressure is routinely measured without attempting to control the subject's activity before the rest period which generally precedes the measurement, or the time which has elapsed since his last meal. If the results of the measurements may influence his future activities, as when he was being examined for service in the armed forces or for life insurance, the subject's eagerness, fear or anxiety may increase his blood pressure readings. For these and other reasons it is doubtful whether indirect readings may be relied upon

* RT = right arm.
† LT = left arm.

to give results which are nearer than 10 mm. of mercury above or below the true value, which could be measured only by far more elaborate methods. Since this is generally known by those experienced in making and interpreting the measurements, they are guided accordingly in distinguishing between normal and abnormal or pathologic values. Normal values, then, represent an order of magnitude rather than a precise figure. Most of the reference values apply to measurements taken under everyday routine conditions. These are, however, adequate to show variations with age, weight and sex.

Though we do not have results from acceptable studies on all age groups, it has been established that normally there is an increase in the systolic and diastolic pressures up to the age of about sixty-two years and a more rapid increase from sixty-two to eighty-five years, after which they may decrease. Blood pressure of newborn infants has been reported as 80/46 mm. of mercury, with the standard deviations of 8.1 and 8.2 mm., respectively, for systolic and diastolic pressures (results of *direct* measurement). No significant differences in blood pressures of boys and girls have been reported up to the age of ten to twelve years, at which time the systolic pressure in girls is slightly higher. After puberty, when adult levels have been attained, the blood pressures in young men exceed those in women. The pressures for male adults are given as 110/70 mm. of mercury at twenty years of age to 140/90 mm. of mercury at sixty-five years of age. After menopause, the systolic pressure of women may exceed that of males in a corresponding age group. Heavy people show somewhat higher values than persons of normal weight.

If the subjects have been resting in bed, and have not eaten for three to five hours, systolic pressures may decrease by 15 to 30 mm. of mercury and diastolic from 5 to 10 mm. Similar values are also observed in normal, quiet sleep.

SUMMARY

The spurting of blood which occurs when an artery is cut demonstrates that the blood within the arteries is under pressure and that the pressure varies with the phase of the cardiac cycle.

The peak which occurs during ventricular systole is called systolic pressure; the minimum value which occurs during ventricular diastole is known as diastolic pressure.

In young adults the systolic pressure is about 120 mm. of mercury, and the diastolic is 80 mm. of mercury.

Blood pressure is the result of the pumping action of the heart which empties the blood into an already filled series of elastic tubes, the arterial system. The work of the heart is expended in overcoming the friction of the smaller vessels, in energy of flow, and in the capillaries in supplying filtration pressure. There is therefore a gradation of pressure from the mean arterial pressure of about 100 mm. of mercury to the venous pressure of 12 to less than zero mm. of mercury.

The velocity of blood flow decreases as the cross-section area of the vessels increases. Blood flows rapidly in the large arteries and veins, but slows down in the small vessels and the capillaries.

The arterial pulse is the result of the pressure variations which occur in an artery during a cardiac cycle causing expansion and relaxation of vessel walls.

The pulse may be taken wherever an artery approaches the surface of the body. It may be felt in the radial, carotid, superficial temporal, popliteal and dorsalis pedis arteries.

The measurement of blood pressure by the direct method is usually limited to experimental animals.

Blood pressure in man is measured with a sphygmomanometer by an indirect method. The principle of the method is to balance the pressures in the artery with an externally applied air pressure and to observe the air pressure by means of a mercury or aneroid (air-pressure gauge type) manometer.

QUESTIONS FOR DISCUSSION

1. Explain the meaning of systolic and diastolic pressures in terms of the work of the heart.

2. What is the relation of the pulse to (*a*) the sounds heard in taking blood pressure by the auscultatory method; (*b*) the velocity of blood flow; and (*c*) circulation time?

Chapter 19

The Maintenance and Regulation of Blood Pressure

FACTORS INFLUENCING BLOOD PRESSURE

THE RELATIVELY narrow range of blood pressures which are maintained during rest and light activity may be extended by a variety of circumstances encountered in everyday living. The upper range for systolic pressure may be increased to 180 to 200 mm. of mercury and for diastolic pressure to 100 to 110 mm. under conditions of maximum exercise or extreme emotion. Other circumstances involving emotional reactions, such as particularly distressing or distasteful situations, may result in so great a fall of blood pressure as to cause fainting or unconsciousness. For the most part, however, extreme variations are prevented or minimized by compensatory reactions, and blood pressure is nicely adjusted to the state of bodily activity. Blood supply, locally and throughout the body, is regulated to the degree of activity. The mechanisms of these adjustments are discussed in the following sections.

Cardiac Output. The amount of blood which is pumped by the heart is, of course, one of the principal factors in determining both pressure and supply. Variations in cardiac output in response to bodily activity are determined by changes in (1) venous return (the rate at which venous blood is returned to the heart), (2) force of the heart beat, and (3) frequency of the heart beat.

Venous return to the heart is increased during exercise by the contraction of the skeletal muscles, which tend to force the blood toward the heart by compressing the thin-walled veins, since veins have valves which prevent blood flow in the opposite direction. The deep and rapid breathing which occurs during exercise also aids venous return, since deep inspirations lower the pressure within the chest, aspirating the blood toward the heart. The descent of the diaphragm compresses the abdominal viscera, forcing blood from the veins in this area.

The *tone* of capillary vessels also influences venous return. If any extensive area of capillary dilatation occurs, the capacity of the circulatory system is increased so that the rate of flow of venous blood into the atrium is decreased. Gravity also has its influence, since blood below the heart level must return against the force of gravity, while the flow of blood from areas above the heart level is aided by gravity. This effect may be easily demonstrated by observing the veins of the hand when the arm is allowed to hang by the side of the body and then raised above the head. Standing quite still for a relatively short period of time may cause fainting, since the venous return is reduced by (*a*) the effects of gravity and (*b*) by lack of the muscular movements which normally aid the flow of blood in the veins.

The *force* of the heart beat is determined chiefly by the chemical environment of the heart and by the length of the cardiac fibers at the onset of systole. Carbon dioxide in moderate amounts and an adequate supply of oxygen are favorable for strong contractions. The strength of contraction is related to the length of the cardiac muscle fibers at the time of contraction. This relation in heart muscle was called by Starling the "Law of the Heart." The law states that, within physiologic limits, *the greater the initial length of heart muscle fibers at the beginnings of systole, the more forcible is the contraction.* If venous inflow is increased, the heart muscle fibers will be stretched to a greater extent by the greater filling during diastole. Presystolic volume may also be increased by a rise in arterial pressure. In this case the heart is at first unable to empty itself completely, so that at the beginning of diastole a small amount of blood remains in the heart. When normal inflow has been added to this remainder, the heart enters the following systoles with an increased volume, so that in several beats the force of the heart beat has increased sufficiently to empty against the greater pressure.

The output per minute may also be increased by the heart's beating more times per minute. It follows however that with the faster rate, diastole is shortened and less time is available for cardiac filling, so that the rate of filling must rise if the output is to increase.

Resistance Offered by the Peripheral Blood Vessels. The caliber of the arterioles may be altered to a considerable extent by chemical and nervous influences. Change in arteriolar caliber is the principal factor in regulating peripheral resistance in normal man. When the diameter of the arterioles is relatively large, there is little resistance to flow and little energy is lost through friction of the blood with the vessel walls. As the caliber of the vessels is reduced, the friction is increased; more precisely, the friction is inversely proportional to the square of the radius (r) of the vessel, i.e., the fall in pressure between two points, P1 and P2, is proportional to $1/r^2$ when all other factors remain constant. When the arterioles constrict, the blood escapes more slowly from the arterial tree into the capillary bed and blood pressure rises. This in turn may increase initial cardiac filling in subsequent heart beats as the heart empties against the greater pressure.

The degree of constriction of the arterioles is the chief factor in determining the peripheral resistance. The caliber of these vessels is regulated by chemical and nervous influences.

Capacity of the Closed Vascular Bed. The pressure in the closed elastic system is dependent upon the total volume capacity of vessels, and upon the quantity of fluid which they contain. Local changes in capacity occur due to the elasticity of the vessels and are evidenced by the pulses. More widespread changes in the capacity of the system may occur by constriction or closure of some of the vessels. The minute vessels, because of their tremendous total cross-sectional area, exert a considerable influence on the volume of blood that can be accommodated by the system.

If considerable loss of blood occurs, as in hemorrhage, there is some compensatory reduction of the capacity of the vascular bed, so that no noticeable change in blood pressure may occur. At some point however, hemorrhage will result in such a disparity between the content and the capacity of the system that blood pressure will fall until the blood volume is restored.

Blood Volume. The blood volume undergoes relatively small changes under physiologic conditions in spite of wide variations in fluid intake and fluid excretion. This is the result of the finely adjusted balance between the fluid component of the blood which leaves the blood stream at the arterial end of the capillary bed to form tissue fluid and lymph, and the return of fluid to the blood stream from the tissue spaces at the venous end of the capillary bed. The kidneys constitute another such mechanism for regulation; here large quantities of plasma are filtered out into the renal tubules (Fig. 281, p. 480), but much of the fluid is reabsorbed into the blood stream.

Normally, man has about 70 to 100 cc. of blood per kilogram of body weight, or roughly about 6 liters of blood for an average person. Hemorrhage, exercise or various conditions which modify water balance will cause some variations from these values.

Viscosity of the Blood. The more viscous a fluid, the greater is the force required to set it in motion. Blood is about five times as viscous as water, so that it aids in maintaining blood pressure by its resistance to movement. Viscosity is an expression of the friction which results from the sliding of molecules past one another in a moving fluid. The blood corpuscles and the plasma proteins are the main factors determining blood viscosity.

Elasticity of the Arterial System. During ventricular systole, blood is forced into the arterial system faster than it can escape into the capillaries and veins; the arteries are thus stretched to greater capacity. As the blood pressure starts to fall at the end of ventricular systole, the elastic recoil of the arterial walls presses upon the blood within and forces it onward through the vessels until the arteries return to the presystolic caliber.

Before systole the arterial system contains more blood than it would if the principal vessels were not stretched to some degree. The additional energy which was stored up during the further stretching of the elastic tissues during systole is expended between heart beats. In consequence, the blood pressure is maintained between heart beats, and the flow of blood into the capillaries and veins is continuous. As people become older, some elasticity of the vessels is lost; this is compensated for, in some degree, by an increase in the caliber of the vessels, so that they receive the systolic output with a lesser rise in pressure than would otherwise occur. If the vessels became increasingly inelastic and no change in the presystolic capacity occurred, enormously high systolic pressures would result. If, on the other hand, the arterial tree were extensible but inelastic, like a paper bag before it is blown up, the blood pressure would fall to zero between heart beats.

To summarize: Under normal physiologic conditions of arterial elasticity, blood volume and blood viscosity, blood pressure represents the product of the cardiac output and peripheral resistance. Compensatory changes in blood pressure are intimately related to the control of heart rate and to the control of the caliber of the peripheral vessels. The mechanism of these controls will be discussed in the following sections.

MECHANISMS CONTROLLING BLOOD PRESSURE

Regulation of the Heart Rate.   The heart is innervated by the *vagus nerves,* which belong to the craniosacral (parasympathetic) division of the autonomic nervous system, and the *accelerator nerves,* which belong to the thoracolumbar (sympathetic) division of the autonomic

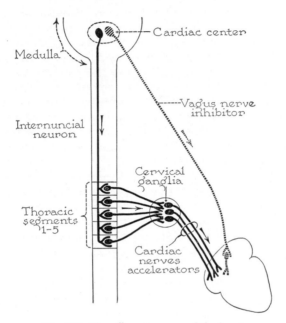

Fig. 227. The efferent nerves of the heart.

nervous system (Fig. 227). The vagi act as inhibitory or depressor fibers to slow the heart rate and to modify the rate of conduction and the strength of atrial contractions. The right vagus (which acts primarily on the sinu-atrial node) plays a major role in decreasing the rate of the heart. The left vagus acts on the atrioventricular node, depressing conduction so that the interval between atrial and ventricular systole is increased or the ventricles do not respond to every beat of the atria. When the level of activity of the left vagus is high, it may also slow the atria as well as diminish the strength of their contractions. The vagus nerves exert their inhibitory action through liberation of a chemical substance, *acetylcholine,* at the nerve endings; this substance is rapidly destroyed, so that, unless the vagus continues to discharge, the heart rate will increase greatly. We speak of vagus tone signifying their continuous activity. High vagus tone indicates that the vagi are exerting a marked effect. The strength of ventricular systole is generally increased during increased vagus tone, since slowing of the heart permits increased ventricular filling and, in consequence, an increased presystolic length of the cardiac muscle fibers. The accelerator nerves act as pressor fibers, tending to increase heart rate and strength of cardiac contractions. Like the vagus, the accelerator nerves act by a *neurohumoral mechanism;* i.e., they liberate a chemical substance upon stimulation. This substance is called *sympathin.* In final analysis, then, heart rate is determined by the basic rate of discharge of the pacemaker under the given conditions of chemical or metabolic environment and the combined activity of the antagonistically acting vagus and accelerator nerves, which mediate their effects through liberation of humoral or chemical agents.

The vagus and accelerator nerves have their connection with sensory nerves and the higher centers of the brain in the medulla oblongata. The areas in which these connections are located are known as the cardiac centers. Sensory nerves from other parts of the body influence these centers, so that either the vagus influence is increased and the heart slowed, or the accelerator nerves are acted upon to increase heart rate. These centers may be acted upon from the higher brain centers; emotions such as anger or excitement may increase heart rate, while sudden shocks may slow it. Stimulation of any somatic nerve may either hasten or retard the rate. In addition, sensory nerve endings located in the circulatory system, which are stimulated by changes in blood pressure or by changes in the chemical environment, have their effects on the heart rate. The chief circulatory receptors which give rise to cardiac reflexes are located in:

1. The aortic arch;
2. The carotid sinus and carotid body;
3. The right atrium and neighboring segments of the great veins.

These reflexes are brought about by stimulation of sensory nerve endings which are sensitive to stretch or tension. Such endings are called *pressure receptors.* Increases in pressure within the blood vessels or in the right atrium stretch the walls of these structures to stimulate the pressure receptors; decreases in pressure diminish the tension and reduce the stimulating effect.

The pressure receptors which are located in the region of the aortic arch (Fig. 228) respond to a rise in blood pressure by increasing the influence of the vagus and slowing the heart rate; a drop in blood pressure reduces vagus influence and the heart beats more rapidly. These responses are reinforced by similar pressure receptors of the carotid sinuses which are located at the bifurcation of the common carotid arteries, where they divide into the internal and external carotid arteries.

Stimulation of sensory nerve endings in the right atrium and great veins causes a reflex acceleration of heart rate. This response occurs when the venous return to the heart is increased and the atrium and

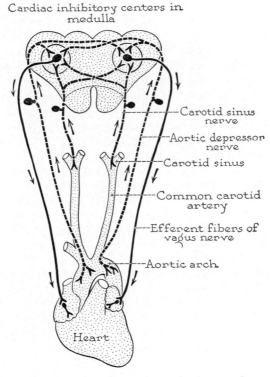

Fig. 228. Diagram showing reflex action of aortic depressor and carotid sinus nerves upon the heart rate.

veins become engorged with blood. The speeding up of the heart rate increases cardiac output and reduces the venous congestion.

In addition to pressure receptors, there are *chemoreceptors* in the region of the carotid sinus (in the carotid body) and the aortic arch which are sensitive to lack of oxygen, increases in carbon dioxide and an increase of the hydrogen ion concentration of the blood. All these chemical changes cause reflex increase in heart rate.

The chemical environment also has its influence on the heart by direct action on the heart muscle and on the cardiac centers, in that the activity of these tissues is depressed by excesses of carbon dioxide and by oxygen lack.

Epinephrine causes a reflex slowing of the heart rate by raising the blood pressure and stimulating the carotid sinus and aortic nerves; it acts directly on a denervated heart to quicken the heart. Thyroxine and an increase in body temperature accelerate heart rate.

Control of Peripheral Resistance.   It has been stated that the arterioles constitute the chief factor in determining peripheral resistance. Changes in the caliber of these vessels have a marked effect on blood pressure. The efferent nerves which bring about changes in the diameter of the vessels are called *vasomotor nerves.* There are two types: the vasoconstrictor nerves, which are distributed chiefly to the arterioles of the skin and viscera, and to a lesser extent to the arterioles of the muscles and mucous membranes; and the vasodilator nerves, supplying the arterioles of the salivary glands, tonsils, pharynx and erectile tissues of the penis and the clitoris.

The arterioles are regulated by the activities of the vasomotor centers in the medulla oblongata. The vasoconstrictor center acts to decrease the caliber of the vessels, and the vasodilator center acts to increase their diameter. The balance of the two activities determines the state of the arterioles. The vasoconstrictor center is tonically active; that is, it is constantly sending out vasoconstrictor impulses. The activity of the vasodilator center is intermittent. Both centers are influenced by nervous and chemical factors.

The vasomotor centers are affected by impulses from the higher centers, so that emotional stress or excitement may cause constriction of the arterioles, while disagreeable or shocking experiences may cause dilatation of the arterioles, a fall in blood pressure and fainting. The respiratory center, which is near the vasomotor center, causes an increase in vasoconstrictor tone during inspiration.

Sensory nerve endings located in the carotid sinus, the aortic arch and the right atrium, and the great veins respond to blood pressure changes and affect the vasomotor centers. They are pressure receptors which are stimulated in the same manner as the pressure receptors affecting heart rate. A rise in blood pressure in the aortic arch and carotid sinus stimulates the receptors and sets up inhibitory impulses which reach the vasoconstrictor center, decrease its activity and so cause a relaxation of the arteries; decreases in blood pressure result in vasoconstriction. A decrease in the pressure in the right atrium and great veins causes a vasoconstriction.

Stimulation of almost any somatic sensory nerve may cause a decrease or an increase in the caliber of the vessels. The vasomotor centers are affected both directly and reflexly by changes in the chemical environment. An adequate concentration of carbon dioxide is necessary for efficient functioning of the centers, while excess carbon dioxide and oxygen lack act directly to depress them. Moderate increases of carbon dioxide or the lack of oxygen stimulates the chemoreceptors in the aortic and carotid bodies and cause vasoconstriction.

Epinephrine is an important vasoconstrictor hormone. Pituitrin likewise causes constriction. Local metabolites, excesses of carbon dioxide and oxygen lack may act directly on the vessels to cause dilatation. Cold decreases and heat increases the size of the vessels.

Control of Capillary Flow. Since the capillaries lie between the arterioles and the collecting venules, capillary flow is to a great extent regulated by the reactions of these vessels. Capillary flow can be reduced either by arteriolar constriction, which decreases the amount of blood entering the capillary bed, or by constriction of the collecting venules, which reduces the outflow from the capillaries. Dilatation of the arterioles and the venules, on the other hand, would increase the capillary flow. The metarterioles and precapillary sphincteric muscular elements serve to alter local flow through the capillary beds. The responses of the minute vessels are controlled principally by chemical agents (see Summary, p. 380).

The chief evidence for *independent activity* in the capillary vessels in man is found in the reaction of the cutaneous vessels. If the skin of an area which is not commonly exposed (such as the back or the forearm) is stroked lightly with a smooth blunt instrument, a sharply defined white line appears. This is known as the "white reaction." As the color of the skin is due to the blood in the capillaries and subcapillary venous plexus, the reaction is interpreted as being the result of capillary constriction in response to a stretch stimulus. A white reaction is also caused by pricking a drop of epinephrine into the skin.

Capillaries may be dilated by almost any type of injury to the surrounding tissues. If a rubber band is snapped against the skin or if a blunt instrument is drawn forcibly across an area, the underlying tissues are subjected to mechanical injury. A sharply defined red mark appears. This is known as the "red reaction." Heat, exposure to sunlight or ultraviolet light, and an injection of foreign substances cause the red reaction. It has been interpreted as the action of a substance liberated by tissue destruction. When the stimulus has been vigorous, an arteriolar dilatation or flare results; edema or swelling resulting from the passage of increased amounts of fluid from the capillaries to the surrounding tissues may also occur.

External pressure influences the blood flow through the capillaries. Constricting clothing, bandages or pressure from lying in bed, or standing decrease the capillary flow. When external pressures are relieved, the previously constricted area becomes flushed, indicating an increased flow through the dilated capillaries. Examples of this phenomenon may be seen by observing the feet on removing shoes or in other areas which have been subjected to compression. Long-continued external pressures may cause more marked tissue injury such as is seen in skin irritation after long confinement in bed.

SUMMARY

Factors in the Regulation of Blood Pressure and Circulation

Blood pressure depends upon:
  I. Cardiac output
     A. Venous return
        1. Increased by contractions of skeletal muscle (increased activity)
        2. Increased by deep respirations
        3. Increased by gravity in the effect of blood above the heart level
        4. Decreased by gravity in the effect of blood below the heart level
        5. Decreased when there is dilatation of blood vessels over a wide area
     B. Force of the heart beat
        1. Initial length of the muscle fibers of the heart at the beginning of systole
           a. Increased length increases the force of the heart beat
           b. Decreased length decreases the force of the heart beat
        2. Decreased force of heart beat occurs when diastole of the heart is shortened
        3. Effect of changes in coronary circulation
           a. Adequate circulation for proper nutrition maintains the force of the beat
           b. Decreased force with oxygen lack
           c. Decreased force with carbon dioxide excess
        4. Epinephrine or stimulation of the thoracolumbar nervous system increases the strength of the heart beat
     C. Heart rate
        1. Regulated by cardiac nerves
           a. Accelerator nerves increase rate; cardio-accelerator center is in the medulla oblongata
           b. Vagus nerves decrease rate; cardio-inhibitory center is in the medulla oblongata

2. Impulses from higher centers may cause acceleration or inhibition through their effect on the cardioregulatory center
3. Cardiac reflexes
   a. From pressure receptors

(1) Aortic arch (2) Carotid sinus } · · · · · · · · · · ·	Increase in rate results from a fall in blood pressure; decrease in rate results from a rise in blood pressure
(3) Right atrium and great veins } · · · · · ·	Rise in venous pressure causes an increase in rate

   b. Other sensory nerve stimulation may cause a decrease or an increase in heart rate
4. Great excesses of carbon dioxide or marked oxygen lack depresses the excitability of the heart muscle and the cardiac centers in the medulla
5. Rise in body temperature causes increase in heart rate
6. Certain hormones may cause an increase in heart rate

II. Peripheral resistance
  A. Caliber of arterioles and capillaries
    1. Nervous control of these vessels
      a. Vasoconstrictor nerves
        (1) Thoracolumbar nerves constitute the majority of constrictor fibers
        (2) Vagus fibers to coronary arteries
      b. Vasodilator nerves
        (1) Craniosacral nerves
        (2) Some thoracolumbar dilators
        (3) Posterior root dilators
    2. Nervous control may be influenced by:
      a. Impulses from the higher centers
      b. Impulses from the respiratory center
      c. Vasomotor reflexes
        (1) From pressure receptors
          (*a*) Carotid sinus
          (*b*) Aortic arch
          (*c*) Right atrium and great veins
        (2) From chemoreceptors
          (*a*) Carotid body
          (*b*) Aortic arch

     d. Action directly on the vasomotor center
       (1) Carbon dioxide in moderate excess causes vasoconstriction
       (2) Carbon dioxide lack causes vasodilatation
       (3) Great excess of carbon dioxide causes vasodilatation
       (4) Marked oxygen lack causes vasodilatation
     e. Changes in temperature (central action)
       (1) Rise in temperature causes vasodilatation
       (2) Fall in temperature causes vasoconstriction
   3. Chemical and thermal control of vessels
     a. Action on arterioles
       (1) Metabolites
         Carbon dioxide excess ⎱ . . . . vasodilatation
         Oxygen lack   ⎰
       (2) Hormones
         Epinephrine ⎱ . . . . vasoconstriction
         Pituitrin   ⎰
       (3) Histamine . . . . vasoconstriction
     b. Action on capillaries
       (1) Metabolites
         Carbon dioxide lack . . . . capillary constriction
         Carbon dioxide excess ⎱ . . . . . . capillary dilatation
         Oxygen lack   ⎰
       (2) Hormones locally on injection
         Epinephrine ⎱ . . . . capillary constriction
         Pituitrin   ⎰
       (3) Histamine . . . . capillary dilatation
       (4) Temperature, local action
         Rise   ⎱ . . . . capillary dilatation
         Moderate fall ⎰
         Marked fall . . . . capillary constriction

III. Capacity of the closed vascular bed ⎱   ⎧ These factors remain
IV. Elasticity of the blood vessels   ⎰   relatively constant
 V. Blood volume   ⎱   in normal healthy
VI. Viscosity of the blood   ⎰   ⎩ man

QUESTIONS FOR DISCUSSION

   1. How are the numerous factors that control the heart integrated?
   2. Explain the differences in the effects of carbon dioxide excess on the vasomotor centers of the brain and upon the capillaries.
   3. Discuss the physiology of hemorrhage.
   4. Relate changes in skin color to circulation.

Chapter
20

The Lymphatic System

IN EXCHANGES which take place between tissues and blood stream all the products of exchange must pass through the tissue fluid which bathes the cells. Thus a gradient in the concentration of metabolites exists between the cells, the tissue fluid and the blood. The gradients normally favor the passage of oxygen and food materials from the

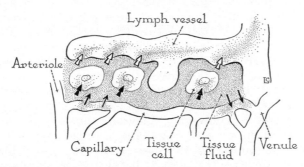

Fig. 229. Diagram showing the course of the tissue fluid. Fluid passing out of the capillary may go into and out of tissue cells, may enter a lymph vessel or be resorbed into the capillary by osmosis.

blood stream to the cells and the passage of the waste products of cellular metabolism in the reverse direction.

The interchange of fluid between the tissues and the blood stream occurs continuously within the body. It is highly probable, however, that the exchange in any one area is intermittent. Fluid passes outwards from the blood stream at a point where (or at a time when) the effective pressure within the minute vessel is greater than the total pressure of the fluid in the tissue spaces. Fluid from the tissue spaces passes back through the wall of the minute vessels when the pressure relations are reversed, or passes into one of two large veins where the blood pressure is low by way of organized channels. On the basis of our studies of the minute vessels, we might consider that, in muscle and the gastrointestinal tract, fluid might leave through the thoroughfare channel or the true capillaries, and that it might return either through the walls of the more distal true capillaries or through those of the postcapillaries. In any case the exchange will certainly be determined by (a) pressure relations and (b) permeability of the capillary wall.

Formation of Tissue Fluid. The outflow of fluid from the capillary is governed by two physical forces: (1) the pressure of blood within the capillaries, the filtration pressure, which forces blood out through the capillary membrane; and (2) the protein osmotic pressure of the blood which acts in the opposite direction. If we assume a pressure of 32 mm. of mercury in the arterial end of the capillary and a protein osmotic pressure of 25 mm. of mercury we have

$$32 \text{ mm. Hg} - 25 \text{ mm. Hg} = 7 \text{ mm. Hg},$$

a force of 7 mm. of mercury favoring formation of tissue fluid. At the venous end of an active capillary the pressure of the blood has fallen to approximately 12 mm. of mercury, while the protein osmotic pressure has increased slightly because of the loss of fluid. As a result, nearly equal amounts of fluid are reabsorbed. It is necessary, of course, to take into account the influence of the pressure in the tissue spaces on the exchange in both directions (Fig. 229).

The Lymphatic System. The lymphatic system consists of lymphatic capillaries, the lymphatic vessels and the lymph nodes or glands.

THE LYMPHATIC CAPILLARIES. These are thin-walled tubes which, like the blood capillaries, are composed of a single layer of endothelial cells. They differ from them, however, in that they begin blindly and their caliber is slightly greater than that of the blood capillaries.

LYMPHATIC VESSELS. The lymph flows from the capillaries in all parts of the body into the lymphatic vessels. These vessels are like the veins in structure, but the walls are thinner and valves (Fig. 230) more numerous. The larger lymphatics converge and finally come together to form two large trunks, the right lymphatic duct and the thoracic duct. The lymphatics of the trunk are shown in Figure 231.

The *right lymphatic* duct is the smaller of the two. It carries the lymph from the right arm, right side of thorax and right side of the head and neck and empties it into the right innominate vein, where it arises from the union of the right internal jugular and subclavian vein. The thoracic duct carries the lymph from all the remaining parts of the body and empties it into the left innominate vein. The *thoracic duct* begins on the posterior abdominal wall at the lower border of the second lumbar vertebra in a pouchlike dilatation called the cisterna

Fig. 230. A lymphatic vessel laid open to show the valves. (Gerrish, Textbook of Anatomy, Lea & Febiger.)

chyli. It continues upward along the bodies of the vertebrae to its termination. Figure 232 shows the areas drained by the right lymphatic and thoracic ducts.

MOVEMENT OF THE LYMPH. The lymph flows from the tissues toward the large lymphatic ducts. The flow is maintained chiefly by the difference in pressure at the two ends of the system. The low pressure end is at the opening of the large ducts into the innominate veins. At this point the pressure may be zero or even negative. At the other end, in the region of the lymphatic capillaries, the pressure is high. This difference in pressure at the two ends is the main factor in moving the lymph.

Accessory factors aiding the flow of lymph are breathing movements and muscular contractions. Respiratory movements aspirate lymph into the veins in the upper chest region. The lymph vessels are alternately compressed and released by the contraction and relaxation of skeletal muscle, and, since the vessels are well equipped with valves, the lymph is moved onward toward the large vessels.

THE LYMPH NODES (Fig. 233). Lymph nodes or glands are oval or bean-shaped bodies located at rather frequent intervals along the

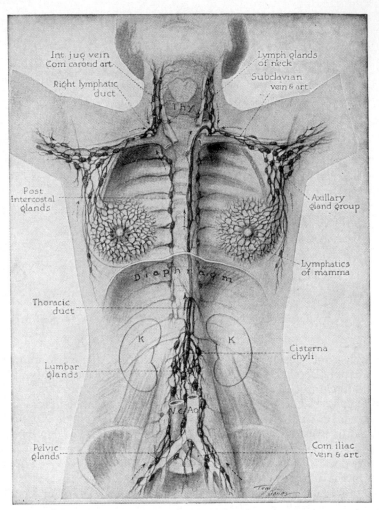

Fig. 231. Lymphatics of the trunk. (Courtesy of S. H. Camp & Co.)

course of a lymph vessel. They consist essentially of networks of reticular and collagenous fibers, the meshwork of which supports masses of lymphocytes and many histiocytes. The node is enclosed in a dense fibrous capsule. Septa or trabeculae from the capsule dip down into the substance of the gland and divide it into separate compartments.

The substance of the node is arranged in an outer cortical and an inner medullary portion. In the cortex are the nodules of lymphoid tissue which contain the germ centers for the production of lympho-cytes. Permeating the organ as a whole are irregular, tortuous channels, the lymphatic sinuses. As a lymph vessel approaches a node, it breaks up into a number of branches, the afferent lymphatics, which enter the gland from the convex surface. The lymph flowing in the vessels

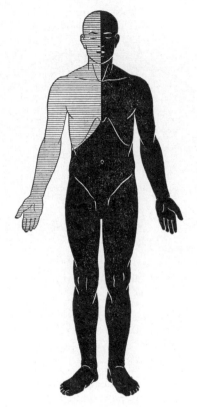

Fig. 232. Diagram to show areas of the body drained by the right lymphatic and thoracic ducts. Solid black, thoracic duct; shaded, right lymphatic duct.

trickles through the sinuses of the node and into the efferent lymphatics, which leave the gland at the indentation or hilus.

Reticulo-endothelial cells of the lymph nodes, particularly the histio-cytes, filter out solid particles, including bacteria, and prevent their entrance into the blood stream. Lymph nodes are hemopoietic in the manufacture of lymphocytes and monocytes. Antibodies and small amounts of plasma proteins are produced in the lymph nodes,

The lymph nodes are usually distributed in groups. Groups found in the *head and neck* are (1) submaxillary nodes, just below the angle of the mandible, (2) pre-auricular nodes, just in front of the ear, (3) postauricular nodes, behind the ear in the region of the mastoid process, (4) the superficial cervical nodes, at the side of the neck over the sternocleidomastoid muscle, (5) the deep cervical nodes, deep in the

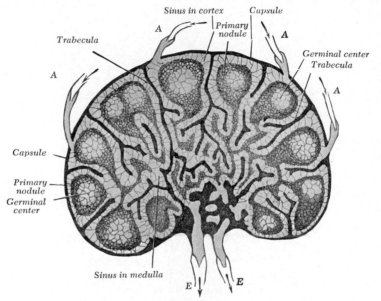

Fig. 233. Diagram of a lymph node. A, Afferent and, E, efferent lymphatic vessels with valves. The arrows indicate the direction of the lymph flow. (Maximow and Bloom.)

neck along the carotid artery and internal jugular vein. In general, each group drains the regions of the head and neck directly above it.

The main group of the *upper extremity* is in the axilla. The axillary nodes receive the lymph from the arm, anterior and lateral walls of the chest, mammary gland and scapular region.

The most important glands of the *lower extremity* are the inguinal nodes, which lie in the groin. They receive the lymph from the leg and from the external genitalia.

Important groups in the *thoracoabdominal* cavity are: tracheo-bronchial, mediastinal, gastric, mesenteric, and numerous glands along the main arterial trunks.

Other Lymphatic Tissue. The spleen, the tonsils, the solitary and aggregated nodules of the intestinal tract, and the thymus gland all contain lymphatic tissue. These structures differ from the lymph nodes in that they are not interposed in the lymph stream. Only the spleen, which is the largest mass of lymphatic tissue in the body, will be described.

The *spleen* (Fig. 257, p. 427; Fig. 267, p. 437) is an ovoid organ about 12 cm. long which is located on the left side of the upper abdominal cavity. Its lateral surface is convex and lies molded against the dome of the diaphragm. The medial surface is in contact with the stomach, the pancreas and the left kidney.

The spleen is invested and held in place by a layer of peritoneum. Just beneath the peritoneal covering, a capsule of fibroelastic tissue, containing smooth muscle cells, encloses the organ and, turning inward at the hilum, ramifies through the internal structure to partition it into spaces that are filled with splenic tissue. There are two types of splenic tissue: one, the typical lymphatic tissue or white pulp; the other, atypical lymphatic tissue or red pulp. White pulp, or typical lymphatic tissue, consists of reticular cells, histiocytes and lymphocytes arranged in nodules. Red pulp is in the form of cords or strands and consists of reticular cells, histiocytes, lymphocytes and erythrocytes. The erythrocytes are responsible for the characteristic red color. Running between the cords of red pulp are wide sinuses filled with blood.

The spleen is placed in the course of the blood stream through the splenic artery; in many respects it acts as a filter and a reservoir for the blood. Physiologic changes in the vascular bed may slow circulation of blood through the filtration mechanism of the organ. Epinephrine and appropriate stimulation of nerves cause sudden, strong splenic contractions in dogs and in other species. This active emptying of the spleen releases large quantities of blood into the splenic vein and thence to the portal circulation. In man the muscular trabeculae are poorly developed; so we do not know whether the active phase of emptying is significant.

The spleen manufactures all types of blood cells during fetal life and for a short time after birth. In adult life this function is restricted to the formation of lymphocytes and monocytes. Red blood cells are destroyed in the spleen; the iron from the hemoglobin is stored in the histiocytes and utilized later in the synthesis of new hemoglobin. The histiocytes of the spleen ingest and destroy foreign particles, including bacteria. Because of the large blood sinuses and the slow circulation, the spleen serves as a reservoir for blood. Large numbers of red blood cells are stored in the red pulp, and can be discharged into the blood stream. Another important function of the spleen is the production of antibodies.

SUMMARY

Exchange of products between the tissues and the blood stream takes place through the medium of the tissue fluid, which bathes all cells.

The formation of tissue fluid is governed by filtration pressure and protein osmotic pressure.

The lymphatic system consists of lymphatic capillaries, lymphatic vessels and the lymph nodes or glands.

The lymphatic capillaries resemble blood capillaries in structure. They differ in that they begin blindly.

The lymphatic vessels resemble veins, but are thinner, and the valves are more numerous.

The two largest lymphatic vessels are the right lymphatic duct and the thoracic duct.

Movement of lymph is maintained chiefly by the difference in pressure at the two ends of the system.

Accessory factors aiding the flow of lymph are breathing movements and muscular contractions.

The lymph nodes are located along the course of a lymph vessel.

The gland or node is enclosed in a dense fibrous capsule. The interior consists of a network of reticular and collagenous fibers which support masses of lymphocytes and histiocytes.

Lymph nodes act to filter out solid particles, including bacteria. They produce lymphocytes.

The spleen, the tonsils, the solitary and aggregated nodules in the intestinal tract, and the thymus gland all contain lymphatic tissue. These structures differ from the lymph nodes in that they are not interposed in the lymph stream.

The spleen is located on the left side of the upper abdominal cavity.

There are two types of splenic tissue: typical lymphatic tissue or white pulp, and atypical lymphatic tissue or red pulp.

The principal functions of the spleen are the formation of lymphocytes and monocytes, destruction of red blood cells, phagocytic action of the histiocytes, and the formation of antibodies. The spleen also serves as a reservoir for blood.

QUESTIONS FOR DISCUSSION

1. What is the functional significance of the arrangement and location of lymphatic vessels and nodes?

2. Relate the formation of lymph to the minute vessels of the capillary bed.

3. What physical principles and processes are involved in formation of lymph?

Chapter 21

The Respiratory System

RESPIRATION

RESPIRATION may be defined as the combined activity of the various mechanisms which enter into supplying oxygen to all the cells of the body and effecting the removal of carbon dioxide from the cells. These mechanisms are capable of wide variations in their response, so that respiratory exchange is closely correlated with bodily activity.

It is common knowledge that we are only rarely conscious of breathing, which continues rhythmically without voluntary effort on our part. We have, however, some voluntary control of this vital process, for we can hold our breath for a limited time; we can increase this time by first breathing deeply and rapidly. We can interrupt the outflow of air in speaking, singing and whistling. If we perform work we breathe more deeply and more rapidly. If we take a breath of smoke or irritating gas we involuntarily stop inhaling and then exhale or cough or sneeze. The physiology of respiration helps us to interpret these observations.

The architecture of the respiratory system is closely correlated with function. The respiratory system consists essentially of a series of air passageways that connect outside air with a large expanse of specialized respiratory membrane which lies in close relation to the blood capillaries and affords opportunity for exchange of gases between the air and the blood stream. During its passage through the conducting channels, the air is cleared of the majority of small foreign particles, warmed and humidified. The respiratory membrane, like many areas of the body which are specialized for diffusion or exchange, is arranged so as to provide an epithelial surface of large total area in contact with an extensive capillary network in only moderately sized organs, the lungs. The respiratory apparatus also includes the muscles which provide for a renewal of air in contact with the membranes; these aid in maintaining the gradient (i.e., the difference in levels) of the partial pressures of oxygen and carbon dioxide on the two sides of the membrane and provide conditions favorable for diffusion of gases.

Respiration involves gaseous exchange at two sites. The exchange across the respiratory membrane with the blood in the capillaries of the pulmonary circulation is known as *external respiration;* diffusion of gases between the systemic capillaries and the cells is known as *internal respiration.*

The respiratory system has accessory functions such as coughing and sneezing, which are protective. Talking, which makes possible the communication of ideas and wishes, is also an accessory function of respiration.

Several terms are used to describe conditions in which there is a significant failure in exchange of the respiratory gases. The terms *anoxia* and *hypoxia* are used to describe a condition in which the oxygen supply is inadequate to meet the oxygen requirements for the particular level of bodily activity. That is, the condition is relative. If a man, when working, was receiving an oxygen supply which was just adequate to maintain him while resting, he would become anoxic. If the oxygen deficiency is accompanied by an excessive increase in carbon dioxide in the body, the condition is known as *asphyxia.* Various conditions which result in failure in respiratory exchange will be discussed in the following chapter.

ARCHITECTURE OF THE RESPIRATORY SYSTEM

Air-Conducting Passageways (Fig. 234). The system of passageways which conduct air to the respiratory membrane is made up of the nasal cavity, the pharynx, the larynx, the trachea and bronchi.

THE NASAL CAVITY. The bony structures forming the walls of the nasal cavity, together with the paranasal sinuses, have been described in Chapter 10. The cavity is divided into right and left nasal fossae by a central partition, the septum (Fig. 235). The anterior openings of the fossae are the nostrils or nares; the posterior openings into the nasal pharynx are called the choanae. Each fossa may be divided into a vestibule, lying just inside the nostrils, the spheno-ethmoidal recess lying above the superior nasal concha, and the superior, middle and inferior meatuses, lying underneath the superior, middle and inferior concha, respectively (Fig. 234).

The entire fossa is lined with mucous membrane which is richly supplied with blood vessels. The epithelial lining of the mucosa is highly specialized, being composed of pseudostratified ciliated columnar epithelium in which goblet cells are richly interspersed. The endings of the olfactory nerve lie in the mucosa in the region above the superior concha.

As air enters into the fossae, the fine hairs at the nares screen out the grosser particles of foreign matter. As it passes over the membrane, the air is warmed and takes up moisture from the mucus secreted

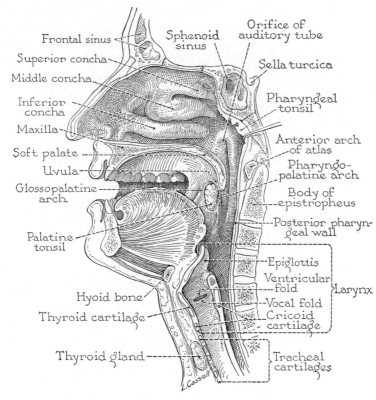

Fig. 234. Sagittal section through mouth, larynx, pharynx and nasal cavity.

by the goblet cells. The ciliary activity of the epithelium removes the finer dust particles.

The nasal cavity has an accessory function in phonation, acting as a sounding board for the voice.

THE PHARYNX (Fig. 234). The pharynx is a musculomembranous tube extending from the base of the skull above to the esophagus below. The posterior wall rests against the bodies of the cervical vertebrae. The lateral wall has openings communicating with the middle ear, while the anterior wall has openings through which connection is established with the nose, the mouth and the larynx. The pharynx is divided accordingly into three parts: nasal pharynx, oral pharynx and laryngeal pharynx. The soft palate separates the nasal pharynx from the oral pharynx. It is a membranous sheet, containing muscle and covered with mucous membrane, which is attached to the bone of the hard palate. On either side it is prolonged downward in the two pillars of the fauces. Of these pillars the one in front (the glossopalatine arch or anterior pillar) passes to the side of the tongue, the one behind (the pharyngopalatine arch or posterior pillar) passes to the posterior pharyngeal wall. Between the two pillars on either side are the palatine

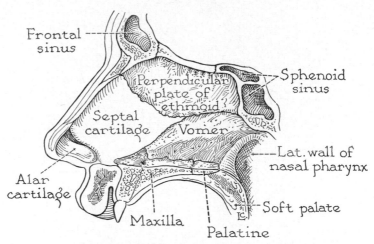

Fig. 235. The nasal septum from the left side. (Redrawn from Spalteholz.)

tonsils. Posteriorly, the soft palate has a median prolongation, the uvula. Soft palate, palatine tonsils and palatine arches are shown in Figure 236.

The *nasal pharynx* is that part of the pharynx which lies behind the choanae or posterior nares and above the soft palate. On each lateral wall is the opening of the *auditory* or *eustachian tube*, which connects with the cavity of the middle ear. The mucosa of the vault of the nasal pharynx contains much lymphoid tissue which constitutes the pharyngeal tonsil or adenoids.

The *oral pharynx* extends from the soft palate above to the level of the hyoid bone below. It opens into the mouth at the glossopalatine arch. The palatine tonsils lie on both sides between the two palatine arches.

The *laryngeal pharynx* lies posterior to the larynx and below the level of the hyoid bone, extending to the cricoid cartilage of the larynx opposite the sixth cervical vertebrae. It communicates anteriorly with the larynx.

The oral and laryngeal portions of the pharynx belong both to the respiratory and digestive tracts. These two tracts cross each other in

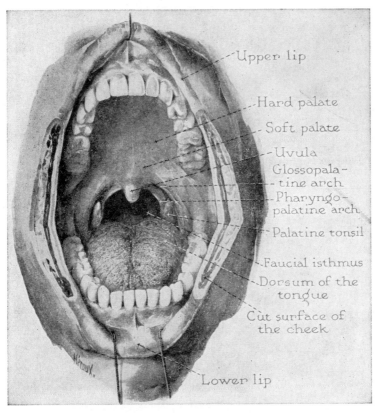

Fig. 236. The mouth cavity. (Modified from Spalteholz.)

the oral pharynx, so that the respiratory is anterior below this point. The nasal pharynx is lined with "respiratory epithelium" like that in the nose; the oral and laryngeal portions are lined with stratified squamous epithelium.

THE LARYNX. The larynx, or "voice box," is placed between the trachea and the root of the tongue (Fig. 234). It forms a prominence in the midline of the neck anteriorly, where it lies close to the surface, covered only by skin and fascia. The five most important cartilages which form the supporting framework are the thyroid, the cricoid, the epiglottis and the paired arytenoid cartilages. The *thyroid* (Fig. 237) is the largest cartilage of the larynx; it is made of two laminae fused

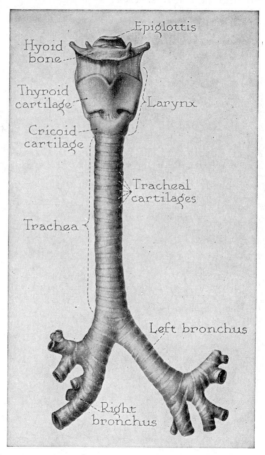

Fig. 237. The hyoid bone, the larynx, the trachea and its principal branches from in front. (Sobotta and McMurrich.)

together at an angle to form a shield-shaped structure, the laryngeal prominence or "Adam's apple." This is considerably larger in the male than in the female. The *cricoid cartilage* is below the thyroid and forms the lower limit of the larynx. It is shaped like a signet ring; the wide portion is placed at the back, and attached to its upper border are the two *arytenoid* cartilages which resemble small pyramids. The *epiglottis* is formed like a leaf; the stem is attached to the thyroid cartilage at the junction of the two laminae. It projects upward behind the root of the tongue anterior to the opening of the larynx. The cartilages of the larynx are connected by ligaments.

Two *vocal folds* (Fig. 234), or vocal cords, pass across the opening of the larynx from anterior to posterior. The vocal folds function in the production of sound and in phonation. They are set into vibration

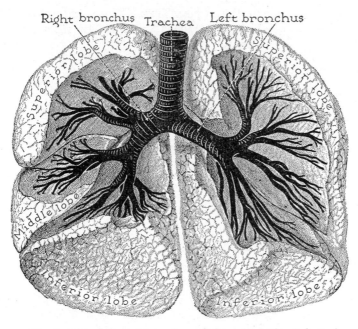

Fig. 238. The lungs with trachea and bronchi. (After Sobotta.)

by outflow of air from the lungs. The variations in pitch which are apparent in speech and singing are the results of changes in the tension of the folds which are acted upon by the muscles of the larynx. The opening between the vocal folds is known as the glottis. Above the vocal folds are two ventricular folds, which do not function in the production of sound. These are sometimes called the "false vocal cords."

The muscles of the larynx consist of two groups: those which act on the vocal cords to open and close the glottis and increase or decrease the tension of the folds; and those which act to prevent the entrance of food during swallowing (see p. 455). The epithelium lining the larynx is mainly of the respiratory type.

THE TRACHEA (Figs. 237, 238). The trachea or windpipe is a cylindrical tube about 11 cm. long. It begins at the lower end of the larynx and, passing into the thorax, terminates by dividing into right and left bronchi at the level of the junction between the manubrium and body of the sternum. The trachea is composed of a fibrous membrane in which cartilaginous rings, sixteen to twenty in number, are embedded. The cartilage gives firmness to the walls and prevents their collapse. The rings are deficient behind, and the interval is filled in with smooth muscle and yellow elastic tissue.

THE BRONCHI AND THE BRONCHIAL TREE. The primary bronchi are the two tubes into which the trachea divides. The right is shorter,

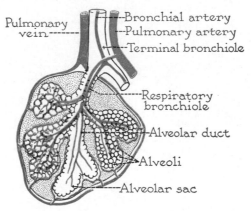

Fig. 239. Structure of a lobule of the lung. (Modified from Bremer.)

wider and more nearly vertical in direction than the left. The structure of the primary bronchi is the same as that of the trachea, except that the cartilaginous rings are complete. On entering the lungs, the primary bronchi divide into a number of branches, secondary bronchi, which in turn break up into smaller and smaller divisions to form the complicated bronchial tree. The smaller divisions are called the bronchioles. Each terminal bronchiole (Fig. 239) continues in one or more respiratory bronchioles. Each respiratory bronchiole gives off several branches called alveolar ducts into which the alveoli open directly or through an intervening structure, the alveolar sac. Given in order the divisions of the bronchial tree are: primary bronchi, secondary bronchi, bronchioles, terminal bronchiole, respiratory bronchiole, alveolar duct, alveolar sac and alveoli. As the secondary bronchi enter the lung substance, the cartilage rings are replaced by irregularly shaped cartilage plates which completely surround the bronchus. As the bronchi decrease in size and the walls become thinner, the cartilage plates are less frequent and the smooth muscle layer completely surrounds the bronchus. Many elastic fibers are distributed among the muscle cells. The cartilage disappears completely when the bronchiole reaches a diameter of 1 mm. The bronchial tree is lined with a ciliated epithelium which extends through the first portion of the respiratory bronchiole, where it gives way to a nonciliated cuboidal epithelium. The epithelium of the alveolar sacs and alveoli consists of a single layer of flattened cells cemented together. Recent studies indicate that the cells of the alveolar lining may be discrete and capable of separation during inflation of the lungs, so that the capillary epithelium may be in direct contact with the air in the alveoli.

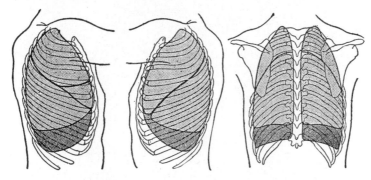

Fig. 240. Thorax, showing surface relation of lungs and pleurae. The heavily shaded areas represent the full extent of pleural cavities beyond the resting lungs. (Homans, A Textbook of Surgery, Charles C Thomas.)

The *bronchial tree* from the trachea to the terminal bronchioles, inclusive, is merely a channel for the passage of air and has no respiratory function. The structures beyond the terminal bronchioles are respiratory in function; that is, gaseous exchanges between blood and air occur here. The group of structures which consists of the respiratory bronchiole, alveolar ducts, alveolar sacs and pulmonary alveoli, together with associated blood vessels and nerves, is the true lung-unit or primary lobule, since it constitutes the functional unit of the organ (Fig. 239).

The Lungs. The lungs are cone-shaped organs which lie in the pleural cavities of the thorax (Fig. 240). The base of each lung lies in contact with the upper surface of the diaphragm, extending to the level of the seventh rib anteriorly and the eleventh rib posteriorly. The apices reach a little over an inch above the level of the clavicles. The interpleural space between the two lungs is called the *medi-*

astinum. It extends from the sternum in front to the thoracic vertebrae behind, and from the thoracic inlet above to the diaphragm below. It contains the heart, the great vessels and some of their proximal branches, the thymus gland, the esophagus, some nerves, a portion of the trachea, and the primary bronchi. Anteriorly, the borders of the

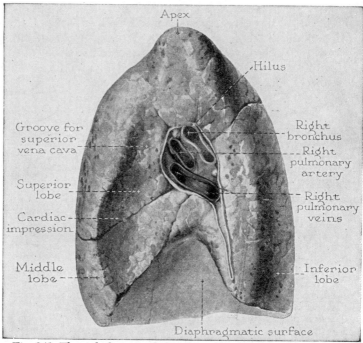

Fig. 241. The right lung, medial surface. (Modified from Spalteholz.)

lungs reach nearly to the midline from the level of the second to the fourth costal cartilages, where they turn laterally, making room for the heart. The posterior borders, which are rounded and less well defined, extend almost vertically from the level of the second rib to the base. The notch for the heart is not apparent in the posterior view.

On the medial surface of each lung (Figs. 241, 242) is a vertical slit, the hilus, where structures enter and leave the lung. These structures, blood vessels, nerves, bronchi and lymphatics taken together, constitute the root of the lung.

The right lung, which is larger than the left, is divided by two inter-lobar fissures into superior, middle and inferior lobes. The left lung is divided into a superior and an inferior lobe; the superior lobe is marked by the cardiac notch. Further subdivisions or *segments* of each lung are distinguished in accordance with the ramifications of the bronchial tree, as shown in Figure 243.

The right and left pleural cavities are formed by two serous sacs into which the lungs are invaginated. The visceral pleura covers the surface of the lung and is reflected from the root of each lung onto

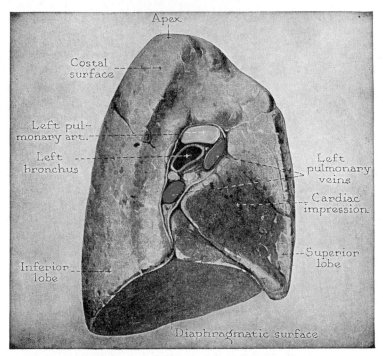

Fig. 242. The left lung, medial surface. (Modified from Spalteholz.)

the inner surface of the chest wall, the diaphragm and the lateral aspect of the mediastinum, to form the parietal pleura.

The two layers of pleura are separated by only a thin layer of fluid about 0.02 mm. thick. Under normal conditions the layers are so closely in apposition that the space between them is potential rather than real. This must be borne in mind when the pleural cavities are mentioned in the discussion of the physiology of respiration. Intrapleural pressures may be measured experimentally by introducing small quantities of air between the layers so as to separate them slightly and inserting a needle connected to a suitable manometer into the small cavity which is formed.

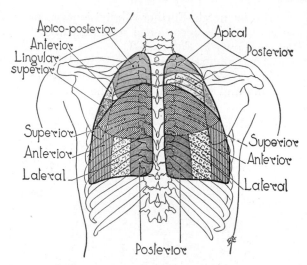

Fig. 243. Diagram of the segments of the lungs; posterior view. (From Sweet: Thoracic Surgery, Ed. 2.)

SUMMARY

Respiration is the process by which oxygen is supplied to the cells of the body and carbon dioxide is removed from them.

The organs of the respiratory system consist of a series of air-conducting passageways and an expanse of respiratory membrane.

Respiration involves exchange of gases at two sites. Exchange between the respiratory membrane and the blood in the capillaries of pulmonary circulation is known as external respiration; diffusion of gases between the systemic capillaries and the cells is known as internal respiration.

The air-conducting passageways consist of the nasal cavity, the pharynx, the larynx, the trachea and bronchi.

The respiratory membrane is composed of the respiratory bronchiole, alveolar ducts, alveolar sacs and pulmonary alveoli. These structures, together with associated blood vessels and nerves, form the true lung unit or primary lobule, since it constitutes the functional unit of the organ.

The lungs are cone-shaped organs which lie in the pleural cavities of the thorax.

The right and left lungs are separated by an interpleural space, the mediastinum, which contains the heart, the great vessels, the thymus gland, the esophagus, some nerves, a portion of the trachea, and the primary bronchi.

The right and left pleural cavities are serous sacs with visceral and parietal layers.

QUESTIONS FOR DISCUSSION

1. Explain the functions of the nasal fossae. How do the nasal conchae contribute to these functions?

2. Relate pulmonary and systemic circulations to the respiratory system.

3. Relate the anatomy of the respiratory system to the flow of air and diffusion of gases.

Chapter 22

The Physiology of Respiration

MECHANICS OF EXTERNAL RESPIRATION

WHILE THE respiratory membrane is in free communication with the outside air through the conducting passageways, the interchange of gases by diffusion alone is too slow a process to meet the bodily requirements of oxygen supply and carbon dioxide excretion. The exchange of gases is accelerated by the respiratory movements which increase the oxygen content and diminish the carbon dioxide content of the gases exposed to the respiratory membrane. The respiratory movements consist of alternate inspiratory and expiratory phases. Inspiration is an active process involving extensive muscular contraction; normal expiration under conditions of rest and moderate activity is largely a passive process.

The thorax constitutes a completely closed compartment surrounding the lungs, while the air passageways within the lung tissue communicate with the external air. The lungs with their pleural coverings are in apposition to the chest wall at all times. The 0.02 mm. layer of fluid between the two layers of pleura "links" the lungs to the chest wall, yet permits the lungs (lower lobes) to glide over the parietal pleura lining the inside of the chest. A simple experiment will serve to illustrate this type of linkage. Place a drop of water on a clean glass microscope slide, cover it with a second slide and press them together. The thin layer of water will hold the two slides firmly together, so that considerable force will be required to separate them, yet they can easily be moved back and forth over one another.

The pressure between the two layers of pleura is below atmospheric pressure (760 mm. of mercury pressure) at all times in the adult. This can be more readily grasped by considering the relations of the lungs to the thoracic cavity at birth and during the initial period of growth. Before birth the lungs are collapsed, as are the alveoli and bronchial walls. The thoracic cavity is completely filled by the collapsed lungs, so that the pressure within the potential pleural cavity is equal to atmospheric pressure. When the thoracic cavity is enlarged during the first inspiration, the intrathoracic or intrapleural pressure decreases, the greater atmospheric pressure expands the collapsed conducting passageways, and air is brought into contact with the respiratory membrane. After having once expanded, the alveoli continue to retain some air even during expiration. Since the lungs are elastic structures, expansion is "resisted" by the tendency to return to the initial size and shape. After initial expansion of the thorax the elastic recoil is, however, limited by the fluid "linkage" between the pleurae. In the newborn, intrapleural pressure is about 755 mm. of mercury, or about 5 mm. less than atmospheric pressure during inspiration, but becomes equal to atmospheric pressure during expiration. As growth occurs and the thoracic content is decreased by the shrinking of the thymus gland and rapid growth of the chest, the volume of the thorax becomes progressively greater than that of the deflated lungs. As a consequence, there is a progressive decrease in the intrapleural pressure which operates to stretch the lungs so that they continue to fill the thoracic cavity. In adults intrathoracic pressure during inspiration is between 4.5 and 9 mm. of mercury below atmospheric pressure; during expiration it becomes 3 to 6 mm. of mercury below the pressure of the outside air. Intrathoracic pressures are spoken of as negative pressures since they are always compared with atmospheric pressure; the values given above may be written as "—4.5 to —9 mm. of mercury" during inspiration and "—3 to —6 mm. of mercury" during expiration.

Inspiration. The size of the thorax is increased in all its diameters by the contraction of the muscles of respiration (Figs. 244, 245). When the diaphragm contracts, it descends and increases the vertical diameter. Contraction of the external intercostal muscles elevates the anterior extremities of the ribs so that they attain a more nearly horizontal position and the sternum becomes tilted about its upper articulation. This increases the anteroposterior diameter of the thorax. In addition, the lower ribs, whose axes are directed downward and outward, move outward as they are elevated. This, together with the eversion of the ribs as they are elevated, results in an increase in the lateral diameters of the thorax. The increase in the thoracic volume decreases the intrapulmonic pressure, so that atmospheric pressure causes air to enter the lungs and distend the alveoli until intrapulmonic pressure reaches that of the outside air.

Expiration.　On relaxation of the diaphragm and the accessory inspiratory muscles the thoracic volume is decreased. This is accomplished by the rebound of the costal cartilages which have been placed under tension during inspiration, the return of the somewhat stretched abdominal wall and the elastic recoil of the lungs; in addition, the force of gravity aids in restoring the chest to the expiratory position. It is now established that some muscular activity also is involved in the expiratory act. The muscles involved are the interosseous portions of the internal intercostals and, in some persons, the abdominal muscles, which show moderate contraction even during quiet respiration.

PULMONARY VENTILATION

Air Volumes in the Lungs.　The maximum volume of air which the lungs can contain may be divided into four portions. Three of these portions can be controlled voluntarily and constitute *vital capacity;* this represents the maximum volume of air which may be exchanged in a single respiration. A fourth portion represents the air volume which remains in the lungs as long as the thoracic cavity remains an air-tight compartment.

This volume, which is about 1200 cc. in the adult, is known as the *residual air.* Such a low volume can be attained only at the end of the most forcible expiratory effort. When the lungs are collapsed as a result of opening the thoracic cavity, most of the residual air escapes. Under conditions of quiet respiration (during rest or moderate activity) the lungs contain about 1800 cc. more air at the end of expiration; this portion, which represents the expiratory reserve, is known as *supplemental air.* A quiet inspiration adds an additional 500 cc., which is known as *tidal air.* Tidal air represents the volume which is inspired and expired by a person breathing quietly under conditions of rest or moderate activity. At the end of a normal inspiration an additional 1800 cc. may be taken in by a forcible inspiratory effort; this portion, which represents the inspiratory reserve, is known as *complemental air.*

These volumes are summarized in relation to respiratory exchange in Table 12.

It must be understood that, though the figures in the table are representative values, large variations exist in normal persons. Men have greater average vital capacities than women. People who show relatively low respiratory rates usually show large tidal volumes.

Respiratory Rates. In adults during rest the normal range of respiratory rate is between 12 to 20 per minute, although rates of 2 to 30 a minute have been observed in normal persons. In children rates of 20 to 25 per minute are normal.

Minute Volume. The minute respiratory volume is the product of the volume of air taken in at each breath and the number of breaths per minute. Minute volume is a more significant index of pulmonary ventilation than either rate or depth alone, since it is the product of these two that determines the supply of oxygen available for diffusion and the elimination of excess quantities of carbon dioxide. The initial adjustment to increased bodily activity is an increase in the depth of

Table 12

Air Volumes in Lungs

COMPONENT	VOLUME OF AIR REMAINING IN THE LUNGS AT THE END OF				VITAL CAPACITY
	Forcible Expiration	Quiet Expiration	Quiet Inspiration	Forcible Inspiration	
Residual air	1200 cc.	1200 cc.	1200 cc.	1200 cc.	
Supplemental air		1800 cc.	1800 cc.	1800 cc.	1800 cc.
Tidal air			500 cc.	500 cc.	500 cc.
Complemental air				1800 cc.	1800 cc.
Total air volume	1200 cc.	3000 cc.	3500 cc.	5300 cc.	4100 cc.

Table 13

Composition of Air in Volumes Per Cent

	INSPIRED AIR	EXPIRED AIR	ALVEOLAR AIR
Oxygen	20.96	15.8	14.0
Carbon dioxide	0.04	4.0	5.3
Nitrogen	79.00	80.2	80.7

respiration. As bodily activity reaches a high level and there is a demand for further increase in ventilation, the respiratory rate is increased.

Types of Respiration. Normal quiet breathing is known as *eupnea*. Increase in depth of respiration is called *hyperpnea;* if the depth is increased and expiration is forcible, it is called *dyspnea.* Respiration which is characterized by a rapid rate is designated by the term *polypnea;* when exceedingly high rates are attained, it is known as

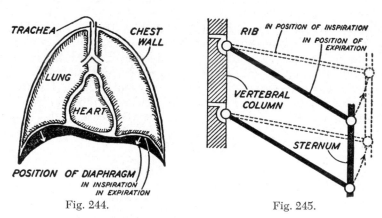

Fig. 244.   Fig. 245.

Fig. 244. Contraction of the diaphragmatic muscle in inspiration causes the diaphragm to descend (indicated by white arrows). The resultant increase in chest volume is indicated in black. A corresponding volume of air is drawn into the lungs. (Carlson and Johnson, The Machinery of the Body, University of Chicago Press.)

Fig. 245. Diagram of rib movements in breathing. Elevation of the front ends of the ribs, or of the sternum to which the ribs are attached, causes an increase in the front-back diameter of the chest. (Carlson and Johnson, The Machinery of the Body, University of Chicago Press.)

tachypnea. Cessation of respiration for short intervals of time is known as *apnea.*

Composition of the Air in Pulmonary Ventilation. It is apparent that if tidal inspiration and expiration involve an exchange of only 500 cc. of air and if the lungs contain 3000 cc. of air at the end of a normal expiration, the exchange of air in the alveoli must be far from complete. It would not, therefore, be expected that alveolar air would attain the same composition as atmospheric air at any phase in the respiratory cycle.

The degree of exchange of alveolar air is dependent upon (1) the volume of tidal air and the respiratory rate, (2) the capacity of the trachea, bronchi and bronchioles, which constitute the dead space in the air passageways, and (3) volume of air remaining in the lungs at the end of expiration.

The dead space of the air passageways has a volume of about 140 cc. of air, so that of 500 cc. of air taken in during a quiet inspiration only 360 cc. remain to be mixed with the 3000 cc. in the alveoli. From these figures it may be calculated that only 12 per cent of the air is renewed in a quiet respiratory cycle. Examination of Table 13 indicates the differences in composition in the inspired and expired air after their admixture with alveolar air. The composition of the alveolar air is maintained at physiologic levels of carbon dioxide and oxygen by the relatively small percentage renewal of the air during conditions of rest or light activity. The percentage renewal is increased during periods of greater activity by portions or all of the increases available through the exchange of supplemental and complemental volumes of air.

Nitrogen is an inert gas which is only slightly soluble in plasma. The nitrogen content of the blood is determined only by the amount which will dissolve in the plasma at nitrogen pressure in the alveolar air; nitrogen does not enter into the formation of compounds with the constituents of the plasma or corpuscles.

TRANSPORT OF BLOOD GASES

Oxygen Carriage. The exchange of oxygen between the alveoli and the blood stream takes place so rapidly that the arterial blood is nearly completely saturated; i.e., it has taken up oxygen to the extent of its capacity for the existing partial pressure of oxygen so that no increase would occur if the time were prolonged. One hundred centimeters of arterial blood contain about 20 cc. of oxygen; 19.5 cc. of the gas is carried in combination with hemoglobin (HHb) within the erythrocytes, and about 0.5 cc. is physically dissolved in the plasma. The combination of oxygen and hemoglobin is known as oxyhemoglobin (HHbO$_2$). One gram of hemoglobin can combine with 1.36 cc. of oxygen, when the partial pressure of the oxygen is 150 mm. of mercury or more. Since there are normally about 15 gm. of hemoglobin per 100 cc. of blood, we would expect the hemoglobin, under optimal conditions, to carry a little more than 20 cc. as oxyhemoglobin; i.e., the oxygen capacity would be 20 cc. per 100 cc. of blood. The degree of *oxygen saturation* is determined by the ratio, oxygen content : oxygen capacity. Since the oxygen partial pressure in the lungs is less than 150 mm. of mercury, the arterial blood is not completely saturated.

Hemoglobin is well adapted to respiratory functions since it is 97 per cent saturated at oxygen partial pressures of 100 mm. of mercury and about 90 per cent saturated at 70 mm. of mercury. This shows that it can take up a high per cent of its maximum load of oxygen at pressures which are lower than those normally occurring in alveolar air. Further, formation of oxyhemoglobin is favored by relatively low pressures of carbon dioxide; its dissociation is favored by the low oxygen pressures and the high carbon dioxide pressures which occur in the tissues. These properties are illustrated in Figures 246 and 247.

In the lungs the alveolar oxygen pressure is about 100 mm. of mercury and the carbon dioxide pressure about 40 mm. of mercury; the oxygen tension or pressure in the mixed venous blood returning to the lungs is about 40 mm. of mercury, and the carbon dioxide tension is

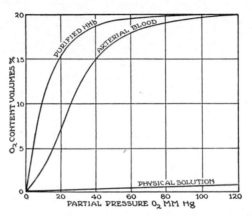

Fig. 246. Oxygen contents of arterial blood and plasma (physical solution) and solution of purified hemoglobin at various partial pressures of oxygen. Note difference in shape of absorption curves of purified hemoglobin and arterial blood and small amount of oxygen carried in physical solution. (After Barcroft.)

about 46 mm. of mercury. These pressure gradients and the affinity of hemoglobin (HHb) for oxygen favor oxyhemoglobin formation ($HHbO_2$); since oxyhemoglobin is a stronger acid than hemoglobin and since there is a lower partial pressure of carbon dioxide in the alveolar air than in the venous blood, the conditions are favorable for the release of carbon dioxide from the blood. During internal respiration, where pressures of oxygen in the tissues may be 30 mm. of mercury, or according to some observers considerably less, and the carbon dioxide pressures may be 50 to 60 mm. of mercury, conditions are strongly in favor of the breakdown of oxyhemoglobin and the release of oxygen to the cells. Since the blood is in motion, there is not time for diffusion to continue until the oxygen pressures in the blood and tissues are equal. The venous blood upon returning to the heart shows average values of 14 cc. of oxygen per 100 cc. of blood. In some of the circulatory pathways, reduction of the oxygen content of the blood may be carried further, especially if the local tissues are active. In other circuits the venous blood may show values for oxygen which are almost equal to those of arterial blood; resting tissues and marked local vasodilatation usually minimize the percentage reduction in oxygen content.

Carbon Dioxide Carriage. The pressure gradient of carbon dioxide between the tissues and the blood stream favors diffusion of this gas out of the tissues. Venous blood contains about 56 cc. of carbon dioxide per 100 cc. of blood. Ninety-five per cent of the carbon dioxide is carried in chemical combination with constituents of the blood, while the remaining 5 per cent is physically dissolved in the blood. As the carbon dioxide diffuses from the tissues to the blood stream, most of the gas enters into the red blood corpuscles; some of it enters directly into chemical combinations with the constituents of the plasma. The major chemical and physical changes are as follows:

I. *In the corpuscles:*

1. Carbon dioxide unites with water to form carbonic acid. This reaction is speeded up about 600 times by the presence of the enzyme carbonic anhydrase:

(*a*) $CO_2 + H_2O \xrightarrow{\text{carbonic anhydrase}} H_2CO_3$

Carbonic acid then dissociates into hydrogen and bicarbonate ions.

(*b*) $H_2CO_3 \rightleftarrows H^+ + HCO_3^-$

These ions interact with potassium hemoglobinate, capturing the K ion from the hemoglobin.

(*c*) K hemoglobinate + carbonic acid $\longrightarrow$ K bicarbonate + acid hemoglobin:

$$K\,Hb + H^+ + HCO_3^- \longrightarrow KHCO_3 + HHb.$$

2. A small fraction of the carbon dioxide is carried by hemoglobin as a carbamino type of compound.

$$HHb\,NH_2 + CO_2 \longrightarrow HHb\,NHCOOH$$

II. *In the plasma:*

1. Small amounts of HCO_3^- diffuse out of the cell and form sodium bicarbonate with the sodium ions of the plasma. The Cl^- ions of the plasma sodium chloride enter the corpuscles, replacing the HCO_3^- which has passed in the opposite direction. This exchange continues until an equilibrium is reached.

2. The carbon dioxide content of the plasma is increased by the migration of HCO_3^- from the corpuscles.

3. About 5 per cent of the carbon dioxide is physically dissolved in the plasma.

In the lungs the processes are reversed, with carbon dioxide leaving the corpuscles and plasma and the Cl⁻ ion leaving the red blood corpuscles.

The degree of alkalinity of the blood is determined chiefly by the ratio of carbonic acid (physically dissolved carbon dioxide) to the bicarbonates (HCO_3^- in combination with Na^+ and K^+). Respiration tends to maintain the blood in a slightly alkaline state by keeping this ratio nearly constant even under widely varying degrees of bodily activity.

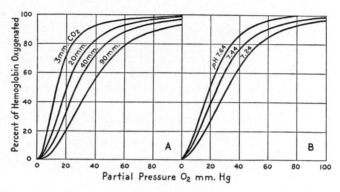

Fig. 247. *A*, Effect of carbon dioxide on oxygen dissociation curve of whole blood. (After Barcroft.) *B*, Effect of acidity on oxygen dissociation curve of blood. (After Peters and Van Slyke.)

REGULATION OF RESPIRATION

Ventilation of the lungs as affected by the depth and rate of respiration is under control of the respiratory center in the medulla oblongata. The respiratory center consists of an inspiratory center and an expiratory center. These centers in the medulla have nervous connections with higher centers in the brain. Impulses from various levels of the central nervous system act upon one another and affect the control of respiration. Afferent impulses, initiated by stimulation of stretch receptors located in the lungs, reach the medullary centers by way of afferent fibers in the vagus nerve; these afferent nerves also play a major role in the control of respiration. Efferent nerves pass from the centers to the muscles of respiration. The most important of these are the *phrenic nerves*, which arise from the cervical region of the cord and pass down, one on either side of the heart, to the diaphragm. The intercostal nerves arise from the thoracic portion of the cord to supply the intercostal muscles. Other efferents travel to the larynx, the muscles of the mouth, the external nares and the smooth muscles of the bronchioles. Figure 248 illustrates the nervous control of respiration.

The mechanism of rhythmic respiratory exchange may be visualized as being initiated by the action of the inspiratory neurons in the medulla, which are subject to constant chemical stimulation by their internal fluid environment, which, in turn, is dependent upon the composition of arterial blood. The expiratory neurons are also subject to constant chemical stimulation, but in general they are considered as having a higher threshold of response. The discharge of the inspiratory neurons spreads to the motor units which control inspiration. The excitation may reach the "pneumotaxic" center in the pons and to other levels. Experimentally, it may be shown that vagus afferent impulses from the lungs or impulses from the pneumotaxic center may terminate inspiration. In normal man the afferent vagus impulses, acting on the medullary centers directly or through the higher centers, exert the primary reflex control in terminating inspiration. Quiet breathing appears to result from repetitive interruption of a dominant activity of the inspiratory center. In rapid breathing the expiratory center becomes increasingly active in determining respiratory rate. These basic patterns of activity of the medullary centers are continually modified by afferent impulses from many nerves and by chemical influences which affect the centers directly or reflexly.

The most important factor in this chemical influence is carbon dioxide, which acts directly on the respiratory center and reflexly through chemoreceptors in the carotid and aortic bodies. Increase in the carbon dioxide content of the blood stimulates respiration, while a marked decrease in carbon dioxide content causes a decreased respiration or a period of apnea. The effects of carbon dioxide lack may be readily demonstrated by voluntarily breathing deeply and rapidly to blow off the carbon dioxide in the alveoli and diminish its content in the blood. After this period of overventilation, automatic breathing ceases entirely for a time and will not be reestablished until the carbon dioxide accumulates and its concentration again approaches the normal level.

With increased bodily activity there is consequent increase in the production of carbon dioxide and an increase in its content in the blood. This in turn raises the carbon dioxide content in the alveolar air so that the gradient between the blood and the alveoli is decreased and diffusion is initially reduced. As a result the blood retains more of the gas in passing through the lungs and the excess stimulates the respiratory center and the chemoreceptors. This acts to increase the discharge from the respiratory center which in turn brings about increased activity of the muscles concerned with respiration through

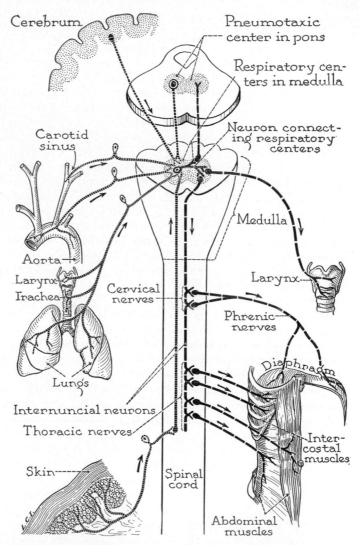

Fig. 248. Diagram to illustrate the nervous control of respiration. Nerves on the left carry impulses to the respiratory centers; those on the right carry impulses from the respiratory centers to the muscles of respiration. The course of afferent impulses from the muscles is not shown.

excitation of their motor nerves. The resulting increase in ventilation augments the renewal of alveolar air and lowers its carbon dioxide content. The decrease in carbon dioxide content increases the passage of carbon dioxide from the blood. Changes in H^+ ion concentration which are intimately related to dissolved and combined carbon dioxide of the blood may cause changes in respiration by acting either directly or reflexly in the same manner as carbon dioxide.

Oxygen lack acts upon the chemoreceptors of the carotid body and aortic arch to increase respiration. This mechanism is called into play only when the oxygen content of the blood is significantly reduced. It is probable that the only effect of decreased oxygen on the respiratory center is a depression such as is characteristic of its action on nerve tissues in general. Oxygen excesses may stimulate respiration; the mechanism of this response has not been explained to the satisfaction of many observers.

The reflex mechanism initiated by stimulation of the proprioceptor endings of the vagus nerve, which has been described as a major factor in the control of respiration, is known as the *Hering-Breuer reflex*. As the lungs become inflated during inspiration, sensory nerve endings within the lung tissue are stimulated by stretching. This starts a series of inhibitory impulses in the afferent nerves traveling to the respiratory center. This discharge of impulses occurs at a progressively increased rate as inflation proceeds until it reaches a critical level for inhibition of the inspiratory phase. There is evidence for the existence of a second set of receptors which act to terminate expiration, but these endings come into action only when there is marked deflation of the lungs.

Stimulation of almost any sensory nerve may result in either inhibition or stimulation of respiration. Cold or painful stimulation of the skin or other parts of the body modifies respiration. If an irritating gas such as ammonia is inhaled, inspiration is suddenly arrested. The fumes of the gas reaching the trachea and larynx set up nerve impulses which act upon the center to inhibit inspiration and stimulate expiration. This is a protective reflex by which injury to the lungs may be prevented. The presence of fluids in the region of the larynx similarly inhibits inspiration and causes closure of the glottis. Respiration is normally inhibited during swallowing.

Evidence for the influence of the higher centers on respiration may be seen in the extent of voluntary control in talking, singing, whistling, blowing and in holding the breath for a limited time. Under usual conditions respiratory movements proceed automatically and rhythmically.

The major components entering into control of respiration have been summarized in the chart on page 414.

Factors in the Regulation of Respiration

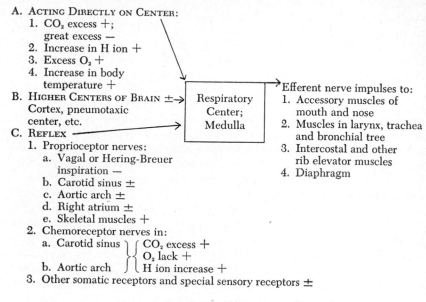

A. ACTING DIRECTLY ON CENTER:
   1. CO_2 excess +;
      great excess −
   2. Increase in H ion +
   3. Excess O_2 +
   4. Increase in body
      temperature +
B. HIGHER CENTERS OF BRAIN ±→
   Cortex, pneumotaxic
   center, etc.
C. REFLEX
   1. Proprioceptor nerves:
      a. Vagal or Hering-Breuer
         inspiration −
      b. Carotid sinus ±
      c. Aortic arch ±
      d. Right atrium ±
      e. Skeletal muscles +
   2. Chemoreceptor nerves in:
      a. Carotid sinus ⎫ ⎧ CO_2 excess +
                        ⎬ ⎨ O_2 lack +
      b. Aortic arch   ⎭ ⎩ H ion increase +
   3. Other somatic receptors and special sensory receptors ±

Respiratory
Center;
Medulla

Efferent nerve impulses to:
1. Accessory muscles of
   mouth and nose
2. Muscles in larynx, trachea
   and bronchial tree
3. Intercostal and other
   rib elevator muscles
4. Diaphragm

THE ANOXIAS

Failure at any link in the chain of events in external or internal respiration may result in anoxia. If the supply of oxygen from the outside air is reduced or cut off, the condition is known as *anoxic anoxia.* This would occur if the trachea were closed either by a foreign body or by choking; it may also result from the decreased partial pressure of oxygen at high altitudes. The percentage of oxygen remains constant with increasing altitude (i.e., 20.9 or roughly 1/5), but the partial pressure is reduced. For example, the total barometric pressure at 30,000 feet is 326 mm. of mercury; $1/5 \times 326 = 65.2$ mm. of mercury oxygen partial pressure in outside air. This is insufficient to sustain life, so that consciousness is soon lost and death results if the inspired air is not enriched by the addition of pure oxygen within a short time. It is for this reason that modern transport aircraft pressurize their cabins so that the cabin pressure is not less than the barometric pressure at 8000 feet (i.e., 560 mm. of mercury) even when the flight altitude is 25,000 or 30,000 feet.

If the transport of oxygen is interfered with by circulatory failure, the resulting condition is known as *stagnant anoxia;* if transport fails through stable chemical combination of carbon monoxide with hemoglobin which prevents the formation of oxyhemoglobin, or through a marked decrease in the amount of hemoglobin in the blood, the condition is known as *anemic anoxia*. Poisoning of the enzyme systems which catalyze the reactions in internal respiration results in *histotoxic anoxia*.

SUMMARY

In inspiration the size of the thorax is increased in all its diameters by the contraction of the muscles of respiration. The intrapulmonic pressure is thereby decreased, and air rushes into the lungs until intrapulmonic pressure again equals atmospheric pressure.

In expiration, relaxation of the muscles of respiration decreases the thoracic volume. Intrapulmonic pressure is now greater than atmospheric pressure, and air rushes out during this period until the pressure within the lungs is reduced to that of the atmosphere.

Intrathoracic pressure is less than atmospheric pressure at all times, but this negative pressure is increased to a considerable degree during inspiration.

The vital capacity of the lungs represents the maximum volume which can be exchanged in a single respiration.

The vital capacity is about 4100 cc. It consists of the complemental, supplemental and tidal air.

The residual air is the portion which can exist in the lungs at any time as long as the thoracic cavity remains an air-tight compartment.

The minute volume is the product of the volume of air taken in at each breath times the respiratory rate per unit of time.

Oxygen is carried in the blood in solution in the plasma, and in combination with the hemoglobin of the red blood corpuscles as oxyhemoglobin.

Carbon dioxide is carried in the blood in solution in the plasma, in the form of $NaHCO_3$ in the plasma, and as $KHCO_3$ and a carbamino compound in the red blood corpuscles.

Respiration is under the control of the respiratory centers in the medulla and pons.

The activity of the center is continually modified by impulses reaching it over afferent nerves or by chemical influences which affect the center either directly or reflexly.

The term "anoxia" is used to describe a condition in which the oxygen supply is inadequate to meet the oxygen requirements for the particular level of bodily activity. The types of anoxia include anoxic anoxia, stagnant anoxia, anemic anoxia and histotoxic anoxia.

QUESTIONS FOR DISCUSSION

1. Distinguish between intrapulmonic and intrathoracic pressures.

2. List all the factors which tend to decrease the thoracic volume in expiration.

3. Compare the amount of oxygen carried by blood plasma with the amount carried by the hemoglobin of the erythrocytes. Estimate approximately the number of cubic centimeters of oxygen carried by the total blood volume of the body.

4. Give an example which shows the close correlation of the respiratory mechanisms with bodily activity.

5. Describe the influence of eating and of talking on the respiratory pattern. Give illustrations of the influence of the cerebral cortex on respiration.

Chapter 23

The Digestive System

INTRODUCTION

THERE ARE two drives which cause man to seek food: one of these is called hunger; the other is called appetite. *Hunger* is a primitive, elemental sensation which is subjectively perceived as a dull or gnawing pain referred to the midchest region or somewhat below it. It is caused by waves of contraction of the musculature of the empty stomach.

Table 14

Time After Swallowing

	ARRIVAL IN STOMACH	ARRIVAL IN SMALL INTESTINE	ARRIVAL IN LARGE INTESTINE	EXCRETION OF RESIDUES FROM G. I. TRACT
From	6 sec. (liquids)	5 min.	4– 5 hrs. ⎫	
To	30–60 sec. or more (solids)	4 hrs.	12–15 hrs. ⎬	24–72 hrs.

Appetite, on the other hand, is a cerebral response. It is the wish for desirable or palatable foods which may arise from seeing or smelling foods or even merely thinking of them.

Once the food is eaten, the entire digestive system is directed toward its preparation for absorption into the blood stream. This preparation involves both chemical and mechanical activities. For proper nutrition to result, sufficient time must be allowed in each of the divisions of the digestive tract so that the digestion and absorption may continue to completion. Table 14 indicates the approximate time during which food remains in the different portions of the digestive tract.

417

The structures involved in the chemical and mechanical processes in the mouth are under the control of the central nervous system (see p. 126). In the remainder of the alimentary tract these activities are under the control of the autonomic system or chemical mechanisms, so that we are not normally aware of their occurrence. Final elimination of food residues by defecation is normally under voluntary control in that it may be consciously inhibited or facilitated.

ARCHITECTURE OF THE DIGESTIVE SYSTEM

The Alimentary Canal. The digestive system (Fig. 249) consists of the alimentary canal, a tube about 9 meters long extending from the mouth to the anus, and a number of related portions, the accessory organs. The alimentary canal is formed by the mouth, pharynx, esophagus, stomach, small intestine, large intestine and rectum. Associated with the canal are the accessory structures, salivary glands, liver, gallbladder and pancreas.

Though the different regions of the alimentary tract have individual and special features, the tube conforms to a definite structural plan from the esophagus to the rectum. From within outward there are the following layers: mucous, submucous, muscular and serous (Fig. 250).

The *mucous layer* is composed of a superficial epithelium, an underlying supporting connective tissue and a relatively thin arrangement of smooth muscle fibers, or muscularis mucosae. In the esophagus, the epithelium is of the stratified squamous type, but the stomach and intestines have a simple columnar epithelium. The cells of the mucosa secrete digestive juices and mucus. Those secreting digestive enzymes are usually arranged in the form of tubular glands. Sensory nerve fibers have been found in the epithelium. Accumulations of lymphoid tissue often occur in the connective tissue of the mucosa.

The *submucous layer* is composed of areolar connective tissue which connects the mucous and muscular coats and provides an adjustable basis for movements and changes in size of the tube. This layer supports numerous lymphatics, blood vessels and nerves. Thoracolumbar nerve endings from cells in the celiac, superior and inferior mesenteric ganglia are found around the blood vessels. Ganglion cells of the submucous plexus of Meissner synapse here with craniosacral endings from vagal and sacral nerves.

The *muscular coat* consists of smooth muscle arranged in two layers: an inner circular one surrounding the tube, and an outer longitudinal one whose fibers run parallel with the long axis. Contraction of the circular layer narrows the lumen of the tube, and contraction of the longitudinal layer shortens the tube. At several points along the canal

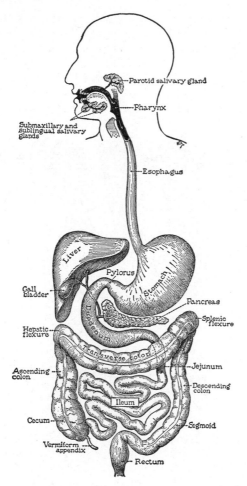

Fig. 249. Diagram of the organs of the digestive system. (Clendening, The Human Body, courtesy of Alfred A. Knopf, Inc.)

the circular layer is thickened to form sphincters, or valves, which are closed by contraction of these muscle fibers. Autonomic nerve endings comparable to those of submucosa are located in the muscular coat. Vagal and sacral nerves synapse with ganglion cells of the myenteric plexus of Auerbach.

In the esophagus the *serous* layer is lacking and the outer coat is fibrous in nature. The portions of the alimentary tract lying below the esophagus are contained in the abdomen; these structures are covered with the outer serous layer, the peritoneum. The *peritoneum* has two layers: a parietal layer, which completely lines the abdominal cavity, and a visceral layer, which is reflected over the organs contained within the cavity (Fig. 251). The term "abdomen," or abdominal cavity, is used here to indicate the region enclosed by the muscular and bony walls, and the term "peritoneal cavity," the spaces which may exist between the parietal and the visceral layers of the peritoneum.

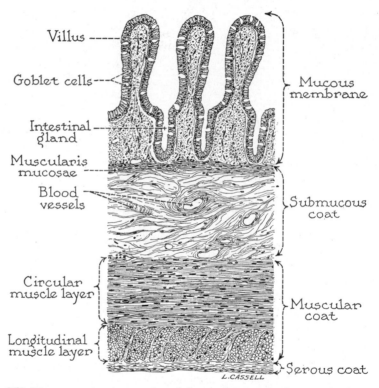

Fig. 250. Diagrammatic cross section of the small intestine, showing the four coats which form a conspicuous structural feature throughout the gastrointestinal tract.

Certain folds of the visceral layer receive special names. The portion which passes from the inferior surface of the liver to the lesser curvature of the stomach is the *lesser omentum;* the fold extending from the greater curvature of the stomach to the transverse colon is the *greater omentum.* This fold is the most conspicuous of all and spreads out like an apron over the intestines. From the transverse colon the peritoneum is carried backward to the posterior abdominal wall as the *transverse mesocolon*. A fan-shaped membrane, the *mesentery*, attaches the small intestine to the posterior abdominal wall. The peritoneum is arranged in such a manner that two cavities are formed; the greater or main cavity, and the lesser cavity or omental bursa (Fig. 251). The omental bursa lies posterior to the stomach; its walls

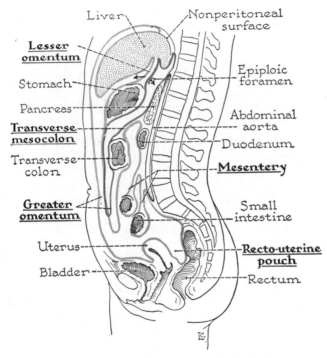

Fig. 251. Diagrammatic midsagittal section of female body to show peritoneal reflections. The greater sac of the peritoneum is shown in green; the omental bursa in red.

are formed principally by the lesser omentum, greater omentum and transverse mesocolon. A connection between the two cavities is provided by the epiploic foramen.

MOUTH. The mouth is the first division of the alimentary canal. The lips form the anterior boundary and the glossopalatine arch the posterior limit, at which point it leads into the pharynx. The roof is formed by the palate, the floor by the tongue, and the lateral walls by the cheeks. It houses the teeth, which are embedded in the upper and lower jaws. It is lined with stratified squamous epithelium which is continuous with that of the pharynx. The salivary glands empty their secretions into the mouth.

The *tongue* is a muscular organ. The mucous membrane covering the upper surface shows numerous elevations, the *papillae*. There are three varieties: filiform, fungiform, and vallate. Figure 252 and Figure 69, page 134, show papillae on the dorsal surface of the tongue.

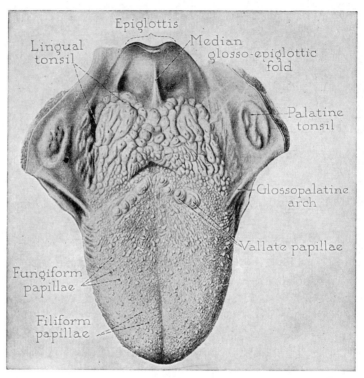

Fig. 252. The dorsal surface of the tongue. (Sobotta and McMurrich.)

The filiform and fungiform papillae are scattered over the anterior two-thirds of the tongue; the latter, less numerous, appear as red points chiefly near the edges. The vallate papillae, numbering ten to twelve, are arranged in the form of a V on the posterior part of the tongue. The apex of the V is directed toward the pharynx. The end organs of taste, the taste buds, are distributed over the surface of the tongue, but are most conspicuous on the sides of the vallate papillae. The tongue is supplied through the cranial nerves (p. 126) which serve the functions of taste, general sensation and movement.

TEETH.   The teeth begin to form early in embryonic life, about the seventh week. They develop from the ectoderm (oral epithelium) and mesoderm, but do not begin to erupt until the infant is about six or seven months old.

There are two sets of teeth: first the deciduous or milk teeth, and later the permanent teeth. The *deciduous teeth* are twenty in number, ten in each jaw. Beginning at the center in each half jaw there are

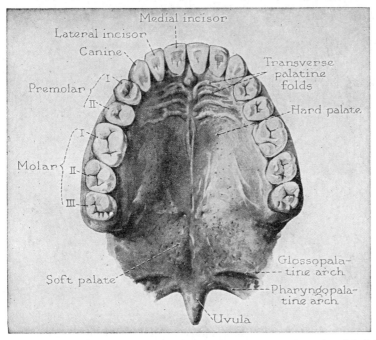

Fig. 253. The palate with superior dental arch seen from below. (Modified from Spalteholz.)

two incisors, one canine and two molars. Their eruptions begin about the sixth or seventh month and end usually at two and one half years. The *permanent teeth* (Figs. 253, 254) are thirty-two in number, sixteen in each jaw. Beginning at the center in each half jaw there are two incisors, one canine, two premolars and three molars. The permanent teeth begin to erupt about the sixth year, and the full complement may not be attained until the twenty-fifth year. The incisors have sharp, chisel-like edges for biting and tearing; the premolars and molars have flattened, irregular surfaces for grinding. The third molars are called the "wisdom teeth."

The structure of a tooth consists of an exposed portion protruding from the gums, called the *crown,* a portion embedded in the socket, or alveolus, of the jaw bone, called the *root,* and a portion connecting the crown and root, known as the *neck.* The neck is covered by the gum.

Examination of a vertical section of a tooth (Fig. 255) shows it to be composed of a solid outer portion and a central pulp cavity. The solid portion consists of an ivory substance, dentine, which forms the

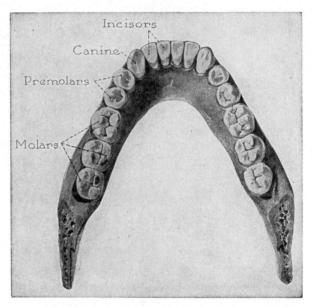

Fig. 254. The inferior dental arch from above. (Modified from Spalteholz.)

main body of the tooth, and an adamant substance, enamel, which covers the crown. The enamel is the hardest substance in the body. The root of the tooth is covered by a thin layer of hard material, the substantia ossea or cement. The tooth socket is lined with periosteum which supplies nourishment and serves to attach the tooth to the socket. The pulp cavity extends lengthwise through the center of the tooth; blood vessels and nerves enter it through openings in the root tip.

PHARYNX.   The structure of the pharynx has been described on page 391. The *palatine tonsils* are on the lateral walls of the oral pharynx between the glossopalatine and pharyngopalatine arches. They are oval masses of lymphoid tissue in the connective tissue of the mucous membrane. Ten to twenty deep crypts open on the exposed surface. The tonsils participate in the formation of new lymphocytes; this is the only established function which can be ascribed to them. The oral and laryngeal portions of the pharynx serve as a channel for the passage of both food and air; food is conducted through it from the mouth to the esophagus, and air from the nasal pharynx

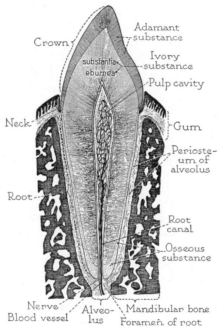

Fig. 255. Longitudinal section of a tooth in its alveolus (diagrammatic). (Sobotta and McMurrich.)

to the larynx. When swallowing occurs, the soft palate is pushed backward against the posterior pharyngeal wall, closing the passage to the nose; the larynx is elevated, and its superior aperture is protected by a projecting ledge formed by the epiglottis.

ESOPHAGUS. The esophagus is a muscular tube about 25 cm. (10 inches) long, which conveys food from the pharynx to the stomach. It lies posterior to the trachea and the heart and just in front of the vertebrae. In the lower part of its course it sweeps in front of the aorta, passing through the diaphragm at the left of the median line to end in the stomach. Its walls conform to the general plan described earlier in this chapter.

The remaining portions of the alimentary canal are contained in the abdomen, which is the largest cavity in the body and extends from the thorax to the floor of the pelvis. For descriptive purposes, the abdomen or abdominal cavity is artificially divided into an upper portion, the abdomen proper, and a lower part, the pelvis. The abdomi-

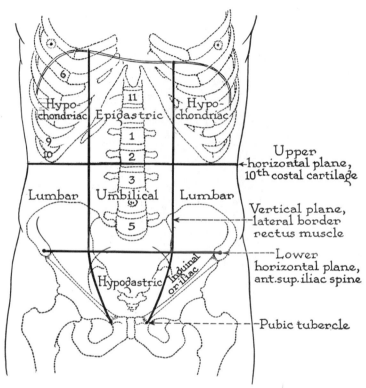

Fig. 256. Diagram of the abdominal regions.

nal cavity proper is bounded above by the diaphragm, below by the brim of the lesser pelvis, behind by the vertebral column, quadratus lumborum and psoas muscles, and in front and at the sides by the abdominal muscles and the iliac muscles. The upper boundary formed by the dome of the diaphragm extends high into the thorax and lies well under the shelter of the ribs.

In order to locate the organs of the abdominal cavity proper, the anterior surface of the abdomen is divided by two horizontal and two vertical planes into nine regions (Fig. 256). The upper horizontal plane passes through the body at the lowest point of the tenth costal cartilages; the lower horizontal plane passes through the anterior superior iliac spines. The longitudinal planes coincide with the lateral margins of the rectus muscles extending from the costal borders to the pubic spines. The central regions from above downward are epigastric, umbilical and hypogastric. On either side in the same order are the right and left hypochondriac, the right and left abdominal or lumbar and right and left inguinal or iliac regions.

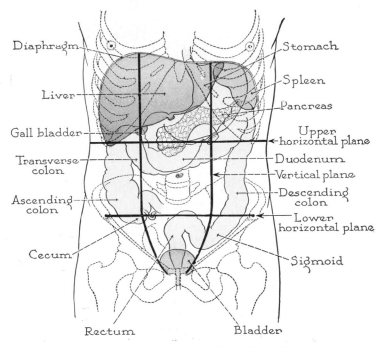

Fig. 257. Surface projection of the abdominal viscera.

STOMACH (Fig. 258). The stomach is a dilated portion of the alimentary canal lying in the upper abdomen just under the diaphragm on the left. It may be thought of as a retaining and mixing reservoir in which the chemical phases of digestion begin. The opening into the esophagus is called the *cardiac orifice*, since it is just below the heart; and the opening into the small intestine is the *pyloric orifice*. The two borders of the stomach pass between these orifices. The right border or lesser curvature is short and somewhat concave; the left border or greater curvature is long and convex.

The stomach is composed of a central portion, the body, a balloon-like portion to the left, the fundus, and a constricted portion to the right, the pylorus. A notch on the lesser curvature, the incisura angularis, marks off the body from the pylorus. The shape and position of the stomach show great variations, not only among different people, but in the same person at different times. The organ is situated in the left hypochondriac and epigastric regions, but frequently, especially

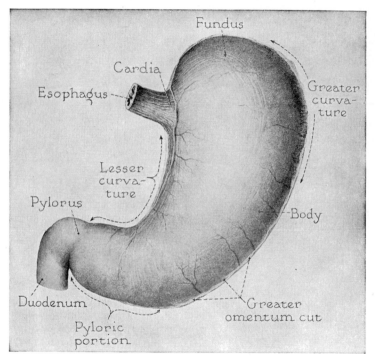

Fig. 258. The stomach with its peritoneal covering, from in front. (Sobotta and McMurrich.)

when distended, it extends into the umbilical and right hypochondriac regions. X-rays taken of man standing erect show that when the stomach is filled with food it assumes an almost vertical position and has a tubular shape. Because of the sharp angle formed at the junction of body and pylorus, its shape has been likened to the letter J. The mucous membrane is smooth when the organ is full, but is thrown into folds, called *rugae*, when empty. The mucous membrane contains the secreting cells of the stomach, which are arranged in small tubular units to form the gastric glands. The glands of the fundus (Fig. 259) and body are most important in the secretion of gastric juice. There are four types of cells in these glands; the chief cells and the parietal cells will be described. The *chief* or *zymogenic cells* are simple colum-

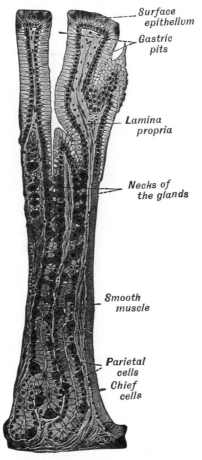

Fig. 259. Fundic glands of the stomach of an executed man. Chief or zymogenic cells, gray; parietal cells, dark gray. × 130. (Maximow and Bloom, after Braus.)

nar cells which form a continuous lining for the tubule; they secrete *pepsin* and *chymosin* or rennin. The *parietal cells* are scattered here and there along the tubule between the chief cells and the underlying membrane; they secrete *hydrochloric acid.*

The muscular coat, in addition to circular and longitudinal layers, has an inner layer in which the fibers run obliquely. The circular layer is thickened at the cardiac and pyloric orifices to form sphincters.

SMALL INTESTINE. The small intestine is a thin-walled muscular tube about 7 meters (20 feet) long. It is divided into three portions; the duodenum, the jejunum and the ileum. The *duodenum*, the shortest of the three, is 25 cm. long. It is attached to the posterior abdominal wall and arranged in a horseshoe shape to enclose the head of the pancreas. The bile and pancreatic ducts open into the duodenum

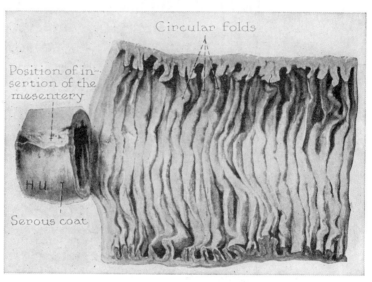

Fig. 260. Circular folds of small intestine as seen in a portion of the jejunum. (Modified from Spalteholz.)

about 8 to 10 cm. from the pylorus. The jejunum and ileum continue from the duodenum until the latter connects with the large intestine at the cecum. The *jejunum* is about 2.2 meters (7½ feet) long, the ileum is between 3 and 4 meters. These two portions of the small intestine are suspended from the posterior abdominal wall in the fan-like fold of peritoneum, the mesentery.

Although the three portions differ slightly, their structural principle is the same throughout. The four coats of the alimentary canal previously described are most perfectly represented in the small intestine. Certain features of especial interest are the villi, the circular folds and the glands. The circular folds and the villi of the mucous layer are structural devices which increase the surface enormously. Beginning a short distance from the pylorus, the circular folds (Fig. 260) are numerous and high in the duodenum and first portion of the jejunum, but from this point on they gradually become less numerous and smaller and fade out completely about the middle of the ileum. They are permanent structures and do not disappear when the wall is distended. The villi (Fig. 261) are small finger-like or leaflike out-

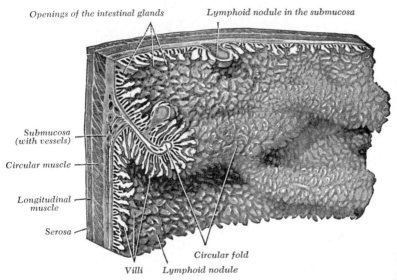

Fig. 261. Portion of wall of small intestine, showing villi and a circular fold. (Maximow and Bloom, after Braus.)

growths of the mucous membrane. They are closely crowded over the entire surface of the mucosa, covering the sides and crests of the folds as well as the spaces between them. They give a velvety appearance to the surface. Each villus is covered by a layer of simple columnar epithelium and contains a capillary loop, a central lymphatic (lacteal), connective tissue and smooth muscle (Fig. 262). The presence of about 5,000,000 villi in the intestine provides an absorbing surface of some 10 square meters.

The *intestinal glands* or crypts of Lieberkühn are found throughout the small and large intestines. They have the form of a simple tube. In the small intestine they are placed between the villi and secrete the intestinal juice containing the digestive enzymes.

The *duodenal glands* or Brunner's glands are found only in the duodenum. They are tortuous and branching; their secretion is alkaline and contains mucus.

Lymphoid tissue is present in the form of nodules throughout the small intestine. The nodules may appear singly as the solitary nodules or be massed together as the *aggregated nodules* or Peyer's patches (Fig. 263). The solitary nodules are scattered all over the intestine, but are larger and more numerous in the distal part. Aggregated nodules are found chiefly in the ileum. They are always located on the side of the intestinal wall opposite to the line of attachment of the

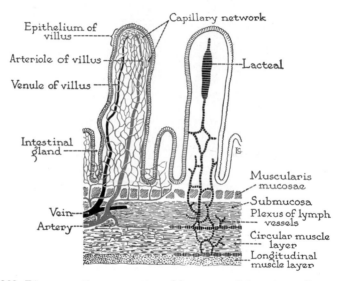

Fig. 262. Diagrammatic cross section of human small intestine; villus at the left shown with blood vessels only, that at the right with lacteal only, but both occur in all villi. (After F. P. Mall.)

mesentery. They are oval, slightly elevated areas varying in length from 12 to 20 mm.

LARGE INTESTINE (Fig. 257). The remaining portion of the alimentary canal is the large intestine. It is about 1.5 meters long and is divided into cecum, colon and rectum.

The *cecum* is that part of the large intestine below the attachment of the ileum. It is a blind pouch from the lower portion of which projects the appendix. At the opening of the ileum into the cecum is the colic or ileocecal valve, a true sphincter, which controls the passage of the intestinal contents into the cecum.

The *colon* is divided into ascending, transverse, descending and sigmoid portions.

The ascending colon passes upward on the right of the abdomen from the cecum to the anterior surface of the liver, where it bends to become the transverse colon. This bend is called the hepatic flexure. The transverse colon sweeps across the abdominal cavity from right to left below the stomach. It is attached to the posterior abdominal wall by a peritoneal fold, the transverse mesocolon. At the spleen it bends downward to become the descending colon. This bend is the splenic flexure. The descending colon extends downward along the left side of the abdomen to the brim of the pelvis. From this point the colon

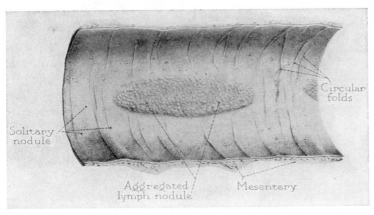

Fig. 263. Portion of lower ileum opened along its entire length, showing an aggregated lymph nodule. (Sobotta and McMurrich.)

courses in a curve like the letter S as far as the third segment of the sacrum, where it becomes the rectum. The S-shaped curve is called the sigmoid colon.

The walls of the large intestine (Fig. 264) conform to the general structural plan and have the usual four layers. The mucous layer is like that of the small intestine, but there are no villi and no circular folds. The intestinal glands are present, but they secrete chiefly mucus. Lymphoid tissue is present in solitary nodules, but there are no aggregated nodules. The muscular layer shows a striking difference; the longitudinal layer does not completely surround the intestine, but is confined to three narrow bands called teniae, placed at nearly equal distances from each other. The teniae shirr the tube into sacculations known as haustra. The inner aspect presents semilunar folds between the haustra which correspond to the creases on the outer surface. The serous coat is marked by little pouches of peritoneum containing fat. These are the *epiploic appendages*.

RECTUM. The *rectum*, which is 15 to 20 cm. long, descends along the hollow of the sacrum and coccyx to end in the lower opening, the anus. The opening is guarded by two sphincters, internal and external. The internal sphincter is smooth muscle tissue and is formed by a thickening of the circular fibers of the muscular coat. The external

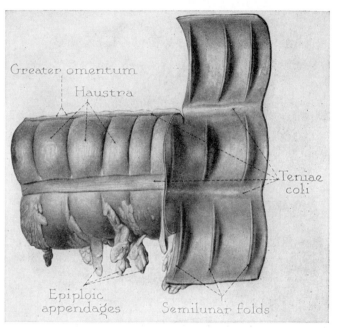

Fig. 264. A portion of the transverse colon from in front and below. The right end is opened up. (Sobotta and McMurrich.)

sphincter is striated muscle tissue formed by a separate muscle encircling the lower end of the rectum.

Accessory Digestive Organs. The glandular accessory digestive organs develop in the embryo as epithelial evaginations from the entoderm layer. They retain their connection with the alimentary canal through their ducts. These organs are the salivary glands, liver, gallbladder and pancreas (Figs. 265, 266, 267).

SALIVARY GLANDS (Fig. 265). The large salivary glands consist of the parotid, in front of and below the ear, the submaxillary, below the mandible, and the sublingual, in the floor of the mouth under the tongue. Ducts from the three pairs of glands open into the mouth.

The glands are classified according to the type of their secreting cells into mucous, serous and mixed glands. The mixed glands contain both serous and mucus-secreting cells. The parotid gland is a serous gland; the submaxillary and sublingual glands are mixed glands. These glands secrete only in response to mechanical, thermal and chemical stimuli applied to the mucous membrane of the mouth or as a result of psychic or olfactory stimuli.

THE LIVER (Fig. 266).   The liver is the largest gland of the body, weighing 1.5 kilograms in men and somewhat less in women. It is

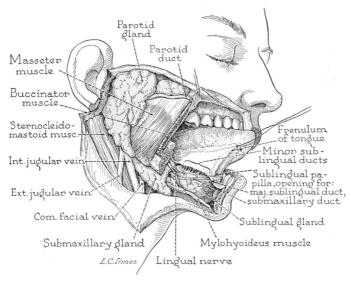

Fig. 265. The salivary glands on the right side of the face.

a soft, plastic organ, which is molded by surrounding structures. It occupies chiefly the upper right hypochondriac and epigastric regions directly beneath the diaphragm. There are two principal *lobes,* the right and the left. The right lobe consists of the right lobe proper, with the small quadrate lobe on the inferior surface and the caudate lobe on the posterior surface. The line of demarcation between the right and left lobes is indicated on the anterior and superior surfaces by the falciform ligament, which passes from the liver to the diaphragm and the anterior abdominal wall. The ligament is a remnant of the anterior mesentery and conveys on its free border a fibrous cord, the occluded umbilical vein, now the *round ligament.* The surface of the liver is covered with peritoneum with the exception of a small area on its posterior surface which is attached directly to the diaphragm. Beneath the peritoneum is a dense connective tissue layer called the capsule of Glisson, which covers the entire surface of the organ, and at the hilum or porta is continued into the liver substance, forming a framework for the branches of the portal vein. hepatic artery and bile ducts.

MICROSCOPIC STRUCTURE (Figs. 268, 269).   The cells of the liver are arranged in architectural units, called *lobules*. These are elongated polygonal structures, having five, six or seven sides. Running lengthwise through the center of the lobule is the central or intralobular vein. Encircling the periphery of the lobule are the branches of the portal vein, called interlobular veins, interlobular bile ducts and branches of the hepatic artery. The interlobular veins break up into sinusoids which enter the lobule at the periphery. A study of the diagram of a lobule (Fig. 268) in connection with the microscopic section (Fig. 269) will help in the understanding of the structure of a liver lobule.

The liver cells are arranged in cords which radiate from the central vein to the periphery of the lobule. Between the cords lie the liver sinusoids. Each liver cell cord consists of two adjacent rows of hepatic cells between which runs a thin bile canaliculus which passes to the periphery of the lobule to join the interlobular bile ducts. The close relationship of hepatic cells, bile canaliculi and sinusoids allows an easy exchange of nutrient materials from circulation to liver cells, and the products of their metabolism back to circulation, while the bile manufactured by hepatic cells can be emptied readily into bile canaliculi (Fig. 268).

The sinusoids are irregular blood channels formed by a discontinuous layer of squamous cells to which histiocytes are attached by delicate strands. The histiocytes of the liver are called Kupffer's cells (Fig. 270). The sinusoids lead in a radial manner toward the middle of the lobule, like the spokes of a wheel to the hub, and empty into the central vein. They receive branches of the hepatic artery at the periphery of the lobule.

SUMMARY OF CIRCULATION.   Blood is brought to the liver from two sources: from the digestive tract and spleen by the portal vein, and from the aorta through the hepatic artery.

The *portal vein* is unique in that it is interposed between two capillary beds: one in the liver, the other in the digestive area which it drains. The portal vein on entering the liver divides into branches approximating the circumference of the lobule (Figs. 268, 269). These branches in turn give off interlobular veins which run between the lobules. These give rise to the sinusoids which run between the cords

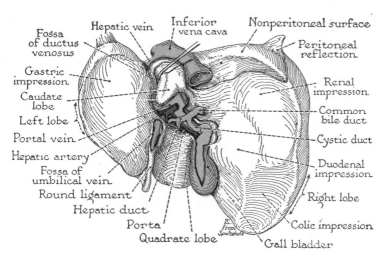

Fossa of ductus venosus — Hepatic vein — Inferior vena cava — Nonperitoneal surface

Gastric impression

Caudate lobe

Left lobe

Portal vein

Hepatic artery

Fossa of umbilical vein

Round ligament

Hepatic duct

Porta

Quadrate lobe

Peritoneal reflection

Renal impression

Common bile duct

Cystic duct

Duodenal impression

Right lobe

Colic impression

Gall bladder

Fig. 266. The liver from below and behind. (After Spalteholz.)

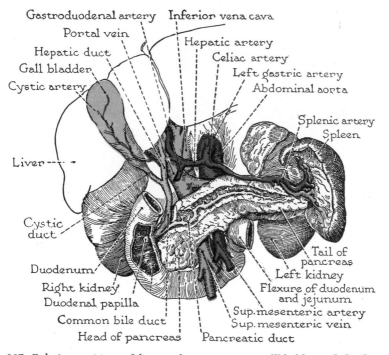

Gastroduodenal artery   Inferior vena cava

Portal vein

Hepatic duct

Gall bladder

Cystic artery

Hepatic artery

Celiac artery

Left gastric artery

Abdominal aorta

Splenic artery

Spleen

Liver

Cystic duct

Duodenum

Right kidney

Duodenal papilla

Common bile duct

Head of pancreas

Tail of pancreas

Left kidney

Flexure of duodenum and jejunum

Sup. mesenteric artery

Sup. mesenteric vein

Pancreatic duct

Fig. 267. Relative positions of liver, spleen, pancreas, gallbladder and duodenum.
(Eycleshymer-Jones, Hand Atlas of Clinical Anatomy. Lea & Febiger.)

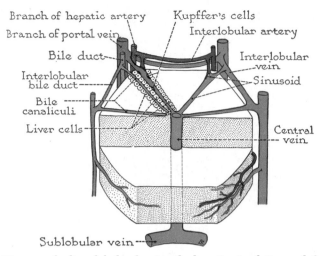

Fig. 268. Diagram of a liver lobule, showing the hepatic circulation and the relation of liver cells to sinusoids and bile canaliculi.

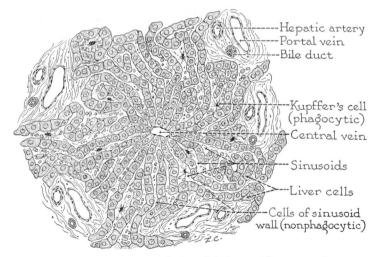

Fig. 269. Cross section of a liver lobule, semidiagrammatic.

of hepatic cells to enter the central veins. Central veins of several lobules join to form the sublobular veins, which in turn unite to form the hepatic veins. The hepatic veins, usually two or three in number, empty into the inferior vena cava.

The *hepatic artery* is distributed chiefly to the interlobular connective tissue and its contained structures. Its finest branches empty into the sinusoids at the circumference of the lobule. The hepatic artery contributes about one fourth of the total blood supply of the liver. However, the liver is dependent upon this fraction for its oxygen supply.

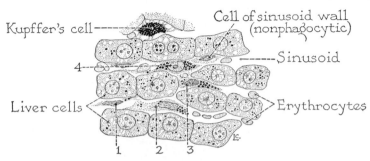

Fig. 270. Liver of a rabbit injected intravenously with India ink. Kupffer's cells (histiocytes) have engulfed granules of India ink. Kupffer's cell at top is packed with granules; cells (1–4) in sinusoids below are in transitional stages. (Redrawn from Maximow and Bloom.)

FUNCTIONS.   The functions of the liver are summarized to describe the extent and versatility of the activities of this important gland. They include:

1. Formation of bile
2. Activity of reticuloendothelial tissues
   Hemopoiesis in the embryo
   Production of plasma proteins and antibodies
   Destruction of red blood cells
   Phagocytosis (Kupffer cells)
3. Metabolism of carbohydrates, lipids and proteins preparatory to use or excretion
   Glycogenesis and glycogenolysis to maintain normal blood sugar
   Desaturation of fats and conversion to phospholipids
   Synthesis of amino acids
   Formation of serum albumin, serum globulin, antibodies, heparin, fibrinogen and prothrombin
   Deamination of amino acids
   Conversion of protein to carbohydrate and fat
   Formation of urea and uric acid; destruction of uric acid
4. Storage depot
   Glycogen
   Amino acids
   Fats
   Vitamins A, D, B complex

Antianemic principle
Iron and copper
5. Blood reservoir
6. Heat production

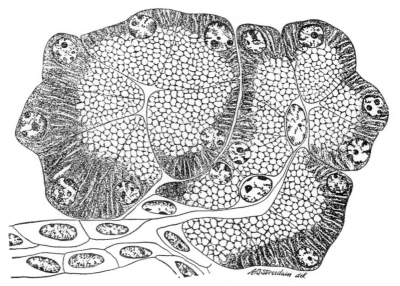

Fig. 271. Pancreatic acinus of guinea pig, showing homogeneous zone at base of cells. In the central portions are the secreting-granule holding spaces. A duct leading off from the acini is shown at the lower left of the figure. (Maximow and Bloom, after Bensley.)

7. Detoxication
Indol, skatol, phenol
Morphine, strychnine, nicotine
Steroid hormones

More detailed treatment of most of these functions is given with related subject matter throughout the text.

GALLBLADDER. The gallbladder is a pear-shaped hollow sac attached to the under surface of the liver (Fig. 267). It ends in the cystic duct, which joins with hepatic ducts to form the *common bile duct*. The bile, which is being secreted continuously by the liver, may not immediately enter the intestines, but, after passing down the hepatic duct, may turn into the cystic duct and enter the gallbladder. The blood vessels and lymphatics absorb water and inorganic salts from the bile so that gallbladder bile may be about ten times more concentrated than that collected from the hepatic duct. The gallbladder serves as a storage for the bile. At intervals during digestion the gallbladder contracts and forces the bile down the cystic duct and into the common bile duct, which opens into the duodenum about 10 cm. below the pylorus. The common bile duct pierces the duodenal wall obliquely and joins with the pancreatic duct to form the *ampulla of Vater*, which opens into the duodenum through a small elevation called the duodenal papilla. The orifice on the summit of the papilla is surrounded by muscle fibers which form a sphincter.

PANCREAS. The pancreas is a long slender organ with its head lying to the right in the loop of the duodenum, its body posterior to the stomach and its tail touching the spleen on the left (Fig. 267). The pancreas forms an external secretion important in digestion and an internal secretion—*insulin*—concerned with carbohydrate metabolism. The organ is a compound tubuloalveolar gland similar in design to the salivary glands. Figure 271 shows secreting cells of the acini and the connection of one acinus with a duct. Ducts from the lobules or acini collect into a long *pancreatic duct,* or duct of Wirsung, extending transversely from the tail to the head. At this point the pancreatic duct is usually joined by an *accessory pancreatic duct,* or duct of Santorini, draining the head of the gland. The pancreatic duct empties into the duodenum with the common bile duct at the ampulla of Vater as described above. Scattered throughout the gland between the alveoli are groups of cells somewhat paler than the others which are called the *islets of Langerhans* (Fig. 297, p. 512). They secrete the insulin.

SUMMARY

The digestive system consists of the alimentary canal and related or accessory organs.

The alimentary canal is formed by the mouth, pharynx, esophagus, stomach, small intestine, large intestine and rectum.

The accessory structures are the teeth, tongue, salivary glands, hard and soft palates, liver, gallbladder and pancreas.

The alimentary tract from esophagus to rectum conforms to a definite structural plan. The layers from within outward are mucous, submucous, muscular and serous. In the esophagus the serous layer is lacking, and the outer coat is fibrous in nature.

The organs of the digestive system contained in the abdomen are covered with the serous coat, the peritoneum. The peritoneum has two layers, the visceral and parietal.

Certain folds of the visceral layer receive special names: lesser omentum, greater omentum, transverse mesocolon, and mesentery.

The mouth is the first division of the alimentary tract.

Important structures of the mouth are the tongue, which contains the end organ for taste, and the teeth, which divide and mix the food.

There are two sets of teeth, first the deciduous or milk teeth, and later the permanent teeth.

The palatine tonsils are on the lateral walls of the oral pharynx between the palatine arches.

The oral and laryngeal portions of the pharynx serve as a channel for the passage of both food and air; food is conducted through it from the mouth to the esophagus, and air from the nasal pharynx to the larynx.

The esophagus conveys food from the pharynx to the stomach.

Two horizontal and two vertical planes divide the anterior surface of the abdominal cavity proper into nine regions.

The stomach is a dilated portion of the alimentary canal lying in the upper abdomen just under the diaphragm. It is a retaining and mixing reservoir in which chemical breaking down of food begins.

The circular muscle layer is thickened at the pyloric and cardiac orifices to form sphincters.

The glands of the fundus and body are most important in the secretion of gastric juice. They are formed mainly of chief and parietal cells.

The small intestine is a thin-walled muscular tube about 7 meters long. Its three portions are duodenum, jejunum, and ileum.

The bile and pancreatic ducts empty into the duodenum.

Special structural features of the small intestine are the villi and the circular folds.

The intestinal glands or crypts of Lieberkühn secrete the intestinal juice containing the digestive enzymes.

The large intestine is about 1.5 meters long and is divided into cecum, colon and rectum.

Special structural features of the large intestine are teniae coli, haustra, semilunar folds and epiploic appendages.

The large salivary glands consist of the parotid, the submaxillary and the sublingual. Ducts from the three pairs of glands open into the mouth.

The liver is the largest gland in the body. It is directly beneath the diaphragm on the right side of the abdomen.

The liver cells are arranged in architectural units, called lobules. The bile capillaries and sinusoids lie between chains of liver cells in the lobule.

Branches of the portal vein, bile duct and hepatic arteries encircle the periphery of the lobule.

The liver secretes bile and has many other important functions in relation to reticuloendothelial activity; metabolism of carbohydrates, lipids and proteins; heat production; and detoxication of certain substances. It is a storage depot and blood reservoir.

The gallbladder is a pear-shaped hollow sac attached to the under surface of the liver. It concentrates the bile and stores it.

The pancreas is a long slender organ with its head to the right in the loop of the duodenum, its body posterior to the stomach and its tail touching the spleen on the left.

The pancreas forms an external secretion important in digestion and an internal secretion, insulin, concerned with carbohydrate metabolism.

QUESTIONS FOR DISCUSSION

1. At this point in the text all reticuloendothelial tissues have been mentioned in their locations in the body. Where are they and what functions do they perform?

2. Relate the circulatory supply of the liver to its functions.

3. What analogy of structure exists between the respiratory and digestive systems?

Chapter
24

The Physiology of Digestion

CHEMICAL FACTORS IN DIGESTION

THE CHEMICAL phase of digestion consists in the breaking down of large nondiffusible molecules into small diffusible molecules which will pass through the cells of the digestive tract. Hydrolysis, which is the principal type of chemical reaction involved, is a decomposition reaction in which a substance combines chemically with water to form simpler substances with smaller molecules:

Maltose   Water   Glucose and Glucose
$$C_{12}H_{22}O_{11} + HOH \rightleftarrows C_6H_{12}O_6 + C_6H_{12}O_6$$

The steps in the hydrolysis of the three principal food materials, carbohydrates, fats (lipids) and proteins, are:

Carbohydrates:

1. Starch, a polysaccharide which must be changed to a monosaccharide before absorption can occur

   Starch $\longrightarrow$ dextrin $\longrightarrow$ maltose $\longrightarrow$ glucose

444

2. Disaccharides, which are hydrolyzed to monosaccharides

    Maltose $\longrightarrow$ glucose and glucose

    Sucrose $\longrightarrow$ fructose and glucose

    Lactose $\longrightarrow$ galactose and glucose.

Fats:

    Fats $\longrightarrow$ glycerol and fatty acid.

Proteins:

    Protein $\longrightarrow$ proteoses $\longrightarrow$ peptones $\longrightarrow$ peptides

    $\longrightarrow$ amino acids.

Hydrolytic reactions in digestion are accelerated by the action of enzymes.

Enzymes are substances produced by living cells which act as catalysts. A catalyst is a substance which speeds up chemical changes without itself entering into the reaction. Enzymes have definite characteristics. They are specific; that is, an enzyme usually acts on a particular substance, but has no effect on any other substance. There are certain combinations of conditions which favor the activity of the enzymes; those which are most favorable for a specific enzyme are said to be optimum conditions. Some require an acid medium, others neutral or alkaline media. They have an optimum temperature at which they bring about changes most rapidly; this is usually body temperature.

There is a system of naming enzymes which is used to some extent. The suffix *-ase* is added to the name of the substance acted upon; thus a starch-splitting enzyme is called an *amylase*, a fat-splitting enzyme is a *lipase*, and a protein-splitting enzyme is a *protease*. Usually another name is included to indicate the source of the enzyme, as, for example, *pancreatic lipase*. However, the older names ptyalin, pepsin and trypsin continue to be used.

Table 15 (p. 446) includes the more important digestive enzymes. A study of the table shows some duplication and overlapping of enzyme action. For example, three enzymes act on protein: pepsin, trypsin, and erepsin. Pepsin in the gastric juice starts protein digestion by changing it to proteoses and peptones; trypsin from the pancreas changes proteoses and peptones to peptones and peptides; erepsin in the intestinal juice changes peptones and peptides to amino acids.

REGIONAL DIGESTION

In the Mouth. Digestion in the mouth is largely mechanical. The food is broken up by the teeth, ground into small particles, and moistened and softened by the saliva. Human saliva is slightly acid, generally having a *p*H of 6.35 to 6.85. The amount secreted in twenty-four hours is about 1300 cc. It consists of 99.5 per cent water and 0.5 per

Table 15

Digestive Enzymes

DIGESTIVE FLUID	ENZYME	SUBSTANCE ACTED UPON	PRODUCTS FORMED
Saliva	Ptyalin or salivary amylase	Boiled starch and dextrins	Dextrins and maltose
Gastric juice	Pepsin	Protein casein	Proteoses and peptones
	Rennin Gastric lipase	Emulsified fat	Insoluble paracaseinate Fatty acids and glycerol
Pancreatic juice	Trypsin	Proteins, proteoses, peptones Chymotrypsinogen	Polypeptides Chymotrypsin
	Chymotrypsin	Proteins, proteoses, peptones	Polypeptides
	Carboxypolypeptidase	Polypeptides	Peptides and amino acids
	Amylopsin or pancreatic amylase	Starch and dextrins	Maltose
	Steapsin or pancreatic lipase	Fat	Fatty acids and glycerol
Succus entericus	Erepsin (enzyme complex) Aminopolypeptidase; et al. Dipeptidase Enterokinase	Polypeptides Dipeptides Trypsinogen	Peptides and amino acids Amino acids Trypsin
	Maltase Sucrase Lactase	Maltose Sucrose Lactose	Glucose and glucose Glucose and fructose Glucose and galactose
	Intestinal lipase	Fat	Glycerol and fatty acids

cent total solids. Its chief constituents are water, inorganic salts, mucin, serum albumin and serum globulin, and salivary amylase or ptyalin. One chemical change is effected by salivary amylase, which acts on the boiled starch, changing it to dextrin and possibly to maltose. It is unlikely that this change occurs to any extent while the food is in the mouth, but the ptyalin may continue to act on the starch within the bolus of food for some time after it enters the stomach.

Salivary digestion is important in preparing the food for the changes that follow. Saliva dissolves some of the solid substances so that they are brought in contact with the taste buds; thus they stimulate appetite and result in a series of reflexes which increase the flow of gastric juice and augment salivary secretion. Moistening food with saliva enables it to be rolled into a plastic mass and gives it a lubricant coating to facilitate swallowing.

In the Stomach. The food which reaches the stomach is mixed with saliva and is semisolid in consistency. It accumulates in the fundus, and the mass thus formed is not penetrated to any extent by the gastric juice, so that salivary digestion can be continued for some time. Gradually, however, owing to muscular movements, the food is mixed with the gastric juice and the acidity so increased that the action of the ptyalin ceases. The reaction of the gastric juice is acid, pH 0.9 to 1.5. The more important constituents are hydrochloric acid, mucin, pepsin, rennin and gastric lipase.

The first step in gastric digestion is the action of hydrochloric acid upon protein. The acid causes the protein to swell to a gelatinous mass (acid metaprotein) which goes rapidly into solution in the acid gastric secretions. Pepsin then hydrolyzes acid metaprotein to proteoses and peptones. Protein digestion does not go beyond the peptone stage in the stomach; it is completed in the intestines. Gastric *rennin* is a milk-curdling catalyst which acts upon the caseinogen of milk, transforming it into paracasein. The curd is subsequently acted upon by pepsin in the usual manner. Rennin may be absent from or inactive at the pH of the gastric contents of the normal adult. In the infant, whose food is largely milk, the pH of the gastric contents is about 5 to 6.5, which is favorable for the action of the enzyme. Gastric lipase is a weak enzyme which is of little importance in fat digestion. It acts only on emulsified fats such as milk and egg yolk. There is no carbohydrate enzyme in the gastric juice, but some of the cane sugar (sucrose) is hydrolyzed by the hydrochloric acid.

As a result of muscular movements which mix the food with the gastric juice, and of the various chemical changes caused by the gastric enzymes, the gastric contents are reduced to a semifluid, more or less homogeneous, creamy mass called *chyme*. At intervals, portions of the chyme are ejected through the pylorus into the duodenum.

In the Small Intestine. Before discussing digestion in this part of the alimentary canal, let us consider the condition in which we find the various food substances of the chyme as it enters the duodenum. Much of the protein has been reduced to proteoses and peptones, carbohydrate digestion has barely begun, some of the starch is converted to dextrin and small amounts as far as maltose, disaccharides are in solution, but not digested except for hydrolysis of a portion of sucrose by hydrochloric acid in the stomach. Fats are melted and emulsified fats hydrolyzed to some extent. Much remains to be done.

As the acid chyme enters the *duodenum,* the secretions from the liver and the pancreas mix with it, and it also comes in contact with the succus entericus or intestinal juice, secreted by the intestinal glands. Intestinal juice is alkaline in reaction because of the presence of sodium carbonate and bicarbonate. The chief enzymes are enterokinase, which activates trypsinogen; a proteolytic enzyme erepsin which completes protein digestion by changing polypeptides to amino acids by the action of its components; an enzyme for each disaccharide; sucrase, maltase, and lactase, which act upon corresponding disaccharides to reduce them to monosaccharides; and lipase, which acts in the digestion of fats. The intestinal juice is secreted continuously, though in variable quantities, and the composition differs greatly with conditions. It may be watery at one time and slimy with mucus at another. The concentration of enzymes shows considerable variation.

The pancreas contributes an alkaline fluid in which there are three important enzymes, trypsin, amylopsin, and steapsin. Trypsin, or pancreatic protease, is secreted in an inactive form known as trypsinogen. It is changed to the powerful proteolytic trypsin by enterokinase. Trypsin and its related factors hydrolyze proteins, proteoses and peptones to peptides. Amylopsin or pancreatic amylase changes starch, glycogen and dextrin to maltose. Pancreatic amylase, unlike salivary amylase, is capable of digesting unboiled starch. Steapsin acts upon the fat molecule, reducing it to fatty acid and glycerol. Some of the fatty acids made soluble in the presence of bile react with the alkali in the intestinal fluid to form soaps. Bile salts and the soaps thus formed lower surface tension and have important effects in the emulsification of fats. Lowering the surface tension facilitates the division of fat into small globules and, by increasing the total surface area exposed to the action of the enzyme, correspondingly enhances the effect. Bile contains no digestive enzymes. The function of the bile salts in the absorption of fats is discussed on page 466.

In the Large Intestine. The large intestine contains the feces, which are composed of bacteria, material secreted through the wall of the intestine and the bile, leukocytes, epithelial cells and food residues. The contents of the ileum are fluid in consistency, but as they pass through the large intestine, water is absorbed, so that under normal conditions the feces are solid or semisolid. The glands of the large intestine secrete mucus, but no enzymes. The mucus helps to hold the feces together and facilitates evacuation.

The large intestine serves as a channel of excretion for calcium, magnesium, iron and phosphate. Substantial amounts of calcium, magnesium and phosphate are also eliminated in the urine, but practically all iron is excreted in the large intestine and appears in the feces as iron sulfide.

CONTROL OF DIGESTIVE JUICES

The glands of the gastrointestinal tract which are responsible for elaboration of digestive secretions are controlled by nervous and chemical action. The flow of digestive secretions is frequently started by reflexes initiated by the sight or smell of food. As soon as food enters the mouth or stomach, additional reflex secretion results from mechanical or chemical stimulation of sensory nerve endings in the alimentary tract. This secretion of the "ignition" juices (the juices responsible for starting digestion and secretion) is for the most part of too short duration to insure complete chemical breakdown of the foodstuffs. Action of these "ignition" juices does, however, result in some digestion of the food with the liberation of substances called secretagogues. *Secretagogues* are products of digestion of food which act to cause secretion of digestive juices by chemical stimulation. It seems highly probable that the initial digestive juices, together with the secretagogues or digestive products of the foods, are responsible for bringing into play the chemical mechanism which insures the continuance of the secretions of the glands of the stomach and small intestine, and accessory digestive glands until digestion is complete. The ignition juices and the secretagogues play an important role in the elaboration of the digestive hormones and colyones, which are the substances that constitute the chemical control of digestion. These hormones are chemical messengers which are formed in various parts of the digestive system, absorbed into the blood stream and carried to various parts of the gastrointestinal tract, where they stimulate secretion and mechanical activity. Colyones, which are formed and absorbed in a similar manner, inhibit secretion and movements of the digestive tract.

Salivary Secretion. The salivary glands are entirely under nervous control (Fig. 272). They are stimulated reflexly through chemical and mechanical excitation of nerve endings in the mouth. The type of salivary secretion varies with the stimuli; acid, noxious substances and dry or finely pulverized matter bring about a copious watery secretion, while moist foods and larger particles result in a scant, sticky saliva.

Conditioned reflexes (see Chap. 7) play an important part in salivary (and gastric) secretion and afford a physiologic interpretation of the advantages of palatable food, well cooked and tastefully arranged. The sight and smell of appetizing food may cause a watering of the mouth. This is the result of action of the higher centers which, because of former association of sight and smell with taste and mechanical

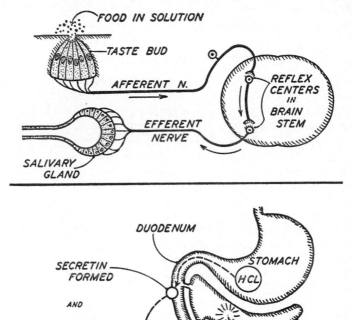

Fig. 272. Nervous control of salivary secretion (*above*) and chemical control of pancreatic secretion (*below*). By means of these distinctly different mechanisms, saliva flows when food is present in the mouth, and pancreatic juice is secreted when food and HCl enter the small intestine. Arrows (*above*) indicate the direction of nerve impulses. Dotted arrows (*below*) indicate course taken by chemicals. (Carlson and Johnson, The Machinery of the Body, University of Chicago Press.)

stimuli which result in salivation, bring about the salivary flow even before the mechanical and chemical stimulation has started.

In addition, mechanical and chemical stimulation by the presence of food in the esophagus and in the stomach causes salivary secretion; these reactions are known as the esophagosalivary and gastrosalivary reflexes, respectively. The former is of value when particles and incompletely masticated food become temporarily lodged in the esophagus.

Gastric Secretion. Secretion of gastric juice has three phases: (1) the cephalic phase, (2) the gastric phase and (3) the intestinal phase.

The *cephalic phase,* which is responsible for secretion of the "ignition" gastric juice, has a conditioned reflex and an unconditioned reflex component. The conditioned reflex functions as in the case of salivary secretion. The unconditioned reflex flow of the secretions is brought about by the presence of food in the mouth. The *gastric phase* insures continuation of secretory activity; it is excited by the distention of the stomach probably resulting in elaboration of a hormone and by the liberation of the hormone gastrin. This hormone is formed by the secretagogues which act on the mucosa of the pyloric portion of the stomach; gastrin, when absorbed into the blood stream, stimulates the gastric glands. The *intestinal phase* is important in that it may either excite or inhibit gastric secretions. The presence of food, secretagogues or even nonabsorbable or poorly absorbable substances in the intestine will cause elaboration of the hormone intestinal gastrin. The presence of fat in the intestine has an inhibitory influence on gastric secretion (and also on gastric motility). This is due to the colyone enterogastrone, which is elaborated from the duodenal mucosa.

Pancreatic Secretion. Experiments indicate that pancreatic secretion is a continuous process, but that the rate of secretion is increased two or three minutes after a meal and rises to a maximum in two or three hours. The initial augmentation appears long before digestion could have released secretagogues for hormone formation, so that it must be ascribed to nervous control. The continued secretion is brought about by the hormone secretin, which is liberated from the intestinal mucosa by the presence of acids, soaps, fatty acids and bile (Fig. 272). The pancreatic secretion resulting from nerve stimulation contains trypsin in active form in contrast to the juice excited by hormone control which contains trypsinogen, an inactive form of trypsin. Pancreozymin, a constituent of succus entericus, is synergistic with secretin, increasing the enzyme content of pancreatic juice. Secretin also excites the secretion and flow of bile and possibly the formation of intestinal juices.

Bile Formation and Excretion. In considering the role of bile in digestion it must be borne in mind that there are two components in its mobilization for use: (1) formation and (2) release into the gastro-intestinal tract.

Bile formation may be affected by nervous influences to a minor degree. By far the most effective stimulus, however, is bile salts. Bile is being continuously secreted, but, if it is drained out of the body, secretion soon stops; nerve stimulation is without effect, but intravenous injection serves to reestablish the flow. Secretin is probably a normal factor in stimulating bile formation.

The emptying of the gallbladder is primarily under chemical control. The hormone, *cholecystokinin*, which is formed when egg yolk, cream and certain other substances containing fat enter the duodenum, is specific for contraction of the gallbladder.

Intestinal Secretion. Secretion of the succus entericus may be largely the result of mechanical stimulation of the intestinal mucosa by intestinal contents. However, trypsin appears to be an excellent excitant; secretin may also stimulate secretion.

The glands of the large intestine respond chiefly to mechanical stimulation.

Correlation of the Mechanisms of Secretion. So far the control of the secretions has been discussed without indicating established or probable interrelations. Though the nervous secretions are initiated promptly, they do not continue throughout the period of digestion. The nervous mobilization of secretions may, however, start the chemical mechanisms (1) by the actions of the digestive secretions themselves, either locally or at a lower level in the gastrointestinal tract, and (2) by acting upon the ingested food with the formation of secretagogues which act directly or through the formation of hormones.

Once the chemical activity is initiated, the opportunity for continuous reexcitation of secretion will exist throughout the period of digestion. Table 16 indicates such possible interrelations.

MECHANICAL FACTORS IN DIGESTION

The mechanical factors of digestion are those which (1) have direct action in breaking up the ingested foods; (2) are effective in causing a mixing of the foodstuffs with the digestive secretions; (3) effect a renewal of the surfaces of the nutrient material presented to the absorbing surfaces of the gut; (4) serve to hasten or retard the progress of foodstuffs through the gastrointestinal tract; (5) effect the evacuation of the exogenous and endogenous residues, through defecation.

The muscular tissues of the alimentary canal consist largely of smooth muscle; the exceptions are the striated muscles in the mouth, pharynx, upper part of the esophagus and the external sphincter of the rectum. Smooth muscle has certain characteristics which distinguish it from striated muscle; its contractions are sluggish, it has greater extensibility, is able to sustain contraction at varying lengths with small expenditure of energy, it has the power of rhythmic contraction and is especially sensitive to the mechanical stimulus of stretching.

Mastication and Deglutition. Mastication is the process by which food is broken up by the action of the teeth, tongue, cheeks and hard palate. The divided particles are mixed with saliva and formed into a ball or bolus. Deglutition or swallowing involves the use of both smooth and striated muscles (Fig. 273). The first movement brings the bolus of food on the tongue, which is then moved backward so that the bolus is pushed through the glossopalatine arches into the pharynx. Up to this point the act is under voluntary control. Once the food enters the pharynx, reflexes are set up which propel the food into the esophagus and prevent its entrance into the respiratory passages. The nasal cavity is blocked off by the raising of the soft palate. The entrance to the mouth is closed by elevation of the tongue to the hard palate and contraction of the palatine arches. Muscular contraction elevates the larynx and places it under the shelter of the base of the tongue and the epiglottis, which acts as a protecting shelf to deflect food from entrance into the trachea. The approximation of the vocal cords closes the glottis. Just before swallowing, a slight inspiration is taken which is followed by inhibition of respiration for about five seconds. During the third stage of swallowing food passes through the esophagus. The time required for its passage will vary with the composition of the food; liquids travel more rapidly than solids. Powerful contractions of the striated muscle in the upper part of the esophagus insure the rapid movement of food through the region lying immediately posterior to the trachea. Smooth muscle then takes over the task of propelling the food by a series of peristaltic waves (Fig. 274). A *peristaltic wave* is a band of constriction, involving the circular muscles, which travels along the esophagus and other parts of the digestive tube for varying distances. This wave is sometimes preceded by a wave of relaxation. Food may be passed through the cardiac sphincter of the stomach by the peristaltic wave, or it may be delayed until the arrival of a succeeding wave. During a meal there is less and less tendency for the cardia to close between swallows.

Movements of the Stomach. The normal stomach has a remarkable ability to adapt its capacity to the volume of food with little change in intragastric pressure. Normally, the peristaltic wave which forces the bolus through the esophagus and relaxes the cardia also diminishes the tone of the fundus.

In considering movements of the stomach it becomes necessary to state the condition of gastric filling, since the motility resulting from the ingestion of small quantities of liquid or food is not the same as that following a full meal. When a small amount of food enters the stomach it passes at once to the pyloric region. Liquid may pass directly through the pyloric sphincter into the duodenum without being propelled by gastric contractions. The initial effect of food or liquid is

Table 16

Secretory Correlations

SECRETORY CORRELATIONS

SECRETION	INITIAL SECRETIONS	CONTINUED SECRETIONS	FURTHER RELATIONS OF SECRETIONS
Saliva	Conditioned reflexes	Unconditioned reflexes: (a) chemical and mechanical stimuli from mouth (b) esophago-salivary (c) gastrosalivary	
Gastric juice	Cephalic phase: (a) conditioned reflexes (b) chemical and mechanical stimuli from mouth	Gastric and intestinal phases: (a) distention of stomach (b) initial gastric secretions (ignition juices) aiding in elaboration of: (1) secretagogues (2) gastrin (3) intestinal gastrin (4) inhibitory effects of enterogastrone	Initial and conditioned gastric juice + secretagogues + partially digested food pass into intestine to stimulate or aid in the elaboration of ⟩ cholecystokinin secretin enterogastrone intestinal gastrin
Pancreatic juice	Nervous control: conditioned? unconditioned?	secretin	pancreatic juice containing trypsin → stimulates succus entericus with its enterokinase pancreatic juice containing trypsinogen → trypsin
Bile formation	Nervous control	secretin bile salts	bile salts ⟩ aid in elaboration and absorption of secretin
Emptying of gallbladder	Nervous control	cholecystokinin	release of bile which aids in elaboration and absorption of secretin
Succus entericus		secretin trypsin mechanical stimulation	enterokinase in succus entericus activates trypsinogen of pancreatic juice to trypsin

to inhibit any motor activity which may be occurring in the empty stomach. However, motor activity is soon renewed. The tone of the body and fundus increases. Small peristaltic waves may arise from constricted rings of high tone in the fundus and pyloric regions. When larger portions of food are ingested, the body and the fundus become filled and soon develop an increase in tone. The peristaltic waves start in the region of the body of the stomach and travel toward the pyloric valve. As digestion proceeds, the waves begin higher up on the stomach and gradually encroach on the main mass of food in the fundus. Two

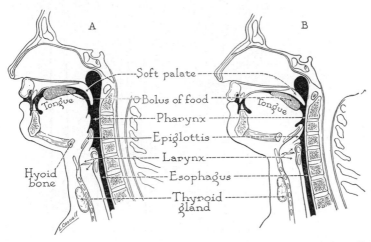

Fig. 273. Deglutition. A, Before swallowing begins, parts in normal position. B, Nose closed off, larynx raised, tip of tongue pressed against the roof of the mouth.

or three hours after a meal the waves may originate almost at the cardiac orifice and sweep over the entire organ. The complex movements serve to mix the food with the gastric juice and propel it toward the duodenum.

Emptying of the Stomach. The emptying of the stomach depends upon two fundamental factors: (1) the existence of an opening between the stomach and the duodenum and (2) the existence of a higher pressure in the stomach than in the duodenum at the time of the passage of stomach contents. It is established that emptying of the stomach requires some time, that it is emptied in small portions and that the transport of these portions is the result of vigorous peristaltic waves. If the observations of prominent investigators in this field are combined, the mechanism may be summarized by the following description:

Liquid passes directly through the pyloric sphincter, which is either open or exhibiting low tone at the beginning of the filling of the stomach. If, because of its consistency and chemical composition, it fails to excite the myenteric reflex, no closure of the pyloric valve results and emptying continues. The *myenteric reflex* may be described as the constriction of circular muscles of a valve or of the digestive tube at any point immediately above the site of stimulation of the intestine. Food or liquids which cause mechanical or chemical stimulation of the mucosa when entering the duodenum may cause constriction of the pyloric sphincter lying immediately above by eliciting the myenteric reflex. Emptying would then cease until the chyme was moved out of the first portion of the duodenum and the intragastric pressure

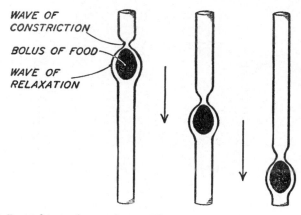

WAVE OF
CONSTRICTION

BOLUS OF FOOD

WAVE OF
RELAXATION

Fig. 274. Peristalsis in the esophagus. Three stages in the downward movement of a solid bolus of food are shown. (Carlson and Johnson, The Machinery of the Body, University of Chicago Press.)

increased over that of the intestine. Chyme in the duodenum may delay emptying, not only through the myenteric reflex, but by elaboration of enterogastrone, which inhibits gastric motility. Thus as successive portions pass through the pyloric valve they may cause closure of the valve and a decrease in motility (and hence a decrease in intragastric pressure); as the chyme is passed along these influences are removed and further emptying of the stomach takes place. This may account for the delays in emptying caused by large particles of food in the chyme (myenteric reflex) and the presence of fats in the stomach (enterogastrone).

The closure of the sphincter precedes and lasts throughout contraction of the duodenum so that regurgitation is normally prevented.

Movements of the Small Intestine.   Two main kinds of movement are observed in the small intestine: peristaltic waves, which carry the chyme onward, and rhythmical segmentation, which churns and mixes it with digestive juices.

Peristaltic movements appear as traveling waves of constriction which when sufficiently strong "strip" the tube and transfer the contents onward. The waves pass for varying distances along the intestine and then fade out. Rhythmical segmentation consists of alternate rings of compression regularly spaced so that they divide the intestinal contents into numerous small segments. When the constriction rings of circular muscle relax, new rings appear in the middle of the previously formed segments. The halves of adjacent segments so divided flow together to form new segments (Fig. 276). As the process is repeated

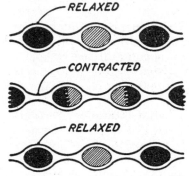

Fig. 275. Churning movements in the small intestine. Three successive stages are shown in a small segment of bowel. Digesting masses of food are shown cross-hatched and in black. The masses of food become thoroughly admixed with one another, and with the digestive juices by means of these movements. (Carlson and Johnson, The Machinery of the Body, University of Chicago Press.)

over and over again, the chyme is mixed with digestive secretions and exposed to the absorptive surface of the mucosa.

These churning or segmenting movements continue in a part of the small intestine for a time and are followed by a peristaltic wave which moves the materials onward into the next portion in which churning movements are repeated.

It seems probable that the existence of an intestinal gradient of activity is responsible for the fact that food passes down the intestine rather than in the opposite direction. The duodenum normally shows the highest rate of muscular contraction with the gradient of motility progressively decreasing as we pass to the jejunum and ileum. The duodenum might be described as the pacemaker of the intestine. Since it exhibits a higher rate of rhythmicity, waves may pass aborally; contractions initiated at lower levels would be more likely to encounter refractory periods or states in the musculature above. Since muscle cannot be excited during the refractory period, the wave is interrupted. Waves passing aborally to the regions of lesser activity are more likely to encounter resting muscle which would favor its propagation in that direction. Under certain pathologic conditions the gradient may be reversed.

Another type of activity taking place in the small intestine is the movement of the *villi*. By exposing the intestinal mucosa of a living animal and examining it under low power magnification, the villi can be seen swaying from side to side and lashing to and fro. Their movements stir the fluids in contact with their surfaces and undoubtedly aid both digestion and absorption. The villi have been called the absorbing units of the small intestine and constitute a total surface area of some 10 square meters.

The colic or ileocolic valve opens at intervals, permitting the passage of the contents from the intestine into the cecum. Swallowing of food causes an initial reflex opening of the sphincter. The ileocolic valve delays the emptying of the intestine, allowing time for digestion and absorption, and aids in preventing regurgitation from the colon into the ileum.

Movements of the Large Intestine. Peristaltic movements in the large intestine have been called mass movements or mass peristalsis. The waves appear from time to time and carry the contents for a distance along the tube. They are frequently preceded by peristaltic waves in the small intestine. Mass movements occur only at long intervals, usually two or three times in twenty-four hours. They often follow the taking of food into the stomach.

The pelvic colon, which serves as a storehouse for feces, becomes filled from below upward, the rectum remaining empty until just before defecation. Entrance of feces into the rectum may follow mass movements or may result simply from overloading the pelvic colon. The emptying of the rectum, or defecation, involves a strong contraction of rectal walls and a relaxation of the anal sphincter. This mechanism is usually reinforced by the contraction of abdominal muscles and diaphragm.

SUMMARY

The chemical phase of digestion consists in the breaking down of large nondiffusible molecules into small diffusible molecules which will pass through the cells of the digestive tract.

Hydrolysis is the principal type of chemical reaction involved.

Hydrolytic reactions in digestion are accelerated by the action of enzymes.

Enzymes are substances produced by living cells which act as catalysts.

Digestion in the mouth is largely mechanical. The food is broken up by the teeth, ground into small particles, and is moistened and softened by the saliva. The action of ptyalin in the mouth is negligible.

In the stomach the pepsin of the gastric juice begins the digestion of proteins, reducing them to proteoses and peptones. Ptyalin may continue to act for a time.

The greater part of digestion takes place in the small intestine. Starch, disaccharides and fats are digested here, and protein digestion which was started in the stomach is carried to completion. Pancreatic juice, bile and intestinal juice play important parts in the digestive processes.

The large intestine absorbs quantities of water and secretes mucus which holds feces together and facilitates evacuation.

The salivary glands are entirely under nervous control.

The secretion of gastric juice has three phases: cephalic phase, gastric phase, and intestinal phase.

Pancreatic secretion is initiated by nervous control and is continued by the action of the hormone secretin.

The most effective stimulus for bile formation is bile salts.

The emptying of the gallbladder is caused by the hormone cholecystokinin.

Mastication is the process by which food is broken up by the action of the teeth, tongue, cheeks and hard palate.

Deglutition or swallowing involves the use of both smooth and striated muscles.

Peristalsis is a band of constriction, involving circular muscles, which passes along the alimentary canal for some distance.

Peristalsis occurs in the esophagus, stomach, small and large intestines and rectum.

Mixing movements take place in the small intestine in addition to peristaltic waves. Mixing results from alternating stationary rings of constriction.

Movement of villi is another type of activity which takes place in the small intestine.

Peristaltic movements in the large intestine are called mass movements or mass peristalsis. They usually occur only two or three times in twenty-four hours.

QUESTIONS FOR DISCUSSION

1. Contrast the functional anatomy of the respiratory system in the transfer of gases to the functional anatomy of the digestive system in its transfer of liquids and solids.

2. Is the chemical or mechanical phase of digestion more important in the mouth? Explain.

3. Test your knowledge of enzyme activity by describing the digestion of a piece of buttered toast and an egg.

4. In this chapter many correlations in time between the secretion of digestive juices and the mechanical phases of digestion are considered. Discuss such time relationships for the three phases of gastric secretion and for the secretion of pancreatic juice.

Chapter
25

Absorption and Metabolism

ABSORPTION

THE DIGESTIVE processes change food to simple materials that can be used by the cells. But until the digestion products, salts, water and vitamins have passed into the blood vessels and lymphatics and become part of the internal environment, they are not available for use by the tissue cells. This passage of digested food material through the wall of the alimentary canal is called absorption. Practically all absorption of food products occurs in the small intestine; water and salts are absorbed in the colon. Absorption involves the selective permeability of the cells as well as the physical processes of diffusion and osmosis. The epithelial cells of the villi actively take up substances from the intestinal contents and pass them into the blood and lymph. The epithelium does not act merely as a passive membrane, but also performs cellular work with the expenditure of energy.

METABOLISM

Phases of Metabolism. Metabolism is the term used to include the sum total of chemical activities occurring within the tissues. The building up or assimilative processes are referred to as anabolism, the breakdown or destructive processes as catabolism. The former results in the construction of protoplasm and thus makes possible growth and the repair of tissues. The latter releases energy needed for muscular activity and the maintenance of vital functions. The source of energy is the chemical energy of the food materials which is transformed by oxidation to heat and mechanical energy, i.e., work. Heat is a form of energy, and it is possible to reduce all other forms to heat. The energy of a food is expressed in terms of the heat it produces. The unit of heat, the *Calorie,* is defined as the amount of heat required to raise 1 kilo-

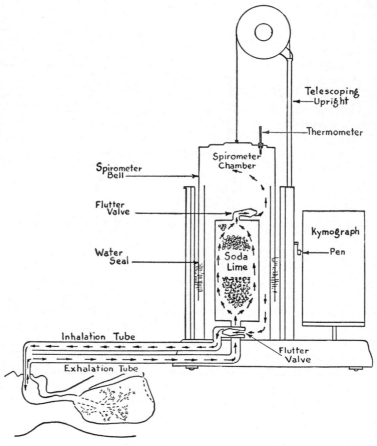

Fig. 276. Diagram showing principle of the recording spirometer (Benedict-Roth principle).

gram of water 1 degree centigrade. The amount of heat liberated by complete combustion of the three types of food has been determined by burning them outside the body. One gram of carbohydrate yields 4 Calories, 1 gm. of fat 9 Calories, and 1 gm. of protein 5 Calories. The same values are found for combustion of carbohydrates and fats within the body. However, only part of the protein can be oxidized in the body, since the nitrogenous portion is incombustible; hence the physiologic oxidiation of 1 gm. of protein yields only 4 Calories.

Utilization of Food Materials. Foods are used in the body as fuel, as building stones for construction of protoplasm and as constituents of the internal environment. The inorganic salts, water and vitamins function chiefly in contributing to the composition of the internal environment. The vitamins regulate various vital processes; minute amounts of them are essential for health, growth and reproduction. Carbohydrates, fats and proteins constitute sources of energy. Carbohydrates form a readily available energy source and are quickly oxidized. Fats have a high caloric value. Protein supplies energy and in addition is essential in tissue growth and repair. Protein forms by far the greatest proportion of the organic constituents of protoplasm, but carbohydrates and fats are present in small amounts.

Metabolic Rate, Basal Metabolism and Respiratory Quotient. The caloric value of food ingested for twenty-four hours must equal the energy utilized by the individual during the same period; otherwise body tissues will be consumed for fuel. The dietary requirements range from 2400 Calories per day for a person leading a relatively sedentary life to 7000 Calories in a lumberman working in winter. In estimating the caloric requirements it is customary to determine the basal metabolic rate first and then add to this the extra calories required for the particular grade of muscular activity.

Basal metabolism is the energy expenditure of a subject who is lying down at complete muscular and mental rest, some twelve to fourteen hours after taking food and in a room with temperature at about 20° C. Figure 276 shows one type of apparatus used to measure metabolism.

Under these basal conditions the three factors which are most powerful in stimulating metabolism—physical exercise, ingestion of food and environmental temperature—have been eliminated. The heat generated under such conditions is due mainly to the activity of heart, blood vessels, alimentary canal, glands and respiratory movements and indicates the energy required to maintain vital processes. It represents the minimum level of cellular activity. The basal metabolism is proportionate to the surface area of the individual and is expressed in terms of Calories per square meter of body surface per hour. On this basis the average metabolism for normal men between twenty and fifty years is from 38 to 40 Calories, and for women between the same ages 36 to 38 Calories. Values 10 per cent above or below these figures are considered within the normal range. In the usual clinical determination of metabolic rate the heat production is computed indirectly on the basis of the oxygen consumed. Knowledge of the volume of oxygen used and carbon dioxide formed is the basis for another valuable determination—the *respiratory quotient*. This is the ratio of the volume of carbon dioxide given off to the volume of oxygen consumed, thus:

$$\frac{\text{Vol. of CO}_2 \text{ given off}}{\text{Vol. of O}_2 \text{ used}} = \text{Respiratory quotient or R. Q.}$$

The value of the respiratory quotient lies in its being a useful indication of the type of food being burned. Since the three food materials differ in the relative amounts of oxygen and carbon in the molecule, the volumes of oxygen used and carbon dioxide produced during the metabolism of each food material also vary. When a person is burning a carbohydrate such as glucose, all the oxygen consumed goes to form carbon dioxide, so that for every molecule of oxygen, 1 molecule of carbon dioxide results. The following equation shows this:

$$C_6H_{12}O_6 + 6O_2 \rightarrow 6CO_2 + 6H_2O$$

$$\text{R. Q.} = \frac{6 \text{ mol. (6 vol.) CO}_2}{6 \text{ mol. (6 vol.) O}_2} = 1$$

When fat is oxidized, some of the oxygen goes to form water and the respiratory quotient is as follows:

Tripalmitin: $$C_{51}H_{98}O_6 + 72.5O_2 \rightarrow 51CO_2 + 49H_2O$$

$$\text{R. Q.} = \frac{51 \text{ mol. CO}_2}{72.5 \text{ mol. O}_2} = 0.703$$

Fats vary somewhat in composition, and the average respiratory quotient is about 0.7, while that of protein is 0.8. When the respiratory quotient is close to 1, the assumption is that diet is chiefly carbohydrate; when it is around 0.7, that it is mainly fat. On a mixed diet the respiratory quotient is about 0.85.

Metabolism of Carbohydrates. Carbohydrates may be ingested as starch or sugar or they may be formed in the body from noncarbohydrate food substances. The polysaccharides and disaccharides are broken down by digestive processes and absorbed as monosaccharides (see p. 455). Carbohydrates pass through the intestine into the blood stream; the direction of transport through the intestinal mucosa is not reversed, i.e., glucose does not pass into the lumen of the intestine. While sugars may be absorbed into the blood from the stomach, the quantities are negligible.

The value of 100 mg. per 100 cc. of blood, which is frequently given as normal for blood sugar determined by routine clinical tests, represents both glucose and other reducing substances in the blood. The concentration of glucose in blood is about 60-80 mg. per cent. The level is maintained remarkably constant except for short periods after the digestion of a meal and under certain conditions which will be considered in discussion of the regulation of the blood sugar. It is not reduced beyond normal range even in prolonged fasting. After a meal rich in carbohydrates the level may be elevated to about 130 to 150 mg. per 100 cc. of blood. The monosaccharides absorbed from the intestines are brought to the liver in the portal blood. Here, galactose and fructose are changed to glucose by the liver cells. The blood sugar may then be (1) oxidized to CO_2 and H_2O to meet the immediate energy requirements of the body; (2) converted to glycogen and stored in the liver or in muscle; or (3) converted into fat and stored. Some glucose passes by diffusion from the capillaries into the tissue fluids and into the cell where it is oxidized through various stages to pyruvic or lactic acid and to its final end products, CO_2 and H_2O. This process proceeds continuously, but at varying rates which depend upon the individual tissues and their levels of activity. The carbohydrates may form compounds with glycerol and amino acids and phosphoric acid.

The process of synthesis of liver glycogen is exactly the reverse of its breakdown (see page 232); phosphorylation of glucose takes place, with hexokinase as catalyst, forming glucose-6-phosphate. ATP serves as donor of the phosphate. There is a change in chemical structure of the glucose-6-phosphate to glucose-1-phosphate through the catalytic action of the enzyme phosphoglucomutase. The final stage, the change to glycogen, is catalyzed by phosphorylase. The process of the formation of glycogen from glucose is called *glycogenesis*. Liver is also capable of forming glucose from other sources, namely from the glycerol portion of fat molecules and certain amino acids. This synthesis of glucose from substances that are not carbohydrate in nature is designated as *glyconeogenesis*. Glycogen which is formed and stored in the liver is constantly being renewed.

The balance between glycogenesis and glyconeogenesis and the reverse process *glycogenolysis* keeps blood sugar at its constant level in spite of the fact that its carbohydrates are being ingested intermittently and consumed continuously by the tissues. The formation, storage, release and consumption of carbohydrates are regulated by hormones secreted in a coordinated, balanced system of endocrine control. The pancreas, adrenal and hypophysis participate. Insulin acts to limit the amount of glucose by increasing its rate of utilization, acting to control glyconeogenesis, increase formation of muscle glycogen and conversion of carbohydrate to fat. Large doses of insulin will cause a marked reduction in blood sugar, a condition known as hypoglycemia. The anterior hypophysis appears to act both directly, and through its influence on the adrenals, in a manner which is antagonistic or opposite to that of insulin. Epinephrine, the sympathomimetic hormone of the adrenal medulla, stimulates glycogenolysis, and so tends to prevent a marked lowering of the blood sugar level. Cortin, or the secretion of the adrenal cortex, appears to stimulate glycogenesis and glyconeogenesis, reduce tissue utilization and conversion of carbohydrate to fat.

If the blood sugar rises excessively in spite of these mechanisms or as the result of diabetes, glucose is lost through the urine. The kidney tubules are capable of reabsorbing normal and even large quantities of glucose from the glomerular filtrate, but at some point after excessive ingestion of carbohydrate, these tubules may become overloaded even in normal individuals so that not all of it is reabsorbed, and *glucosuria* results.

Metabolism of Lipids. The *lipids* are made up of fatty acids in combination with other substances. They can be divided into four groups on the basis of chemical characteristics:

1. Neutral fats and oils, which are esters of fatty acids and glycerol, and waxes which are esters of fatty acids and alcohols other than glycerol.

2. Phospholipids, which are compounds of fatty acids, glycerol, phosphoric acid and a nitrogenous substance; glycolipids, made up of fatty acids and carbohydrate but lacking the phosphoric acid group; and aminolipids, which are the other compound lipids. Lecithin and cephalin are important phospholipids. In general, the compound lipids are miscible with water or water soluble.

3. Sterols, which are secondary alcohols found free or in esters with fatty acids. Important examples include cholesterol and ergosterol.

4. Hydrocarbons, such as carotene, which may be converted into vitamin A in the body.

In digestion the fats are emulsified by the bile, so that their total surface area available for action by the lipases is increased. All except perhaps a small proportion of the fat is broken down *(lipolysis)* into fatty acids and glycerol. The fatty acids form a compound with bile, which renders them water soluble. This *hydrotropic action* aids in the transfer of fatty acids through the intestinal membrane. The combinations break up after passing into the epithelial cells and recombine with glycerol and other substances which have also been absorbed. Some fat, broken into very small particles, may be absorbed without lipolysis. As fat is absorbed and passes through the lacteals (see Fig. 262), the lymph vessels of the mesentery take on a milklike appearance as the result of the great number of fat droplets, called *chylomicrons*, in the lymph. The chylomicrons may also be seen in the blood as they enter the blood stream through the thoracic duct.

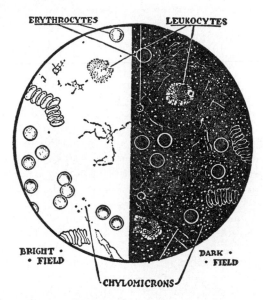

Fig. 277. Shows chylomicrons. (After Gage, from Best and Taylor, The Physiological Basis of Medical Practice, Williams & Wilkins Co.)

The digested fats are transported throughout the body in the plasma as phospholipids, cholesterol esters and neutral fats. The cholesterol and cholesterol ester content of the erythrocyte may also increase during digestion. The phospholipids, lecithin and cephalin, are especially important in fat transfer since they are miscible with water and diffuse readily through cell membranes.

Fats in the body come from ingested fat and conversion from carbohydrate and protein. They are utilized by the body as a source of energy; they serve as a constituent of the tissues, as a padding and insulator of body structures and as a heat insulator of the body as a whole. The fats also carry the fat soluble vitamins A, D, E and K.

Gram for gram, fat contains more chemical energy than either carbohydrate or protein, although it does not appear to be as readily available for rapid release in emergencies. Oxidation of fats may be especially important in the heart. The fats in transport to the tissues or to the liver for oxidation or conversion are *mobile* fats. Those serving as constituents of tissues are called tissue fats; they are found in considerable quantities in cell membranes. Fats not needed immediately for fuel or for building up protoplasm may be stored in fat depots, principally in the superficial fascia under the skin, in the mesentery and omentum, around such organs as the kidneys and the heart, and in the liver. Some fat is excreted in the feces, in the secretions of the skin and, during lactation, in milk.

Two of the important functions of the liver should be mentioned briefly, i.e., storage and oxidation. The liver usually contains 3 to 5 per cent fat, although this may be quite variable, since it serves as a temporary storage during digestion and is concerned with conversion and oxidative processes. Liver fat storage appears to be controlled by the interaction of certain substances. Important among these are choline and chemically related substances, and methionine and proteins containing it, which act to prevent excess fat storage, i.e., fatty liver. This action is opposed by cholesterol, cystine, thiamine and other substances which favor fat storage, and which if taken in large doses may result in excessive fatty infiltration.

Before oxidation occurs, neutral fats are hydrolyzed to glycerol and fatty acid. Apparently, the fatty acids are desaturated in the liver and burned two carbon atoms at a time. Oxidation may be complete or ketone bodies may be formed. The ketone bodies, which are formed only by the liver, are normally oxidized by other body tissues to the final end products, CO_2 and water. When the rate of fat metabolism is greatly increased by lack of adequate carbohydrate, or where a high fat diet is taken, or from other causes, an excess of ketone bodies accumulate and ketosis develops. This may lead to severe acidosis, coma and death.

Metabolism of Proteins. Protein contains carbon, oxygen, hydrogen, nitrogen, sulfur and sometimes phosphorus. The first three constituents are also in carbohydrates and fats; the fourth, nitrogen, is the principal chemical characteristic of protein. Protein, taken in as food, is hydrolized into amino acids in the digestive process; these are absorbed through the small intestine (see Chapter 24).

The amino acids of the blood are (1) used to build new protoplasm as it is needed for growth and repair, (2) oxidized to carbon dioxide, water and urea, (3) converted to carbohydrate or fat and (4) transformed into protein derivatives including creatine, glutathione, epinephrine and compounds with carbohydrates and fats.

Not all proteins have equal dietary importance. Ten amino acids are considered necessary for growth and repair in man. Proteins which contain the essential amino acids are called complete proteins; those lacking amino acids which must be present for growth or for repair, or both, are called incomplete proteins. The amino acids are utilized to considerable extent by liver for the production of plasma protein, and in formation of the protein fraction of hemoglobin. The muscles also utilize large amounts of the amino acids in synthesis of tissue.

The amino acids which are not used for protein synthesis are deaminized in the liver; deaminization is the removal of the amino group, NH_2, from the amino acid.

The following equation shows the oxidative deaminization of the amino acid, glycine, with the formation of nitrogenous and non-nitrogenous portions:

$$\underset{\text{Glycine}}{2H\text{—}\overset{\boxed{H}}{\underset{\boxed{NH_2}}{C}}\text{—}C\overset{O}{\underset{OH}{\diagdown}}} + O_2 \longrightarrow 2\ \underset{\text{Ketoacid}}{H\text{—}\overset{O}{\overset{\|}{C}}\text{—}C\overset{O}{\underset{OH}{\diagdown}}} + \underset{\text{Ammonia}}{2NH_3}$$

The ammonia is the incombustible nitrogenous portion. It changes to urea in two ways. It may combine with carbonic acid and ornithine to form arginine. Arginine, an amino acid, extends the latter reaction to form a cycle. It is hydrolyzed directly to urea and ornithine in a reaction catalyzed by arginase. The ornithine liberated by the decomposition of arginine is used over again. The reactions involving arginine can be summarized as follows:

1. Arginine + water + arginase (in liver) → urea + ornithine
2. Ornithine + ammonia + carbonic acid → arginine

The cyclic response shown above is the principal mechanism for urea formation. Ammonia may also unite with carbon dioxide and water to form ammonium carbonate; this is changed into urea by loss of two molecules of water.

The keto acid, which constitutes the non-nitrogenous portion following deaminization of amino acid, may be oxidized immediately to carbon dioxide and water to yield energy; or it may be synthesized to glucose and subsequently stored as glycogen or fat. Protein not only serves as a source of energy for the body, but acts to increase the release of energy above and beyond the amount which can be derived from the portion of protein ingested. This response is spoken of as the *specific dynamic action* of protein. For example, if we ingest an amount of protein which contains a chemical source of energy approximately equivalent to the basal metabolic rate, the energy derived from the resulting metabolic activities would be approximately 30 per cent in excess of that which could be derived from the ingested protein. The additional heat results from simultaneous oxidation of other foodstuffs already in the body.

In the protein ingested, a balance is maintained between that which is utilized as "building stone" and that which is excreted by the body. The relation between input and output is known as the *nitrogen balance*. This does not imply that the exchange goes on at a constant level. Protein utilization and protein excretion do not proceed at a constant rate, but may vary considerably with age, activity and state of health. The term nitrogen balance does, however, describe the extent to which a balance has been attained. If the nitrogen intake exceeds the total nitrogen excreted, the balance is positive; if the amount excreted is the greater, the balance is said to be negative. The positive balance is associated with growth, pregnancy, muscular exercise and convalescence; a negative balance may occur in starvation, following trauma and in certain wasting diseases.

A number of the important compounds derived from or linked with protein or fractions of protein are discussed in the sections on fat and carbohydrate metabolism; ribonucleic acid was considered in connection with the physiology of the cell.

The urea formed in the liver enters the blood and is excreted by the kidneys. It forms the principal nitrogenous product released by the catabolism of the amino acids. Other waste products containing nitrogen are uric acid, creatinine and ammonium salts. These substances are also excreted by the kidney.

Water Metabolism. WATER BALANCE. Total body water can be measured satisfactorily by determining the dilution of a small measured quantity of heavy water (deuterium oxide) which, when injected into the blood stream, mixes with body water in about one hour. The results by this indirect method agree closely with direct measurement of weight loss of the bodies of small experimental animals following desiccation. The per cent of lean body weight (fat-free body mass) appears to be fairly constant from one normal individual to another. The total water represents 60 to 70 per cent of total body weight.

Total body water and the amounts of it in various tissues and locations are not constant, but vary over a limited range under normal physiologic conditions. The limited extent of the range and the overall constancy is shown by determination of the water balance. Water is taken in liquid form and in food. Water derived from food may be a component of it, be mixed with it, or may result from oxidation; carbon dioxide and water are the principal end-products from the oxidation of all types of foodstuffs. Water is lost from the body by vaporization, by excretion in the stool and as urine. A characteristic daily exchange of water which has been balanced shows the approximate quantities taken in from various sources and lost by various routes under conditions of moderate ambient temperature and humidity, and moderate bodily activity. These are:

Water Intake			Water Output		
SOURCE		AMOUNT (ML.)	LOSS		AMOUNT (ML.)
Drink		1200	Urine		1350
Food			Stool		150
(a)	Mixed with or constituent of	1000	Vaporization		
(b)	from oxidation	350	(a)	Lungs	300
			(b)	Skin	750
	Totals	2550			2550

The ranges of the amounts of the separate losses are not great for moderately active people in moderate weather. For the most part, variations in water intake are balanced by differences in the amount of urine secreted, i.e., between 1 to 1.5 liters. Fifty to 200 ml. may be lost through the intestine in the feces. The losses from the lungs usually fall within the relatively narrow limits of 250 to 300 ml. per day. Loss from insensible perspiration, so called because it is evaporated as fast as it is formed, is influenced to a great degree by the temperature, humidity and air movement of the surrounding environment. It may vary from about ½ to 1 liter.

Water intake increases with increased activity and increased temperature, both separately and in combination; it may reach as high as 13 to 14 liters per day for men doing heavy labor in a hot, dry climate. Water output may be greatly increased under similar conditions by the skin secreting sweat in copious quantities which are lost by evaporation or by dripping from body.

THE PATHS OF THE WATER IN THE BODY. The water taken into the digestive tract is absorbed principally through the small intestine, but also and to a significant extent through the large intestine. It enters the circulation and is carried in the plasma, causing a temporary dilution of plasma constituents. It then passes through the arterial end of the capillaries into the tissues, and from there exchange between the tissue fluids and the cells may occur. Water re-enters the capillary at the venous end. It is again carried by the plasma to be excreted by the kidneys, skin and lungs and through the intestines with the feces. Multiple internal circuits exist where water absorbed from the intestine is poured back as digestive secretion and is reabsorbed. Tissue fluid from the capillaries may enter the lymph circulation and be returned directly through the main lymph ducts, rather than through the venous end of the capillary. The movement and distribution of water within the body must be considered in connection with mineral or inorganic content and the protein content.

THE DISTRIBUTION OF WATER WITHIN THE BODY. Body water is considered as being separated into two principal portions, one which is contained within the cells and the other which lies outside the cells. The water and contained substances lying in the cells is called *intracellular fluid*. The anatomic *extracellular fluid*, which by definition includes all fluid outside the cells, is made up of plasma, lymph, interstitial fluid and extracellular cavity fluids (such as cerebrospinal fluid, synovial fluids and humors of the eye and secretions of the glands and kidneys). Of these, we will be concerned with physiologic extracellular

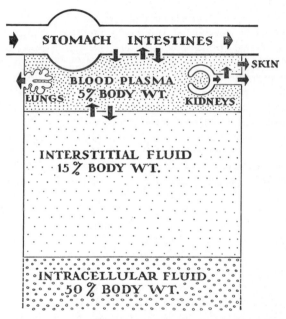

Fig. 278. Diagram of body fluid distribution (after Gamble).

water, i.e., the *plasma* which is in the vascular compartment and the *interstitial* fluid, including lymph, in the interstitial space. The morphologic boundaries of the compartments of the extracellular fluid cannot be definitely defined or its volume precisely measured, since no ideal chemical has been found which will mix only with physiologic extracellular water. While recognizing that there are small inaccuracies of measurement and that it is a somewhat variable quantity, the extracellular fluid volume is known to constitute approximately 25 per cent of total body weight, of which about 6 per cent is plasma and about 15 per cent interstitial fluid. Intracellular fluid makes up about 45 to 50 per cent of the body weight (Fig. 278).

The three body fluids—plasma, interstitial and intracellular—differ not only in distribution, but also in function and composition. The intracellular fluid serves as a medium for the chemical processes of metabolism. The interstitial fluid provides the immediate or internal environment for the body cells. It serves in the transfer of nutrient and essential substances from the plasma to the cell, and of waste products from the cell to the plasma. The plasma serves as the link between the external and internal environments by transporting a wide variety of substances from the gastrointestinal tract and oxygen from the lungs to the interstitial fluid and transporting waste products to the kidneys, lung and skin through which they leave the body and pass to the outside.

THE COMPOSITION OF THE BODY FLUIDS. Our interest in considering the constituents of the body fluids lies not only with the individual chemical substances, but also with the total composition from the point of view of osmotic pressure and of the acid-base balance. We will not concern ourselves here with the nonelectrolytes, i.e., the nutrient substances such as amino acids, waste products of protein metabolism and glucose, etc. (see p. 305).

The chemical composition of plasma and interstitial fluid is closely similar, except that blood plasma contains approximately 7-8 per cent protein, while interstitial fluid contains only small amounts since the walls of most capillaries restrict to various degrees the passage of the plasma proteins. The principal cation of the extracellular fluid is Na^+ and the principal anion is Cl^-. Other cations, i.e., K^+, Ca^{++} and Mg^{++}, and the anions HPO_4^{--}, SO_4^{--} and protein are present in small amounts, while HCO_3^- is present in appreciable amounts. The plasma has a slightly greater osmolar concentration (about 2 mOsm.) than the interstitial fluid, which aids in interchange of water between these two compartments. In the intracellular fluid, K^+ rather than NA^+ is the principal cation. The principal anions are phosphate and protein.

Continuous exchange takes place between the plasma and the interstitial fluid and between the interstitial fluid and the intracellular fluid as the result of differences in hydrostatic pressures and osmotic pressures. While individual ions and molecules change, the amounts of the substances remain remarkably constant. A comparison of the composition of cells and serum (i.e., plasma less fibrinogen) illustrates ionic and osmolar "balance." In such dynamic equilibria, we must use approximate values rather than an absolute value for individual substances; further, we do not know the values for all constituents. In consequence, "balance" does not imply identical totals.

Table 17[*]

Chemical Composition of Human Cells and Plasma
(In Milliosmols and Milliequivalents per Liter H_2O)

CONSTITUENT	SERUM		CELLS	
	mOsm.	mEq.	mOsm.	mEq.
Nonelectrolytes				
Urea	7		7	
Glucose	4		4	
Other	?		?	
Bases				
Na+	150	150	27	27
K+	4	4	135	135
Ca++	3	5	0	0
Mg++	1	2	3	5
Acid				
Cl−	111	111	74	74
HCO_3−	28	28	27	27
Inorgan. HPO_4−	2	3	2	3
Organ. Phos.	trace	†	21	†
SO_4−	1	1	?	?
Protein	1	18	7	62
Total Base		161		167
Total Acid		161		166
Total Milliosmols	312		307	

[*] From Fulton, J. F., Ed.: Textbook of Physiology, W. B. Saunders Co., 1955.
† Not known.

REGULATION OF WATER METABOLISM.   Water intake is influenced by the sensation which we call thirst. While we associate this feeling with a dry mouth and throat, this cannot be the primary stimulus since, when appreciable water losses have occurred, thirst is not satisfied even though discomfort may be slightly relieved by moistening the membranes of the mouth and pharynx. It seems probable that the more diffuse and compelling sensation results from dehydration of cells located in the hypothalamus.

Water in excess of bodily requirements is eliminated primarily by the kidney. In this process water and solutes are filtered off by the glomeruli of the kidney, and then a portion of the water is reabsorbed by the tubules (see Chapter 26). The extent to which the kidney eliminates or conserves water is determined by the nature and the amounts of the solutes which are being excreted and by an *antidiuretic hormone*, ADH, which is secreted by the pituitary (neurohypophysis).

DISTURBANCES IN WATER BALANCE. We have seen that water balance and the distribution of water and electrolytes in the various compartments are dynamic processes. Disturbances in water metabolism may occur, however. Perhaps the most familiar of these conditions are dehydration and retention of excess water, which may be distributed throughout the body or localized in certain areas with a resulting swelling or *edema*.

Dehydration may occur as the result of water deprivation or from excessive water losses. If the loss amounts to approximately 10 per cent of body weight the disturbance becomes serious; if approximately 20 per cent of body weight is lost through dehydration fatal consequences may be expected. Water deprivation may occur among survivors at sea when they are forced to exist in rafts or small boats for extended periods and among soldiers under rigorous combat conditions; occasionally prisoners who go on "hunger strikes" will refuse water. Excessive water losses may be associated with diarrhea, vomiting, profuse sweating, salt deficiency and various types of disease. Water and salt disturbances occur in diabetes and in adrenal cortex insufficiency.

Hydration, or increased water retention, may occur in kidney disease, in certain conditions associated with pregnancy, and upon administration of antidiuretic hormone. Where the increased fluid volume occurs without a corresponding salt retention, "water intoxication" may result. Where salt and water are shifted in excessive quantities to intracellular spaces, the swelling or puffiness characteristic of edema may be seen. Edema may result from many causes; strictly local swelling as in a bruise is caused chiefly by changes in the permeability of the walls of the capillaries.

SUMMARY

Absorption is the passage of digested food material through the wall of the alimentary canal.

Practically all absorption occurs in the small intestine.

Amino acids and monosaccharides are absorbed into the blood capillaries of the villi; fats pass into the lymph vessels, the lacteals.

Metabolism includes the sum total of chemical activities occurring within the tissues.

Building up processes are termed anabolism; breakdown processes are called catabolism.

Carbohydrates, fats and protein constitute sources of energy. Protein is essential in tissue growth and repair.

Inorganic salts, water and vitamins function chiefly in contributing to the composition of the internal environment.

Basal metabolism is the energy expenditure of a person who is lying down at complete muscular and mental rest, some twelve to fourteen hours after taking food and in a room with the temperature at about 20° C.

The basal metabolism is proportionate to the surface area of the individual and is expressed in terms of calories per square meter of body surface per hour.

The respiratory quotient is the ratio of the volume of carbon dioxide given off to the volume of oxygen consumed. The value of the respiratory quotient gives a useful indication of the type of food being burned.

The carbohydrates may be oxidized in the tissue cells to supply energy, they may be stored in liver and muscles as glycogen, and they may be stored as fat.

Fats are oxidized to carbon dioxide and water with the release of energy. Fat not needed for fuel may be stored temporarily in the liver or in fat depots of the body.

The amino acids of the blood are used to build new protoplasm as needed for growth or repair of tissues. The amino acids not so used are deaminized in the liver. The ammonia formed will be synthesized to urea and eliminated by the kidneys. The non-nitrogenous portion may be oxidized to supply energy or synthesized to glucose and subsequently to glycogen or fat.

Glycogenesis is the synthesis of glucose to glycogen; glycogenolysis is the hydrolysis of glycogen to glucose. Gluconeogenesis is the synthesis of glucose from substances of noncarbohydrate origin.

Water is separated into intracellular and extracellular fluid compartments. A continuous exchange takes place between these compartments, which is dependent upon electrolytic composition of the various fluids and certain hormone influences.

QUESTIONS FOR DISCUSSION

1. Describe the absorption of fats.

2. To what substances are carbohydrates reduced for absorption? In what form are they transported in the blood? In what forms are they stored?

3. What part does the liver play in the metabolism of carbohydrates and fats?

4. Explain the fate of the amino acids which are not used by the cells in the construction of protoplasm.

5. How is water metabolism regulated?

Chapter 26

Structure and Function of the Urinary System

Function of the Kidneys. The kidneys perform the important function of excreting the waste products of metabolism from the blood stream. They are also of primary importance in maintaining the water balance of the body and play a prominent role in regulation of the acid-base balance in the blood, and hence in the body as a whole. Their excretory activities are carried out so as to conserve the proper concentration of essential organic and inorganic substances in the blood. Whereas most of the discussion of metabolism thus far has been concerned with the supply of materials for maintaining a constant internal environment, a description of kidney function should aid in an understanding of the role of excretion in keeping the internal environment within physiologic limits.

ARCHITECTURE OF THE URINARY SYSTEM

The organs of the urinary system (Fig. 279) are the kidneys, which secrete the urine; the ureters, or tubes which convey the urine to the urinary bladder, where it is temporarily stored; and the urethra, through which it is discharged from the body.

The Kidneys. The kidneys are paired organs lying on the posterior abdominal wall on either side of the vertebral column and behind the peritoneum (Fig. 279). They are somewhat bean-shaped with a convex lateral border and a concave medial border. The surface of the kidney is smooth and is covered by a thin layer of fibrous membrane called the *capsule.* Each kidney is surrounded by a considerable quantity of

perirenal fat and connective tissue which, together with the peritoneum, afford support to the organ. The notch on the medial border
of the kidney is called the *hilum;* here connections are made with the
ureter and blood vessels. The upper portion of the ureter expands to
form the funnel-shaped renal pelvis with its subdivisions, numerous
small funnels called *calices.*

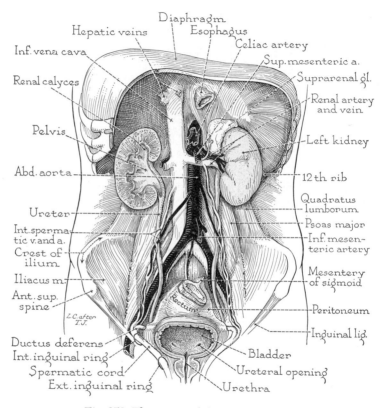

Fig. 279. The organs of the urinary system.

A longitudinal section of the kidney shows an external portion, the
cortex, and an inner part, the *medulla* (Fig. 280). The medulla consists of a number of *pyramids,* the bases of which border on the cortex,
while the apices constitute the papillae which project into the calices.
The cut surface of the pyramid shows striations which represent the
larger collecting tubules of the organ. The cortical substance forms
the peripheral layer and penetrates for some distance between the
pyramids to form the renal *columns.*

The minute structure of the kidneys shows a plan that is familiar— epithelial surfaces in contact with a capillary network. This arrangement is evident in each *nephron,* which constitutes the structural unit of the kidney. The nephron consists of a renal corpuscle with its subjoined tubule (Fig. 281). The renal corpuscle is made up of an elaborate tuft of parallel capillaries, called the *glomerulus,* surrounded by the invaginated end of the tubule known as Bowman's capsule

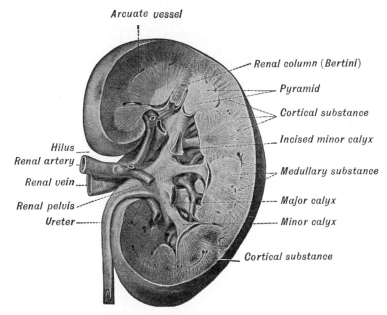

Fig. 280. Cortex, medulla and contents of the sinus of a human kidney, seen from behind after removal of part of the organ. (Maximow and Bloom, after Braus.)

(Fig. 282). *Bowman's capsule* has an outer or parietal layer, which forms the capsular wall, and an inner or visceral layer, which is closely applied to the capillary loops of the glomerulus. Both layers are composed of squamous cells. The capsule empties into the subjoined tubule, which may be divided into three major segments: the proximal segment, which adjoins the glomerulus and is made up of irregular epithelial cells with brush borders on their internal margins; the intermediate or thin segment, made of flat or squamous cells; and a distal segment with columnar cells. The proximal segment, which is loosely coiled, forms the greater part of the cortical substance. The terminal portion of the proximal convoluted tubule continues into *Henle's loop,* the descending limb of which passes downward for some distance into

the pyramid. When near the apex it turns upward to form the ascending
limb of Henle's loop which joins the distal segment. The distal convoluted tubule follows a somewhat tortuous path and finally terminates
in a collecting tubule. The collecting tubules coalesce to form large
collecting tubules which open into the calyx.

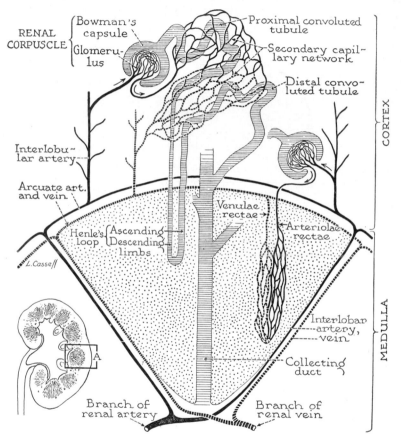

Fig. 281. Diagram of a renal tubule. Inset *A* shows the location of the renal tubule
in the kidney.

The blood supply to the nephrons comes from branches of the renal
artery. As the *renal artery* enters the hilum it breaks up into interlobar
arteries which pass between the pyramids to form arcuate branches
which arch over the bases of the pyramids. The arcuate arteries give
rise to interlobular arteries which pass toward the periphery in the

cortical substance. Each interlobular artery gives off several branches, which, with few exceptions, form the afferent vessels of the glomeruli.

The afferent arterioles break up into the capillary tufts, forming the glomeruli; these capillaries converge into efferent arterioles which have a smaller diameter than that of the afferent vessels. The efferent vessels then divide to form second capillary plexuses which lie in close apposition to the tubules. The afferent and efferent arterioles are surrounded by a cuff of myo-epithelioid cells whose function is as yet undetermined. The efferent arterioles of glomeruli located in the boundary zone between the cortex and medulla give rise to vessels, called arteriae rectae, or arteriolae rectae, which supply the collecting tubules and the loops of Henle. The branches of the arteriae rectae form terminal plexuses about these structures. The venae rectae return the blood to the interlobular veins.

The blood passing through the second capillary network surrounding the tubules drains into a venous plexus, then through interlobular, arcuate, interlobar and renal veins to reach the inferior vena cava (Fig. 281).

Summary of renal circulation:

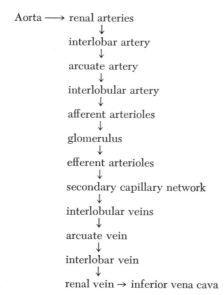

Aorta ⟶ renal arteries
↓
interlobar artery
↓
arcuate artery
↓
interlobular artery
↓
afferent arterioles
↓
glomerulus
↓
efferent arterioles
↓
secondary capillary network
↓
interlobular veins
↓
arcuate vein
↓
interlobar vein
↓
renal vein → inferior vena cava

The Ureters. The ureters are tubes about 27 cm. long which connect the renal pelves with the urinary bladder. They descend beneath the peritoneum on the posterior abdominal wall and cross the pelvic floor to reach the bladder. The wall of a ureter is composed of three layers: an inner or mucous coat covered with transitional epithelium, a middle coat of smooth muscle tissue with inner circular and outer longitudinal layers, and an outer fibrous coat. Peristaltic contractions of the ureters aid in transporting urine to the bladder.

The Urinary Bladder.   The bladder is a muscular bag lying in the pelvis behind the symphysis pubis, in front of the rectum in the male and in front of the vagina and uterus in the female. It serves as a reservoir in which urine is retained until it is eliminated from the body. There are three openings on the floor of the bladder—one in

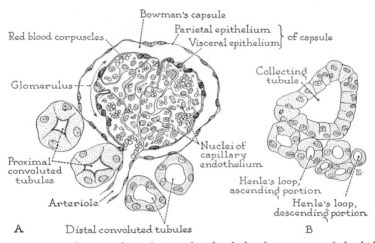

Fig. 282. A, Renal corpuscle with convoluted tubules from cortex of the kidney. B, Henle's loop and collecting tubule from medulla of kidney.

front for the urethra and two at the sides for the ureters. These orifices outline a triangular area called the *trigone*.

The *wall* of the bladder is composed of four coats: (1) An inner mucous coat, which is thrown into folds when the organ is empty. The epithelium is of a special type called transitional epithelium. It is highly elastic; in the contracted state it consists of several layers of polygonal cells, but when stretched in extreme distention only two layers can be seen, a deep row of cuboidal cells and a surface row of large squamous cells. (2) The submucous coat of loose areolar tissue allows free movement between mucous and muscular layers. (3) The muscular coat is arranged in three layers consisting of a middle circular layer between an inner and an outer longitudinal layer. The circular fibers of the middle layer are thickened in the region of the trigone to form the internal sphincter. (4) The outer coat is of peritoneum. It covers the superior surface.

The Urethra. The urethra is the tube passing from the bladder to the exterior. Its character differs in the two sexes. The female urethra is about 4 cm. long. At the junction of the urethra with the bladder the circular muscle layer forms the internal sphincter, while at the periphery striated muscle forms the external sphincter. The urethral orifice is in the vestibule just above and anterior to the vaginal orifice.

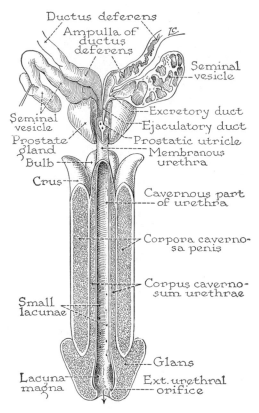

Fig. 283. The male urethra laid open on its anterior (upper) surface.

The male urethra is about 20 cm. long and is composed of three portions, the prostatic, membranous, and cavernous urethrae (Fig. 283). The *prostatic urethra* extends from the bladder to the pelvic floor. It is about 2.5 cm. long and is surrounded by the prostate gland. The *membranous urethra* is the portion which pierces the pelvic wall. It is about 2 cm. in length, and is surrounded by the external sphincter.

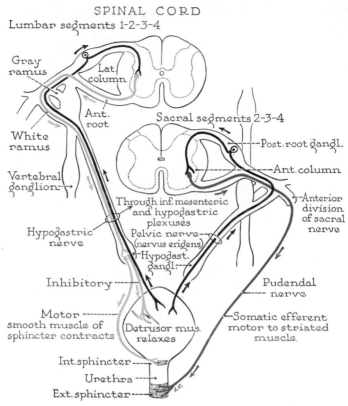

Fig. 284. Diagram of nervous mechanisms controlling the bladder and sphincters in retention of urine (filling the bladder). Reflexes involve the thoracolumbar division of the autonomic nervous system.

The *cavernous urethra* extends through the penis, terminating at the urethral orifice. This portion is about 15 cm. long and is surrounded by the corpus cavernosum of the urethra.

URINE

Composition of Urine. The urine is liquid, colored by the presence of bile pigments. It is usually on the acid side of neutrality. The specific gravity varies between 1.015 and 1.025. The quantity of urine excreted in twenty-four hours normally varies between 1000 and 1800 cc. The amount may be markedly decreased by an increased water loss through the sweat glands. The amount of urine secreted during the day is two to four times greater than the amount secreted during the night.

Water makes up 95 per cent of the urine. Analysis of 1000 cc. of urine yields from 40 to 50 gm. of total solids. Urea constitutes one half of this amount. The solids of the urine consist of inorganic and organic substances. The inorganic compounds are sodium chloride and the sulfates and phosphates of sodium, potassium, magnesium and

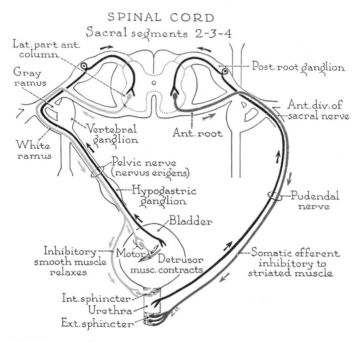

SPINAL CORD
Sacral segments 2-3-4

Fig. 285. Diagram of nervous mechanisms controlling the bladder and sphincters in micturition; reflexes involve the craniosacral division of the autonomic nervous system.

calcium. The chief organic compounds in the urine are urea, uric acid, creatinine and ammonium salts.

Formation of Urine. The relationship between structure and the function of urine formation is readily apparent in the kidney. The glomeruli constitute a system of efficient filters, and the tubules form effective structures for reabsorption.

A protein-free filtrate of blood plasma (i.e., whole blood minus corpuscles and proteins normally present in the blood) is filtered through the glomeruli and Bowman's capsule into the tubules. The energy for the filtration process is supplied by the blood pressure within the glomerular capillaries, which is higher than in other capillaries because of the structural arrangement whereby the efferent arterioles are of smaller diameter than the afferent vessels.

This filtrate of the blood then passes along the renal tubules, and in its course water and certain substances which are normally present in the blood are reabsorbed through the walls of the tubules into the blood stream. When excess quantities of water are ingested, only enough water is reabsorbed to maintain the normal fluid consistency of the blood; the excess water passes along the tubules to the ureters and bladder and is ultimately excreted. Other substances, such as sodium chloride and bicarbonate, are either reabsorbed or excreted, depending upon the amount ingested. For example, if sodium chloride is taken in relatively large amounts it is excreted accordingly. If this salt intake is low it will be reabsorbed through the tubules and little or none will be excreted. Blood sugar is completely reabsorbed from the protein-free plasma filtrate unless it is present in the blood in great excess. These substances are called "threshold" substances. Other substances such as urea, urates and creatinine are almost completely removed from blood plasma. These substances, which are excreted in urine regardless of how low their concentration may be in the blood, are called "nonthreshold" substances. The cells of the tubules perform work in reabsorption. Their activity results in a concentration of the nonthreshold substances in the urine to values far exceeding those in the blood. Urea, for example, is sixty times as concentrated in the urine as in the blood.

The kidneys aid in maintaining a constant acid-base balance in the blood by reabsorption of alkali from the filtrate and by manufacture and excretion of ammonia to neutralize fixed acids. The cells of the tubules may actually add certain substances (creatinine, hippuric acid and phenol red) to the filtrate by secretion.

Micturition. The ureters carry the urine from the kidneys to the bladder. Rhythmic peristaltic contractions pass over the ureters at the rate of one to five per minute, propelling the urine into the bladder. As the urine accumulates, the smooth muscle in the wall of the organ relaxes and stretches (exhibits extensibility) to adjust to the increased volume. When 250 to 300 cc. of urine have collected, the pressure within the bladder increases to about 150 mm. of water. This pressure is sufficient to stimulate afferent nerves. The impulses aroused pass to the central nervous system, and, in turn, efferent discharges culminate in contractions of the bladder wall and the relaxation of both sphincters, and urine is expelled through the urethra with considerable force. The thoracolumbar division of the autonomic system supplies inhibitory fibers to bladder wall and motor fibers to the sphincters and thus allows urine to accumulate in the bladder (Fig. 284). The craniosacral division sends motor fibers to muscles of the bladder wall and inhibitory fibers to the sphincters which, when adequately stimulated, result in micturition (Fig. 285). The voluntary contraction of abdominal muscles while the glottis is closed increases intra-abdominal pressure and assists in emptying the bladder.

SUMMARY

The kidneys excrete the waste products of metabolism from the blood stream and thus aid in keeping the internal environment within physiologic limits.

The kidneys lie on the posterior abdominal wall on either side of the vertebral column behind the peritoneum.

The kidney consists of an external portion, the cortex, and an inner part, the medulla.

The nephron is the structural unit of the kidney. It consists of a renal corpuscle and its subjoined tubule.

The blood supply of the nephrons comes from branches of the renal artery.

The ureters are tubes which connect the renal pelves with the urinary bladder.

Peristaltic contractions of the ureters aid in transporting urine to the bladder.

The bladder is a muscular bag lying in the pelvis behind the symphysis pubis. It serves as a reservoir in which urine is retained until it is eliminated from the body.

The urethra is the tube passing from the bladder to the exterior. The female urethra is about 4 cm. long. The male urethra is about 20 cm. long and consists of prostatic, membranous and cavernous portions.

Water makes up 95 per cent of urine. Analysis of 1000 cc. of urine yields 40 to 50 gm. of total solids.

Urine formation is the result of two processes: filtration, which takes place in the renal corpuscle, and reabsorption, which occurs in the tubules. Some substances may also be added by secretory activity of the cells of the tubules.

Micturition is initiated by the stimulation of afferent nerves in the bladder wall. Pressure of urine of about 150 mm. of water is the adequate stimulus. Impulses thus aroused pass to the central nervous system; in turn efferent discharges culminate in contraction of the bladder wall and relaxation of both sphincters, and urine is expelled through the urethra with considerable force.

QUESTIONS FOR DISCUSSION

1. What is the role of the renal corpuscle in the formation of urine? What is the function of the tubules? What physiologic processes are involved in the formation of urine?

2. What part does the urinary system play in maintaining a constant composition in the internal environment?

3. Explain micturition in terms of nerve control.

Chapter 27

Regulation of
Body Temperature

Normal Temperature of the Human Body. The normal temperature of the human body when taken with a thermometer placed in the mouth is about 98.6° F. (37° C.). It varies slightly above or below this level in different persons. Like other physiologic constants encountered in our study, normal body temperature represents a small range rather than a single value.

The temperature at the surface of the body is far more variable than the temperature of the deep body tissues. In certain parts of the body such as the fingers, toes and ears, where the surface area of the part is great in proportion to the mass of tissues, rather extreme and often painful temperature changes may result upon exposure to cold. When adequately clothed and under the less extreme environmental conditions, the skin of the trunk may be about 95° F.

Poikilothermal and Homothermal Animals. With respect to body temperature, animals may be divided into two classes: those of variable body temperature, or *poikilothermal,* and those with constant body temperature, or *homothermal* (Fig. 286). Poikilothermal (also called "cold-blooded") animals such as the frog or snake have body temperatures which are dependent upon environmental temperature. When it is cold, their metabolic processes are subdued and movements become sluggish. Homothermal animals such as mammals and birds, on the other hand, are able to maintain a fairly constant body temperature in spite of changes in the temperature of the environment (Fig. 287). The body temperature of homothermal animals represents the balance struck between heat production and heat loss (Fig. 288).

Heat Production. Heat is produced by oxidations occurring in the tissues. The muscular tissue and the liver are the chief sources of the body heat. Heat production is stimulated by low environmental temperature, by the intake of food, especially protein, and by muscular activity. It is evident that the rate of heat production must equal the rate of heat loss if constant body temperature is to be maintained. In a cold environment the heat loss is greater and, therefore, heat production is greater. An increase in the tone of skeletal muscles contributes to the general rise in metabolism resulting from a fall in environmental temperature. This increase in tone may continue to the

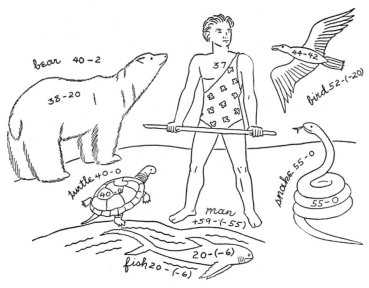

Fig. 286. Homothermal and poikilothermal animals. Body temperature is compared with range of temperature of the environment. The temperatures are given in the centigrade scale. (Lemon, From Galileo to Cosmic Rays, University of Chicago Press.)

point of involuntary muscular contractions which characterize shivering and chattering of the teeth. The heat production of a man shivering at maximal rate but otherwise "at rest" may be in excess of 200 Calories per square meter of body surface per hour. This is comparable to heat production during strenuous work.

The effect of food, especially protein, is important in the chemical regulation of body temperature. The proteins through their specific dynamic action have a stimulating effect upon the tissue cells by which their metabolism is increased (see page 469). At low temperatures the specific dynamic effect of protein may replace heat production which is brought about by muscular contraction. In cold climates, then, protein food may help considerably to increase heat production. Fat also constitutes a valuable food in cold environments because of its high calorific value (9 Calories per gram).

Heat Loss. The body loses heat in the following ways:

1. By convection, conduction and radiation.
2. By vaporization, or evaporation of water from the lungs and skin.
3. By raising of the inspired air to body temperature.
4. By liberation of carbon dioxide from the blood in the lungs.
5. Through the urine and feces.
6. Some heat may be either lost or gained by ingestion of foods below or above body temperature.

Fig. 287. The thermostatic mechanisms in the human body keep its temperature within a degree of normal in spite of activities and outside temperatures. (Lemon, From Galileo to Cosmic Rays, University of Chicago Press.)

Over 80 per cent of the heat loss of the body is effected by conduction, convection, radiation and evaporation from the skin. *Conduction* is simply the passage of heat energy between two objects at different temperatures through molecular vibration. Thus the body will lose heat if immersed in a cold bath or even when objects below body temperature are touched or held. *Convection* is the transfer of heat by molecules of air coming in contact with the body surface; air warmed by the body rises and sets up convection currents renewing the gas particles presented to its surface. *Radiation* is the transfer of infra-red waves through the ether; it occurs without material contact. In this respect the body is acting like the red heater element in an electric heater or in an infra-red therapeutic lamp. The superficial body tissues act as an insulating barrier between the deep tissues and the environment. The effectiveness of the subcutaneous tissues depends to some extent on the amount of fat in the superficial fascia. Fat is a poor conductor of heat and tends to protect the body from excessive heat loss. The degree of insulation provided by the superficial tissues at any time will be greatly influenced by the state of their blood vessels, since these carry blood from the deeper tissues to the surface, where it is "spread out" just beneath the skin. When the body is exposed to a

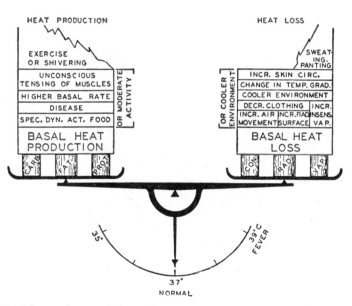

Fig. 288. Scheme showing balance between factors of changing heat production and heat loss. (Wiggers, by courtesy of Du Bois, Ann. Int. Med.)

cold environment, the blood vessels constrict and less blood circulates through the surface vessels. This tends to conserve body heat through reduction in the losses by radiation, convection and conduction. During vasoconstriction, heat may be conducted through the superficial tissues at a rate of about 9 Calories per square meter of body surface per hour for each (Centigrade) degree of difference in temperature between the deep tissues and the body surface. When the body is exposed to warm environmental temperatures, a dilatation of the peripheral vessels occurs; five or six times the quantity of heat, i.e., 45 to 54 Calories per square meter of body surface per hour, may be transferred when the vessels are fully dilated.

Vaporization or evaporation of water from the skin and lungs requires the absorption of about 0.6 Calorie for each gram of water vaporized at 37° C. Water is lost from the skin by "insensible perspiration" even when there is no perceptible sweating. When body temperature increases as a result of high environmental temperature or exercise, the sweat glands are stimulated to increased activity. As the sweat evaporates, the skin surface cools as the result of the heat absorbed in vaporization. High humidity decreases the heat losses through this channel.

Under usual conditions at normal room temperatures about 25 per cent of the heat loss results from vaporization, 15 per cent through convection and 60 per cent by radiation. However, these proportions vary greatly under different environmental conditions. Heat is absorbed when the carbon dioxide of the blood comes out of solution. A small amount of heat is lost in this way.

Temperature-Regulating Mechanism. The temperature-regulating center is in the hypothalamus, the region of the brain in and around the walls of the third ventricle below the thalamus. The cells in the anterior hypothalamus control heat loss; those in the posterior hypothalamus control heat production. There are similar centers in the medulla and spinal cord, but these lower centers are coordinated through the action of the hypothalamus. The hypothalamus is influenced reflexly by afferent nerve impulses from the skin, and locally in the center itself as a result of temperature changes in the blood.

The reflex adjustments occur in response to heat and cold. When receptors for cold in the skin are stimulated, superficial blood vessels constrict, muscle tone increases, and shivering may begin. The effect offsets a fall in body temperature by decreased heat loss in the first instance and increased heat production in the last two effects. When heat receptors in the skin are stimulated, superficial blood vessels are dilated, sweat secretion is increased, muscles are relaxed, and panting may occur. Vasodilatation, sweating and panting increase heat loss; and muscular relaxation decreases heat production so that elevation of body temperature is forestalled.

The center is stimulated directly when the temperature of the blood coursing through it is raised or lowered. Low temperatures set heat-conserving mechanisms into operation and stimulate the center to send impulses over efferent nerves to blood vessels, causing vasoconstriction, and to muscles, increasing tension or initiating shivering. Warming the center produces efferent discharges to sweat glands for secretion, to skin blood vessels for vasodilatation, and to the respiratory center for panting. These discharges result in heat loss.

SUMMARY

The normal temperature of the human body is about 37° C.

With respect to body temperature, animals may be divided into two classes: those of variable body temperature or poikilothermal, and those with constant body temperature or homothermal.

The temperature of homothermal animals represents the balance struck between heat production and heat loss.

Heat production results from oxidation reactions and is termed the chemical regulation of body temperature.

Heat loss depends upon physical processes and is therefore termed physical regulation.

The temperature-regulating center is in the hypothalamus. It is influenced reflexly as a result of afferent impulses from the skin and locally in the center itself as a result of temperature changes in the blood.

QUESTIONS FOR DISCUSSION

1. What advantage do homothermal animals have over poikilothermal animals?

2. Explain the meaning of conduction, convection and radiation in relation to the loss of heat from the body.

Chapter 28

The Endocrine System

The Endocrine System. The endocrine glands comprise the endocrine system. The principal glands are the thyroid, parathyroids, pancreas, suprarenals, hypophysis cerebri, testes and ovaries. Portions of mucosa of the stomach and duodenum may be considered to have an endocrine function. The location of the glands is shown in Figure 289.

The thymus and pineal glands have not been included since their function as endocrine glands has not been established.

Gastrointestinal principles composed of the hormones *gastrin, secretin, pancreozymin, cholecystokinin, enterogastrone* and the *secretagogues* or *parahormones* are discussed in Chapter 24. The hormones of the gonads and placenta which regulate reproductive processes are presented in Chapters 29, 30 and 31 on the reproductive systems.

Our knowledge of the actions of the secretions of endocrine glands and their interrelations is far from complete, although information has been obtained by various methods of study, including: (*a*) the experimental removal of a gland with careful observation of disturbances resulting in both immature and fully grown animals; (*b*) the administration of the active principle of the gland, where it has been isolated, to both normal animals and animals in which the gland has been removed; (*c*) the notation of clinical conditions which can be related to dysfunction of one or more of the endocrine glands. Dysfunction may take the form of either increased hormone secretion (*hyper*function) or a decreased secretion (*hypo*function).

Exocrine and Endocrine Glands Compared. The endocrine glands resemble ordinary glands in that they produce complex compounds from materials derived from the blood or lymph, but differ from them in that they have no ducts for the discharge of their secretions. These compounds, called *internal secretions,* are absorbed into the blood vessels which ramify through the gland. Usually the glands are supplied with vessels which carry away their products. Once in the blood

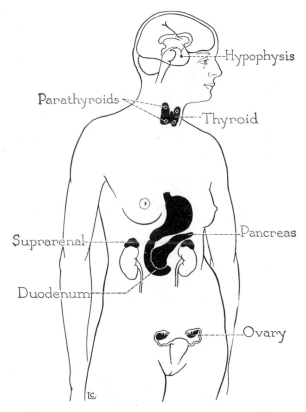

Fig. 289. Location of the glands of internal secretion.

stream, the internal secretions pass to all parts of the body in the systemic circulation and may produce effects in regions remote from the site of origin. The active principles of the internal secretions are called *hormones* or *parahormones.* The latter term qualifies a chemical agent which acts like a hormone, but is not produced by the living cells, although it is distributed in circulation. Glucose and secreta-gogues are examples of parahormones.

Mechanism of Action. Hormones and parahormones are thought to be regulators of enzyme systems within certain tissues or organs of the body. Hence, they do not initiate action themselves, but energize

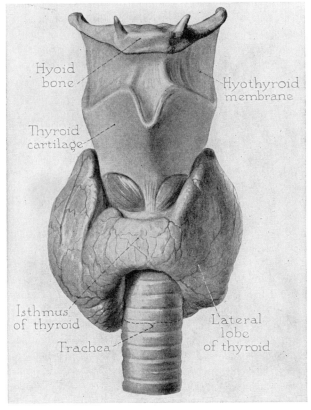

Fig. 290. The thyroid gland, larynx, upper portion of the trachea and hyoid bone from in front. (Sobotta and McMurrich.)

the reactions catalyzed by specific enzymes. In this process, the active principle of the endocrine gland may function independently, or inter-dependent upon a series of complex reactions. In comparison to the nervous system, the endocrine system is adapted to the control of processes requiring slow and long-term adjustment, rather than the rapid adjustments of the former. The ductless glands are usually the last of body coordinating mechanisms to appear in the embryological development of the individual.

Thyroid Gland. This largest of the endocrine glands is located in the neck anterolateral to the trachea at its junction with the larynx. Two lateral lobes lie on either side of the trachea down to the sixth tracheal cartilage and up to the thyroid and cricoid cartilages of the larynx. The lobes are connected by an isthmus passing over the anterior surface of the second to fourth cartilages of the trachea (Fig. 290).

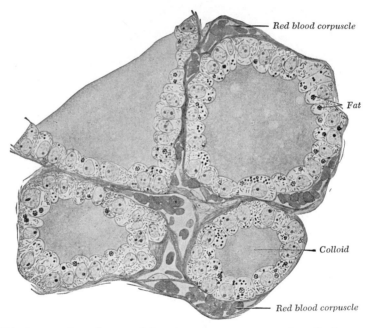

Fig. 291. Section through several follicles of a human thyroid. Colloid is in the lumen of each follicle. (Maximow and Bloom, courtesy of R. R. Bensley.)

A small pyramidal lobe occasionally extends from the isthmus in the direction of the thyroid cartilage. The blood and lymph supply to the thyroid gland is very rich (Figs. 209, 231). Superior thyroid arteries from the external carotid arteries and inferior thyroid arteries from the subclavian arteries form a plexus over the gland which reaches inward toward each follicle as a fine capillary network. Venous blood drains from the capillary plexus to the superior and middle thyroid veins returning to the internal jugular veins, while inferior thyroid veins enter the left innominate vein. The gland is enclosed in two layers of connective tissue forming an outer and inner capsule. Innervation is derived from the autonomic nervous system via the superior and inferior cervical ganglia for thoracolumbar fibers, and superior and inferior laryngeal nerves for craniosacral fibers.

The secretory portion of the thyroid is made up of *follicles* arranged in lobules. The follicles are lined with a single layer of cuboid cells (Fig. 291). The cavities of the follicles possess a homogeneous material called colloid, which contains some of the stored hormone formed by the cuboid cells. The secretion produced by the thyroid gland and stored in the follicles is *thyroglobulin.* Two iodine-containing amino acids may be obtained from the thyroglobulin: *triiodothyronine* and *thyroxin.* Thyroxin, containing approximately 65 per cent iodine, is able to duplicate all the physiologic effects of thyroglobulin, and can be obtained from circulating blood. Only small amounts of triiodothyronine are found in circulating blood. However, thyroxin is deiodinated into triiodothyronine which passes into tissue cells.

The functions of the thyroid gland are presented below, together with some interactions of the effects upon the body.

METABOLISM. The rate of oxidation in all tissue cells is increased probably through hormone action upon respiratory enzymes of the cells.

A vitamin A deficiency results from hyposecretion because the vitamin is improperly synthesized. The same effect is observed in hypersecretion because of too rapid destruction of the vitamin. Deficiencies of B complex and C can be observed in hyperfunction of the thyroid gland.

Protein catabolism is increased and nitrogen balance tends to shift to the negative side. Muscle tissue cannot synthesize creatine phosphate properly without thyroid hormone.

Carbohydrate metabolism is stimulated in a variety of ways, resulting in (a) increased absorption of monosaccharides from the intestine; (b) increased glycogenolysis; (c) increased gluconeogenesis and (d) increased utilization of glucose in tissue cells.

Normal secretion and hypersecretion accelerate oxidation of fats.

Deficiency of thyroid hormone results in collections of fluid high in protein in the tissues.

Sodium is withdrawn from extracellular fluid and calcium from intracellular fluid compartments during hyperfunction of the thyroid.

GROWTH AND DEVELOPMENT.   Thyroxin stimulates anabolism of proteins to release products needed in the growth of tissues.

Endochondral ossification does not proceed properly with a deficiency of thyroid secretion.

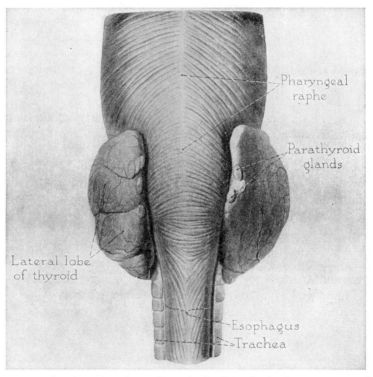

Fig. 292. The thyroid and parathyroid glands with the lower portion of the pharynx and upper end of the esophagus from behind. Usually there are four parathyroid glands, but there may be more, as in this figure. (Sobotta and McMurrich.)

Thyroxin influences normal development and activity of central nervous system.

Tissues and organs innervated by the autonomic nervous system are sensitized to respond more rapidly through thyroid secretion.

EFFECTS OF THYROID FUNCTION UPON THE BODY.   Lack of thyroid secretion may result in cretinism in the young. This condition is characterized by small stature, arrested mental development and retardation in sexual development. In adults, hypofunction of the thyroid results in myxedema. Both of these conditions are associated with edema, skin and hair texture changes and reduction in basal metabolic rate. Excess of this secretion results in a condition known as hyperthyroidism and is characterized by an increased basal metabolic rate, loss of weight, rapid heart rate, increased perspiration, and reduced sensitivity to cold.

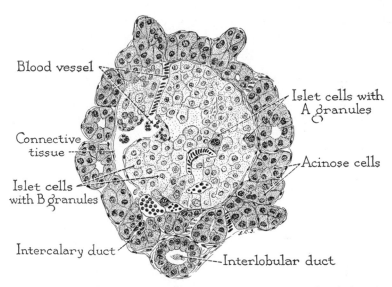

Fig. 293. Section of human pancreas compares endocrine cells of the islet of Langerhans with surrounding glandular cells.

Parathyroid Glands (Fig. 292). These smallest of the endocrine glands consist of four small bodies which lie on the posterior surface of the thyroid gland near the branches of the inferior thyroid artery. Small lobules of parathyroid gland are formed of epithelial cells, partitioned by septa extending from the capsule of the gland inward. The substance secreted by parathyroid cells has been named *parathormone*. The exact mechanism of action of the hormone upon calcium and phosphorus metabolism has not been proven. It is possible that parathormone regulates calcium and phosphorus metabolism by adjusting the activities of osteoclasts and osteoblasts in osseous tissue. It is possible that calcium metabolism is regulated after phosphates are excreted by the kidney because the phosphates are held in the blood plasma under parathormone control.

Approximately 90 per cent of the calcium and 80 per cent of the phosphorus of the body are present in teeth and bone. The normal concentration of blood serum calcium is 9 to 12 mg. per cent and blood serum phosphorus is 2.5 to 4.5 mg. per cent. Marked diminution in the parathormone lowers blood serum calcium and elevates blood serum phosphorus. This condition may cause *tetany*, which is characterized by tonic spasms of the skeletal musculature and increased

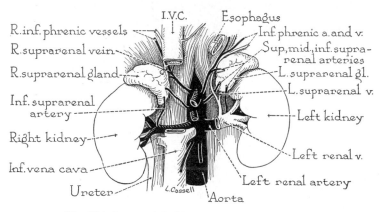

Fig. 294. Suprarenal glands and related structures.

irritability of central and peripheral nerves. A slight diminution of parathormone may lead to improper development of teeth and bones. Increased amounts of parathormone elevate blood serum calcium and lower blood serum phosphorus. Changes in the body which reflect this altered metabolism of calcium and phosphorus include deposition of calcium in intestines, kidneys and heart, hyposensitivity of the nervous system and demineralization and distortion of the skeletal system.

Pancreas. The pancreas lies on the posterior abdominal wall behind and below the stomach (Figs. 267, 289). The head is enclosed in the loop of the duodenum and the tail extends to the spleen. Circulation to the pancreas has been discussed in Chapter 23, with other organs of the digestive system. Thoracolumbar nerve fibers extend to the pancreas through the celiac plexus, and branches of the vagi nerves represent craniosacral innervation. The pancreas develops as an evagination from the wall of the digestive tube in the embryo. This gland contains both exocrine elements, represented by the acini, and endocrine elements in the islets of Langerhans (Fig. 293). In the islets of Langerhans, A and B granular cells can be distinguished. It is generally believed that insulin, the principal hormone of the pancreas, is elaborated by the B cells which predominate in the islet tissue. The protein insulin has a high content of zinc and sulfur.

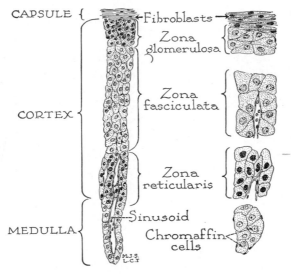

CAPSULE
Fibroblasts
Zona glomerulosa
CORTEX
Zona fasciculata
Zona reticularis
Sinusoid
MEDULLA
Chromaffin cells

Fig. 295. Section through suprarenal gland showing proportional zones of medulla and cortex with their respective types of cells.

Insulin is essential to normal carbohydrate metabolism. This activity is thought to be manifest by enhancing the action of the enzyme hexokinase, so that glucose 6-phosphate is formed. The reactions into which glucose 6-phosphate enters are then augmented so that glycogenesis and the rate of oxidation of glucose to carbon dioxide and water occur more rapidly.

Proper secretion of insulin is essential to life. Normal blood sugar has a concentration of 80 to 100 mg. per cent. Without insulin, there may be an excessive rise of blood sugar to more than 300 mg. per cent, disappearance of glycogen from the liver, glycosuria, and polyuria. Ketone bodies from the incomplete combustion of fat such as beta-hydroxybutyric acid, acetone, and acetoacetic acid will also appear in blood and urine. This condition is characterized as diabetes mellitus. Excesses of insulin may reduce blood sugar to 40 to 50 mg. per cent with resultant fatigue, irritability and hunger. Coma and death may occur in either extreme. It should be remembered that in addition to the insulin activity, the metabolism of carbohydrates is also influenced by a variety of other factors including hormones from the adeno-hypophysis, adrenal and thyroid glands, dietary intake, and conditions affecting the nervous system, circulatory system and urinary system.

There is evidence to suggest that a second hormone, *lipocaic,* is secreted by the pancreas which is concerned with the transportation and metabolism of fats.

Suprarenal Glands. The two suprarenal glands, or adrenal bodies (Fig. 294), are pyramidal structures situated at the upper poles of the kidneys. These glands have one of the best blood supplies of any organ in the body. Thoracolumbar nerve fibers from the celiac plexus innervate the adrenal glands. They consist of an outer portion, the cortex, and an inner portion, the medulla. A relatively dense connective tissue capsule surrounds the glands. Three zones of cells can be distinguished in the cortex which represent various phases of growth, secretion and degeneration occurring in the cortex in that order from periphery to center. Both medulla and cortex cells are arranged in radiating cords with blood sinusoids between the cords, as shown in Figure 295. Cells of the medulla resemble autonomic ganglia cells. The adrenal cortex develops near the kidneys and gonads from mesoderm tissue in the embryo. Adrenal medulla differentiates from the portion of ectoderm, giving rise to the autonomic nervous system.

The secretion of the medulla is known as *epinephrine* or adrenalin. Epinephrine acts upon all structures of the body innervated by the thoracolumbar division of the autonomic nervous system, with the exception of the sweat glands. Its effects are the same as those obtained by stimulation of these nerves. Because of this sympathomimetic action (mimicking the action of the sympathetic nervous system), injection of epinephrine results in (*a*) a rise in arterial blood pressure, constriction of the arterioles (chiefly in the skin and viscera) and increased strength and rate of heart beat; (*b*) inhibition of gastrointestinal musculature, with the exception of the sphincters; (*c*) relaxation of other smooth muscle; dilatation of the pupil of the eye, relaxation of the muscles of the bronchi; relaxation of the coronary arteries; relaxation (or constriction) of uterine muscle; (*d*) liberation of glucose from the

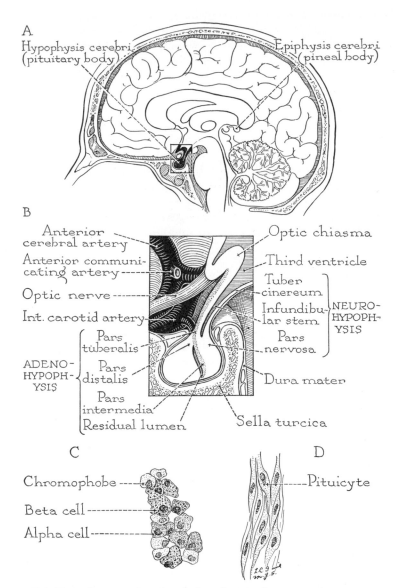

A

Hypophysis cerebri
(pituitary body)

Epiphysis cerebri
(pineal body)

B

Anterior
cerebral artery

Anterior communi-
cating artery

Optic nerve

Int. carotid artery

ADENO-
HYPOPH-
YSIS
{
Pars
tuberalis

Pars
distalis

Pars
intermedia

Residual lumen
}

Optic chiasma

Third ventricle

Tuber
cinereum

Infundibu-
lar stem

Pars
nervosa

NEURO-
HYPOPH-
YSIS

Dura mater

Sella turcica

C

Chromophobe

Beta cell

Alpha cell

D

Pituicyte

Fig. 296. Hypophysis cerebri. *A*, Blackened inset draws attention to relation of hypophysis to gross structures of the brain in midsagittal section. *B* is an enlargement of the inset showing gross details of the hypophysis and surrounding structures. *C* illustrates typical cells of adenohypophysis. *D* illustrates typical cells of neurohypophysis.

glycogen stores of the liver, elevating blood sugar; and (e) increase in the metabolic rate. Compare this action with the effect of stimulation of the thoracolumbar autonomic system described on page 158.

In spite of these marked influences exerted on various bodily functions, the adrenal medullary tissue is not essential to life; its loss does not result in apparent changes in the health or behavior of the animal.

The cortical tissue, however, is essential to life. The six biologically active of about twenty-eight compounds that have been isolated from adrenal cortex are collectively referred to as *corticoids*. No single compound is regarded as the hormone of the gland. All these substances are steroids closely related to the chemical structure of the sex hormones and cholesterol. Some sex hormones are secreted by the adrenal cortex.

The corticoids may be divided into two chemical and physiologic groups. One group, referred to as "salt hormones," will promote the excretion of potassium in the urine and the retention of sodium and chloride, and hence water, in the tissues. The other group, referred to as "sugar hormones," opposes the action of insulin by promoting protein catabolism and protein gluconeogenesis. The "sugar hormones" may also produce an action on electrolyte and water metabolism qualitatively similar to the "salt hormones," and affect membranes in a way to reduce their permeability. Desoxycorticosterone and aldosterone represent "salt hormones" and are formed in zona glomerulosa. Cortisol and cortisone are produced by zona fasiculata and zona reticulata. The latter are adrenocorticosteroids of the "sugar hormones" (Fig. 295).

In the absence of proper cortical secretion, extracellular electrolytes (Fig. 278) are depleted by elimination in the kidney, and intracellular electrolytes become concentrated by changes in membrane permeability. This causes a shift of water into the cells and lowers blood pressure by dehydration. Adrenal cortex secretion maintains normal function of the kidneys in elimination of nonthreshold urea, uric acid and creatinine, threshold electrolytes of sodium, and potassium chlorides, phosphates and sulfates. The total effect of adrenal cortex secretion upon the body includes changes in growth and weight, basal metabolism, reproduction, neuromuscular activity, gastrointestinal function and body fluid balance. Interrelationships exist between the function of the adrenal cortex and adenohypophysis, thyroid gland and gonads.

Hypophysis Cerebri. The hypophysis, or pituitary body, is a small organ about the size of a pea, which lies in the sella turcica of the sphenoid bone (Fig. 296). It is attached to the cerebrum by a stalk which extends downward from the floor of the third ventricle. The optic chiasm lies just above the hypophysis. The adenohypophysis arises from ectoderm of the roof of the mouth, and neurohypophysis arises from ectoderm of the hypothalamus in the embryo. A generous blood supply is available to the gland through small vessels from the circle of Willis, whose capillary bed returns blood to the cavernous sinus. Nerve supply to the gland comes from the carotid plexus and hypothalamus.

ADENOHYPOPHYSIS. The adenohypophysis is composed of the pars tuberalis, pars distalis, pars intermedia, and a residual lumen (Fig. 296B). Pars distalis is commonly referred to as the *anterior lobe* of the pituitary gland. The alpha cells contain large pigment granules that may take an acid or basic stain, although they are usually acidophilic cells. The beta cells are somewhat larger with basophilic granules. It is thought that the chromophobe cells are presecretory and postsecretory phases of the gland, while the granular cells are responsible for secretion of the hormones of the adenohypophysis. Tentatively, it is thought that all the hormones except those affecting the adrenal and thyroid glands are elaborated by the alpha cells.

Among the hormones derived from the adenohypophysis are the following factors:

The *growth factor* influences normal growth. Epithelial and connective tissues in skin and bone seem to respond markedly to this factor, which promotes nitrogen retention as a result of stimulation to protein anabolism. Body growth, however, represents an interaction of several hormones and parahormones, along with the capacity of the tissues involved to respond.

The *thyrotropic factor* (TSH) is responsible for the gross size and vascularity of the thyroid gland and, hence, for its ability to function physiologically.

The *adrenocorticotropic factor* or *hormone* (ACTH) affects the cortex of the suprarenal gland in much the same way as the thyroid is affected, and causes an increase in the production of corticoids or adrenal cortex hormones.

The *diabetogenic* action of the hypophysis indicates that, while the secretion of insulin by the pancreas does not depend upon the pituitary gland, the production and release of insulin do depend upon the blood-glucose level. This, in turn, is partly determined by the pituitary gland through its effect upon the thyroid.

The *gonadotropic factors* include three substances affecting the ovaries or testes. The follicle-stimulating hormone (FSH) causes an increase in the size of the ovary, maintenance of interstitial cells and luteinization of the ruptured ovarian follicle in the female. The FSH influences the size of the testes and seminiferous tubules in the male and the *luteinizing hormone* (LH) stimulates interstitial tissue of the testes. LH in combination with FSH produces a greater effect upon the ovaries and testes than either factor alone. A third factor, *luteotropin*, responsible for the secretion of corpora luteal cells, is considered the same as the lactogenic hormone.

The *lactogenic hormone* or prolactin appears to be a secretagogue or parahormone which will initiate and maintain lactation in mammary glands that have anatomically differentiated for milk production during pregnancy. Lactation depends also on endocrine action of adrenal and thyroid glands and nervous influences.

NEUROHYPOPHYSIS.   The neurohypophysis is composed of the tuber cinerium, infundibular stem and pars nervosa shown in Figure 296B. The pars nervosa portion of the gland is commonly referred to as the *posterior lobe* of the pituitary. This region of the hypophysis is connected by nonmyelinated fibers of the supraopticohypophyseal tract and tuberohypophyseal tract to nuclei of the hypothalamus of the brain. Secretions from cells in the hypothalamus pass along the fibers of these nerve tracts to bring neurosecretory substances into posterior lobe of the pituitary for storage around the pituicytes or release into circulation.

Vasopressin affects smooth muscle of the arteries and arterioles and to a lesser extent the venules and capillaries, resulting in vasoconstriction and an elevation in blood pressure. Antidiuresis, through the action of vasopressin to increase resorption of fluid and increase the output of salt in the uriniferous tubules, has often been attributed to another factor, *antidiuretic hormone* (ADH), attached to vasopressin.

Oxytocin acts directly on the smooth muscle of the uterus, particularly in pregnancy, to cause contraction of the muscle. It aids in release of milk from mammary glands following parturition.

The secretion of the pituitary gland may act directly upon tissues and organs, as with growth factor,vasopressin and oxytocin, or it may affect them indirectly by interaction with other endocrine glands through thyrotropin and adrenocorticotropin, by diabetogenic influence, or by gonadotropic and luteotropic hormones. Because of the widespread influence of the pituitary gland, it is sometimes referred to as the master gland.

SUMMARY

The principal glands of the endocrine system are the thyroid, parathyroids, pancreas, suprarenals, testes, ovaries, placenta and hypophysis cerebri. Certain portions of the stomach and duodenum have endocrine functions.

The endocrine glands resemble ordinary glands in that they produce complex compounds from materials derived from the blood or lymph, but they differ from them in that they have no ducts for the discharge of their secretions.

These compounds, called internal secretions, are absorbed by the blood vessels which ramify through the gland.

The active principles of the internal secretions are called hormones or parahormones.

Methods used in the study of endocrine glands include experimental removal of the gland, administration of the active principle of the gland, and the notation of clinical conditions which can be related to dysfunction of one or more of the glands.

The thyroid gland secretes the hormone thyroxin, which increases the basal metabolic rate and heat liberation after ingestion of food and during exercise.

The parathyroid glands play an important part in the regulation of calcium metabolism.

The islet cells of the pancreas secrete insulin, which is essential to normal carbohydrate metabolism.

The suprarenal glands consist of an outer portion, the cortex, and an inner portion, the medulla.

The medulla secretes epinephrine, which acts upon all the structures innervated by the thoracolumbar division of the autonomic nervous system with the exception of the sweat glands.

The cortex secretes a number of hormone-like substances, i.e., corticoids and sex hormones, which are concerned with maintenance of the salt, sugar and nonprotein nitrogen content of the blood at the physiologic level. They also affect the development of the sex glands and the secretion of the mammary glands.

The hypophysis, or pituitary gland, consists of three parts called anterior, intermediate and posterior portions or lobes.

The anterior pituitary gland appears to be the coordinator of the hormones affecting metabolism, growth and development.

The posterior pituitary gland forms substances which act to constrict the smooth muscle of blood vessels and uterus and to decrease the formation of urine.

QUESTIONS FOR DISCUSSION

1. At this point in the textbook all the major coordinating mechanisms of the body as a whole have been presented. What are they? What main principles are responsible for the individual mechanisms of control?

2. Look up the description of Addison's disease. Relate the symptoms given to your knowledge of the function of the adrenal gland.

3. What hormones are involved in water metabolism in the body?

Unit
5

REPRODUCTION OF THE
HUMAN BEING

THIS UNIT gives consideration to the origin and development of the human body. The reproductive structures of the male and female are described and reproductive processes explained.

Chapter 29

Female Reproductive System

THE FEMALE reproductive organs consist of the ovaries, in which sex cells develop; the uterine tubes, through which the sex cells pass; the uterus, in which the embryo develops; the vagina, a canal which

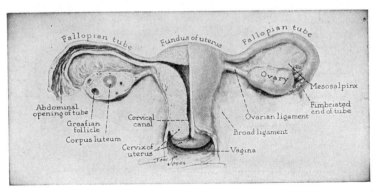

Fig. 297. Uterus and associated organs in the female. (Courtesy of S. H. Camp & Co.)

connects the uterus to the exterior; the external genitalia; and the mammary glands. The ovaries, uterine tubes and uterus are shown in Figure 297.

Ovaries. The ovaries are flattened oval bodies about 2.5 cm. long, which lie on the sides of the pelvis, attached to the posterior surface of the broad ligament and supported laterally by the infundibulopelvic ligament. These ligaments are folds of peritoneum.

The substance of the ovary consists of a connective tissue groundwork or *stroma*. In the central portion, or medulla, the arrangement is loose and blood vessels are numerous. In the outer cortical portion the stroma is more dense and contains many follicles.

The surface of the ovary is covered with a single layer of cuboidal or columnar cells. This epithelium is called the germinal epithelium because it gives rise to the ova and follicles.

Three types of follicles are found in the ovaries: primary, growing, and mature or vesicular follicles (Fig. 298). The *primary follicles* are

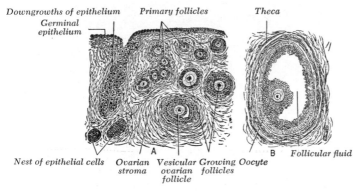

Fig. 298. *A*, Diagrammatic representation of the manner in which the follicles arise during the development of the ovary. *B*, Diagram illustrating the structure of a ripe or vesicular follicle. (Cunningham, Textbook of Anatomy, Oxford University Press.)

the most numerous. They consist of the egg cell surrounded by a few small follicular cells. Some of the primary follicles become *growing follicles* and show marked increase in size. This comes about by increase in size of the ovum and an increase in the number of the follicle cells. Soon spaces filled with fluid appear among the cells; the spaces coalesce to form a single cavity which increases so much in size that the ovum is pushed to one side. With growth of the follicle the connective tissue cells form a capsule around it called the theca. The growing follicle has become the *mature*, or *vesicular*, follicle and is seen bulging from the surface of the ovary. When mature, the follicle either ruptures or undergoes involution. Follicles may degenerate at any stage of development. With rupture of the follicle the follicular fluid and ovum pass into the abdominal cavity. The rupture of the follicle and discharge of the ovum constitute *ovulation*. It occurs usually every twenty-eight days from puberty to menopause.

After ovulation the follicular cells change rapidly into large cells which contain a yellow pigment. The body formed in this way is called the *corpus luteum*. Corpus luteum is rich in pigment and lipids, i.e., cholesterol esters, phospholipids and cerebrosides. If the ovum is not fertilized on its way to the uterus, menstruation follows in about fourteen days and the body is now called the corpus luteum of menstruation. If the ovum is fertilized, menstruation ceases during the period of pregnancy and the follicular body called the corpus luteum of pregnancy continues to develop for five to six months and increases greatly in size. Both types of corpora lutea undergo involution and are reduced to small scars.

In the two ovaries of the newborn infant there are about 400,000 follicles. Currently it is thought that the surface cells of the ovary are not germinal epithelium, and that primordial ova arise from epithelial tissue of the embryonic intestinal tract to migrate to the developing ovary by ameboid motion. It has been estimated that not more than 400 of these follicles mature and discharge their ova during the period of sexual activity of the human female. The rest of the 400,000 follicles gradually degenerate and disappear. This process of degeneration is called *atresia*. It proceeds at a rapid rate up to the time of puberty, after which it continues more slowly and is completed after the menopause.

Uterine Tubes.   The uterine or fallopian tubes are muscular channels about 12 cm. long which lie in the fold of the broad ligament along the superior border. Medially they connect with the uterus; laterally they open into the abdominal cavity. The lateral end of the tube widens out into a funnel-shaped *infundibulum,* the margins of which are frayed into irregular fringes called *fimbriae.* The portion of the tube adjoining the infundibulum is somewhat dilated and is called the *ampulla.* Epithelium of the mucosa of the uterine tube is composed of simple ciliated and nonciliated columnar cells.

The mechanism by which the ovum is transported from the ruptured follicle into the uterine tube is unknown. Vascular changes in the blood vessels of the fimbriae, together with contraction of smooth muscle tissue in these structures, probably effect the transfer. Peristaltic movements of the smooth muscle in the walls of the tube forward the ovum toward the uterus.

Important events occurring in the tube are fertilization, segmentation, and early differentiation of the zygote.

Uterus.   The uterus (Fig. 299) is a hollow organ with thick muscular walls. It is here that the ovum, if fertilized, undergoes its development into the embryo and fetus. The uterus resembles a pear in shape, but is flattened in the anteroposterior direction. It lies in the pelvic cavity between the bladder and the rectum, and is about 7 cm. long, 5 cm. wide and 2.5 cm. thick. The parts of the uterus are the *body,* which is the large upper portion, and the *cervix,* which is the small lower portion. The rounded upper part of the body of the uterus above the entrance of the tubes is the *fundus*. The lower portion of the cervix projects into the upper part of the vagina. The cervical opening is called the *external orifice*. The opening above into the cavity of the body of the uterus is the *internal orifice*.

The wall of the uterus is composed of three layers: an inner mucosa, a middle muscular layer, and an outer serous covering. The mucosa

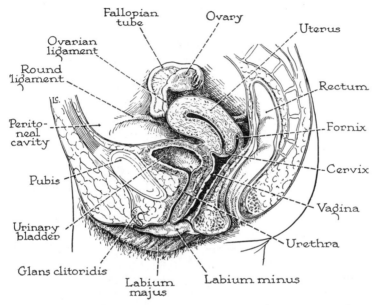

Fig. 299. Diagrammatic sagittal section of female pelvis, showing the genital organs and their relation to the bladder and urethra. (C. D. Turner: General Endocrinology.)

lining the uterus is called the *endometrium*. The epithelium consists of one layer of ciliated columnar cells. The glands, which are simple tubular in type, branch in their deeper portions. The muscular layer of the uterine wall is made up of smooth muscle fibers which run in many directions. Numerous blood vessels penetrate the muscle layers. They are branches of the uterine arteries. The serous layer is the peritoneum.

The peritoneum covering the abdominal wall continues into the pelvis and is reflected over the viscera. It covers the anterior and lateral surfaces of the rectum and is reflected over the uterus, forming the folds of the broad ligament. From the anterior surface of the uterus it passes over the bladder and on to the anterior abdominal wall. Between the rectum and the uterus is a pocket of considerable size, called the *rectouterine pouch* or *pouch of Douglas*.

LIGAMENTS OF THE UTERUS.   The *broad ligament* of the uterus is a wide peritoneal fold which passes from the lateral margin of the uterus to the side wall of the pelvis. Enclosed between its layers are the uterine tubes, round ligaments, vessels and nerves. The *round ligaments* are attached to the lateral angles of the uterus just below the entrance of the uterine tubes. They run outward in the broad ligament to the sides of the pelvis, at which point they enter the inguinal canals to terminate in the tissues of the labia majora. *Uterosacral ligaments* connect the cervix to the sacrum forming recto-uterine folds of peri-

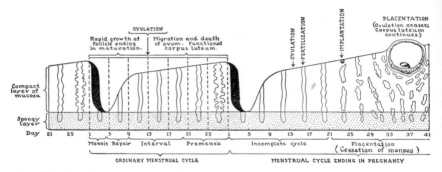

Fig. 300. Graphic presentation of the relations among human ovulation, menstruation and pregnancy. (Arey, modified after Schröder.)

toneum. *Anterior* and *posterior ligaments* are also folds of peritoneum extending from the fornix in front and back to the bladder and rectum respectively. These attachments, though they are called ligaments, have little influence in supporting the uterus. The chief support is afforded by the muscles of the pelvic floor and the *cardinal ligaments* (Fig. 302). The cardinal ligaments are true ligaments arising lateral to the internal uterine os and inserting in the lateral pelvic wall.

CYCLIC CHANGES IN THE ENDOMETRIUM (Fig. 300).   Changes which occur in the endometrium during the menstrual cycle are directly related to ovarian changes. The endometrium of the nonpregnant woman undergoes partial destruction about every twenty-eight days. This destruction of the epithelium is accompanied by a discharge of blood and secretion which constitutes the menstrual flow. The average duration of the flow is from three to five days; approximately 50 cc. of blood are lost each time in this way. The first day of menstruation is considered the first day of the cycle. As the flow ceases, which is usually about the fifth day, a follicle begins to increase in size rapidly. This growth of the follicle is accompanied by marked proliferation of the epithelial cells of the uterine mucosa and the formation in the glands of a mucoid secretion. This stage ends with the rupture of the follicle, which occurs sometime between the tenth and sixteenth days. After ovulation the more active premenstrual changes develop progressively

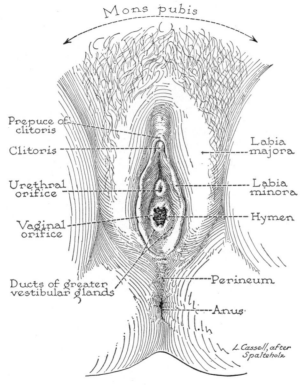

Fig. 301. The vulva. (After Spalteholz.)

for about two weeks. The mucous membrane increases in thickness, and the epithelial cells cease dividing, but increase in size and begin to secrete. The glands grow and become tortuous; the venous capillaries are engorged with blood. The endometrium is now ready to receive the fertilized ovum. If the ovum is not fertilized, menstruation occurs. The distended capillaries burst; the blood and disintegrating epithelium together with secretion of glands are eliminated.

Vagina.   The vagina is a flattened muscular tube about 7.5 cm. long, which extends from the uterus to the vulva. It is posterior to the bladder and urethra and anterior to the rectum. The cervix projects funnel-like into the upper end of the vagina. The circular recess between the vaginal wall and the cervix is called the *fornix*. It is deeper and more conspicuous in the posterior part. The mucous membrane lies in transverse folds called *vaginal rugae*. The epithelium of the membrane is stratified squamous. The vaginal orifice is partially closed by a semilunar or annular fold of mucous membrane called the hymen.

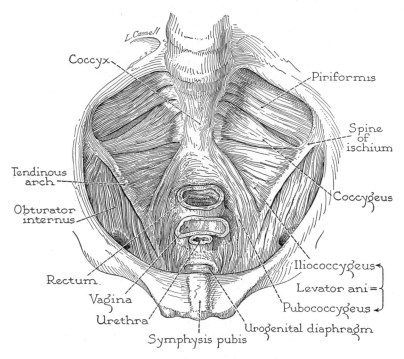

Fig. 302. Muscles of the pelvic floor, viewed from above. (After Tom Jones and F. Netter.)

The vagina is the organ of copulation in the female. It also forms an important part of the birth canal.

External Genitalia. The external genital organs, referred to collectively as the vulva, comprise the mons pubis, labia majora, labia minora, clitoris, vestibule and vestibular glands (Fig. 301).

The mons pubis is the rounded eminence in front of the symphysis pubis. It is composed of fibrous and adipose tissue enclosed by skin, and after puberty is covered with hair. The labia majora are two longitudinal folds of skin which extend downward from the mons pubis

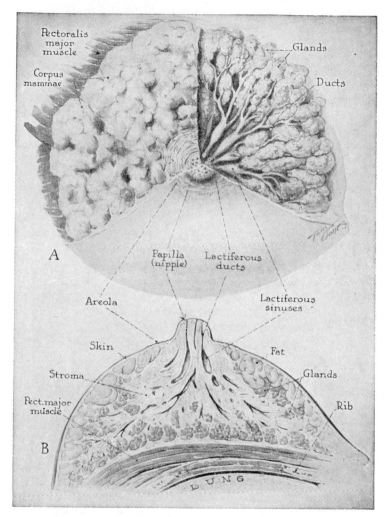

Fig. 303. The breast. A, Dissection of lactating breast. B, Relation of breast to chest wall. (Courtesy of S. H. Camp & Co.)

toward the anus. Between the labia majora are two smaller folds, the labia minora. They meet above to form the prepuce of the clitoris; below, they fuse with the hymen. The clitoris is the homologue of the penis in the male. It consists of two small, erectile, cavernous bodies. The cleft between the labia minora is the vestibule. The urethral and vaginal orifices are in the vestibule. The greater vestibular glands are two glands on either side of the vagina. They correspond with the bulbourethral glands in the male. Their ducts open into the vestibule between the hymen and the labia minora.

Perineum.   It is generally understood that the perineum includes the entire region of the pelvic outlet and contains all structures found between the pubic symphysis and the coccyx. The clinician, however, defines the perineum as the region between the vaginal orifice and the anus.

Muscles of the Pelvic Floor.   The muscles of the pelvic floor close in the outlet of the pelvis and form a diaphragm supporting the pelvic viscera (Fig. 302). The muscles are the levator ani and coccygeus, both paired muscles. The levator ani muscle arises from the pubis, the spine of the ischium and a line, called the tendinous arch, connecting these two points along the lateral pelvic wall. Two portions of the muscle are often described, the one arising from the pubis and called the pubococcygeus, and the other arising from the tendinous arch and called the iliococcygeus. The fibers of both portions pass downward, backward and medialward. The most posterior fibers insert on the coccyx, while the anterior ones unite in the midline with those from the opposite side. The urethra, vagina and rectum lie in the interval between the two muscles anteriorly, and some of the fibers are inserted into the sides of the rectum and vagina.

The coccygeus muscle completes the pelvic floor posteriorly. It arises from the spine of the ischium and is inserted along the side of the sacrum and coccyx. Both muscles support and elevate the pelvic organs. The coccygei draw forward the coccyx after it has been pressed backward during defecation and parturition. The levator ani muscles constrict the lower end of the rectum and vagina and draw the rectum forward and upward.

Mammary Glands.   The breasts or mammary glands resemble sweat glands in structure (Fig. 19, p. 42), but their function places them as accessory organs of the female reproductive system. Figure 303 shows the structure of the glands and their relation to the chest wall.

Each mammary gland is composed of fifteen to twenty-five compound alveolar glands which radiate from the nipple into the surrounding stroma as spokes radiate from the hub of a wheel. The supporting tissue or stroma consists of connective tissue and much adipose tissue. The *nipple* contains some smooth muscle tissue and is surrounded by a pigmented circular area of skin called the *areola*. Under the areola each glandular duct becomes enlarged to form the *lactiferous sinus* and then becomes constricted again as it enters the nipple. Each duct has its separate opening on the summit of the nipple. Preparatory to lactation the glandular tissue shows very active growth during pregnancy.

The numerous *lymphatics* of the breast originate as a network in the interspaces of the glands. They join axillary, sternal and subclavicular lymph nodes.

Endocrine Control of the Female Reproductive System. The production of *estrogens* and *progesterone,* i.e., the female sex hormones which are elaborated by the ovaries, is controlled by the gonadotropic hormones of the anterior pituitary gland. These are steroid in nature and closely related to the chemical structure of cholesterol and corticoids. Sexual development, and establishment of the secondary sex characteristics, are brought about by the estrogens; *estradiol* appears to be the principal controlling factor. The mechanisms by which uterine changes are correlated with ovarian changes are chemical in nature. A simplified schema may serve to illustrate some of the probable interrelations:

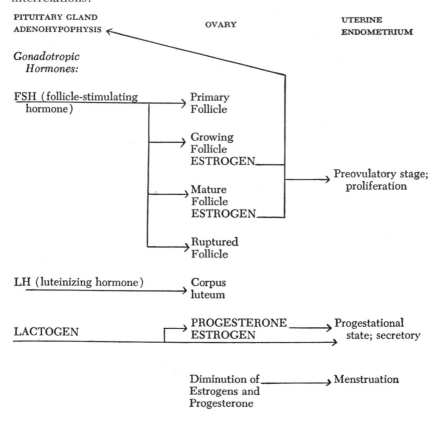

Estradiol, produced by thecal cells of the growing and mature follicles and under stimulation by follicle-stimulating hormone in the presence of small amounts of luteinizing hormone, stimulates follicle growth, proliferation of the endometrium, and uterine contractions; it also acts on the pituitary to stimulate production of gonadotropic hormones. Progesterone from corpus luteum induces the final premenstrual changes occurring during the latter half of the cycle, which prepare the endometrium for the reception of the fertilized ovum; implantation of the embryo depends upon the presence of this substance. Menstruation probably results from cessation or marked diminution of estrogen and progesterone. Progesterone and estrogens elaborated by the placenta inhibit menstruation and uterine contractions during pregnancy.

The combination of estrogens and progesterone, which are greatly increased during pregnancy (see p. 544), causes a development of the duct and areolar system of the breast aided by anterior pituitary factors. The anterior pituitary hormone prolactin (lactogen), together with the secretions of the suprarenal and thyroid glands, stimulates secretion of milk by the mammary glands after gestation. The initiation of lactation or "milk ejection" appears to be under the control of a reflex mechanism. Suckling will initiate the mechanism, which travels proprioceptive pathways to the hypothalamus to cause a release of oxytocin. Oxytocin will cause a contraction of tissue around the alveoli. This, in turn, moves the secretion into ducts and to the lactiferous sinus.

SUMMARY

The female reproductive organs consist of the ovaries, the uterine tubes, the uterus, the vagina, the external genitalia and the mammary glands.

The ovaries lie on the sides of the pelvis attached to the posterior surface of the broad ligament. The outer cortical portion contains many follicles.

The rupture of the mature follicles with the escape of follicular fluid and ovum into the abdominal cavity constitutes ovulation.

After ovulation the follicular cells change to form a body called the corpus luteum.

The uterine tubes connect with the uterus medially; laterally they open into the abdominal cavity.

The uterus is a hollow organ with thick muscular walls. It lies in the pelvic cavity between the bladder and the rectum.

The parts of the uterus are the body and the cervix. The lower portion of the cervix projects into the upper part of the vagina.

The mucous lining of the uterus is called the endometrium. The epithelium consists of one layer of ciliated columnar cells.

The glands, which are simple tubular in type, branch in their deeper portions.

The peritoneum is reflected over the pelvic viscera. Between the rectum and the uterus it forms a pocket called the rectouterine pouch.

The peritoneal reflection over the uterus forms the broad ligament, which passes from the lateral margin of the uterus to the side of the pelvis.

The round ligaments are attached to the lateral angles of the uterus just below the entrance of the uterine tubes. They pass through the inguinal canals to terminate in the labia majora.

The changes which occur in the endometrium during the menstrual cycle are directly related to ovarian changes. The mechanism is chemical in nature, and the hormones of the ovaries constitute the primary regulators. Estradiol, secreted by the follicle, causes proliferation of the endometrium in the first half of the cycle; progesterone from the corpus luteum induces the final premenstrual changes in the latter half of the cycle. The secretion of these hormones is controlled by gonadotropic hormones from the anterior lobe of the pituitary gland.

The vagina is a muscular tube about 7.5 cm. long which extends from the uterus to the vulva.

The vaginal orifice is partially closed by a fold of mucous membrane called the hymen.

The vagina is the organ of copulation in the female. It forms an important part of the birth canal.

The external genital organs, referred to collectively as the vulva, comprise the mons pubis, labia majora, labia minora, clitoris, vestibule and vestibular glands.

The mons pubis is the rounded eminence in front of the symphysis pubis.

The labia majora are two longitudinal folds of skin which extend downward from the mons pubis.

Between the labia majora are two smaller folds, the labia minora. They meet above to form the prepuce of the clitoris; below, they fuse with the hymen.

The clitoris is the homologue of the penis in the male.

The vaginal and urethral orifices are in the vestibule between the labia minora.

The perineum is the region between the symphysis pubis and the coccyx.

The muscles of the pelvic floor close in the outlet of the pelvis and form a diaphragm supporting the pelvic viscera.

The mammary glands are modified sweat glands.

Each gland is composed of fifteen to twenty-five compound alveolar glands, the ducts of which open on the summit of the nipple. Development and secretion of mammary glands are under nervous and hormone influences.

QUESTIONS FOR DISCUSSION

1. Explain the time relations of ovulation and menstruation.

2. Trace the cyclic changes in the endometrium from the first to the twenty-eighth day. Explain the action of the hormones theelin and progesterone.

3. What hormone interactions are responsible for proper development of the female reproductive system?

Chapter
30

Male Reproductive System

THE MALE reproductive system consists of the testes, which produce spermatozoa, a system of excretory ducts with their auxiliary glands, and the penis, an organ of copulation (Fig. 304).

TESTES

The testes are two ovoid bodies which lie in the scrotum. In the embryo the testes develop on the ventral border of the kidneys, and just before birth or afterward they descend beneath the peritoneum and pass through the inguinal canal into the scrotum. The *scrotum* is to be thought of as an extension of the abdominal cavity, although in the adult it is closed off and no connection exists. The temperature within the scrotum is somewhat lower than in the abdomen. The dartos muscle of the scrotum contracts in response to cold and brings the testes closer to the abdomen; heat, on the other hand, relaxes the dartos muscle. In this way the testes are maintained within a relatively narrow temperature range, but below that of internal body temperature, which is too high for the process of spermatogenesis to occur. Each testis is a compound tubular gland, enclosed in a firm fibrous capsule (Fig. 305). Fibrous extensions from the capsule divide the gland into numerous lobules. Within each lobule are found the terminal portions of the *seminiferous tubules*. These tubules unite to form a network from which efferent ducts arise to enter the head of the epididymis. The cells lining the seminiferous tubules are of two types: sustentacular cells, and spermatogenic or germinal cells (Fig. 306).

The *sustentacular cells* serve nutrient and supporting functions. They are elongated, pillar-like cells attached to the basement membrane of the tubule. Like pylons, they give support to the centrally placed spermatogenic elements. The *germinal cells* are arranged in several layers about the periphery of the tubule. The spermatogonia are next to the basement membrane, and the other forms, primary spermato-

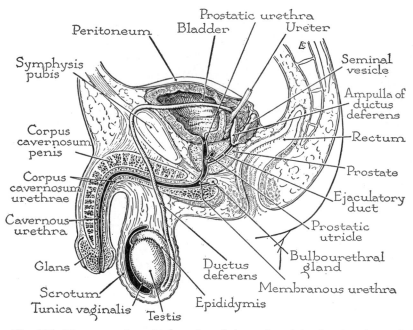

Fig. 304. Diagrammatic sagittal section of the male pelvis, showing the genital organs and their relations to the bladder and urethra. (After Turner: General Endocrinology.)

cytes, secondary spermatocytes, spermatids and spermatozoa, follow in orderly sequence toward the center. The mature spermatozoa become detached from their moorings on the sustentacular cells and are forced out into the lumen of the tubule and finally reach the efferent ducts of the gland.

The interstitial tissue of the testes, which is made up of epithelioid cells within a stroma of connective tissue, lies between the seminiferous tubules. *Leydig cells* of interstitial tissue produce *androgens,* which are the male sex hormones. The androgens are responsible for the secondary male sex characteristics, which include low pitch of voice,

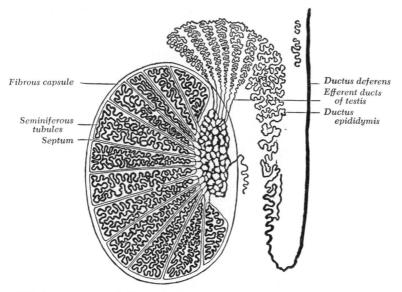

Fig. 305. Arrangement of the seminiferous tubules and the excretory ducts in the testis and epididymis. (Maximow and Bloom.)

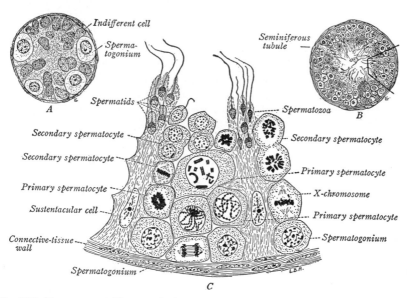

Fig. 306. Human seminiferous tubules in transverse section. *A*, Newborn (× 400); *B*, adult (× 115); *C*, detail of the area outlined in *B* (× 900). (Arey.)

body form, beard and distribution of body hair, and aggressiveness. Androgen production is under the control of the gonadotropic hormones of the anterior pituitary gland; the follicle-stimulating hormone and the luteinizing hormone (see p. 508), acting together, increase androgen production. The testicular hormones, in turn, influence the secretion of the gonadotropins; i.e., there is interaction between the two endocrine glands. The androgens include *testosterone,* which has been produced commercially from the testes of bulls and by chemical synthesis; other androgens, such as androsterone, which is found in human urine, may represent metabolic products of testosterone. Estrogenic substances (see p. 521) have also been extracted from testicular tissues. Other androgens are formed by the adrenal cortex.

EXCRETORY DUCTS

The structures forming the excretory ducts consist of the epididymides, the deferent ducts, the ejaculatory ducts and the urethra. All structures are paired except the urethra (Figs. 304, 307).

Epididymis. The epididymis is an elongated body lying along the upper and posterior parts of the testis. It has a large upper portion or head and narrower body and tail. The efferent ducts of the testis fuse to form the single ductus epididymis, which is a highly convoluted canal 4 to 6 meters in length. Near the lower pole of the organ the duct straightens out and connects with the ductus deferens.

Ductus Deferens. The ductus deferens is a thick-walled tube about 45 cm. long which passes from the epididymis to the ejaculatory duct. It ascends in the scrotum and passes through the inguinal canal to enter the abdominal cavity. Under cover of the peritoneum it crosses the brim of the pelvis, passes to the inferior surface of the bladder, where it ends by uniting with the duct of the seminal vesicle to form the ejaculatory duct. The ductus deferens, spermatic artery, vein and nerves, together with surrounding membranes, form the spermatic cord. The *spermatic cord* extends from the testis and epididymis through the inguinal canal to the internal inguinal ring on the inner wall of the abdomen.

Ejaculatory Duct. The ejaculatory duct arises from the union of the ductus deferens and the duct of the seminal vesicle. It is a short, straight tube which pierces the prostate gland to open into the floor of the urethra at the side of the urethral crest.

Urethra. The urethra, which in the male belongs both to the urinary and reproductive systems, is discussed on page 483. It is divided into three parts by the pelvic wall. The first portion is above the pelvic floor and is surrounded by the prostate gland; the second, or membranous, portion pierces the pelvic wall; the third portion traverses the penis (Fig. 283, p. 483).

AUXILIARY STRUCTURES

Seminal Vesicles. The seminal vesicles are two tortuous pouches developed as evaginations from the ductus deferens. They are placed

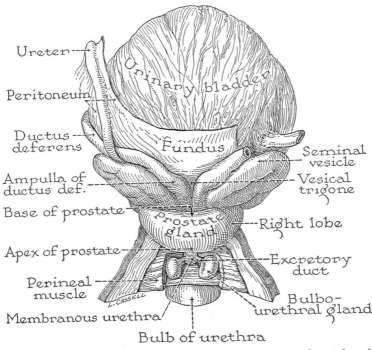

Fig. 307. Posterior view of bladder in male, showing seminal vesicles, ductus deferens and prostate gland. (Modified after Spalteholz.)

between the bladder and the rectum. They elaborate a thick, alkaline globulin-containing secretion which is added to the spermatozoa during ejaculation.

Prostate Gland. The prostate gland is beneath the bladder and surrounds the first portion of the urethra. It is pyramidal in shape, with the base above in contact with the inferior surface of the bladder and the apex directed downward. The prostate gland is an aggregate of about forty tubuloalveolar glands widely separated from each other by smooth muscular and dense fibrous tissue so that the organ is one-half glandular, one-quarter smooth muscle and one-quarter fibrous tissue. Around the urethra the smooth muscle fibers form a ring which is called the internal sphincter of the bladder. The ducts of the glands open into the urethra. The secretion of the prostate is a thin liquid with a slightly alkaline reaction. It neutralizes the acid reaction of the urethra and stimulates the movements of the spermatozoa.

Bulbourethral Glands. These are two small glands that lie on either side of the membranous urethra. They open into the cavernous urethra near its origin. The secretion, which is slimy and viscid, lubricates the urethra.

Penis. The penis is composed of three cylinders of cavernous tissue, called the *corpora cavernosa*. Two of them, the corpora cavernosa penis, form the dorsal and upper part of the organ; the third, the corpus cavernosum urethrae, lies in a groove below the other two. The two *corpora cavernosa penis* separate posteriorly to be attached one on either side to the descending ramus of the pubis. The *corpus cavernosum urethrae* begins at the pelvic floor with the urethral bulb and is traversed throughout its length by the urethra. It ends in a cone-shaped expansion, the *glans penis*. The *bulbocavernous muscle* surrounds the urethral bulb. The circular fold of skin reflected over the glans is called the foreskin or *prepuce*. The tissue of the cavernous bodies of the penis is the erectile tissue. It is spongelike, with large vascular spaces interposed between arteries and veins. In the relaxed state the cavernous spaces are collapsed and contain little blood, but in erection they are filled, resulting in enlargement and rigidity of the organ.

The penis is the organ of copulation in the male by means of which spermatozoa are deposited in the vaginal tract of the female.

COURSE OF THE SPERMATOZOA

The spermatozoa, with the secretions of the ducts and auxiliary glands added to them, constitute the *semen*. The spermatozoa, which are formed in the testes, pass slowly through the epididymis and may remain in the tail for months. Here they are nourished and ripened by the viscid secretion of the epithelial cells lining this canal. The ductus deferens serves for rapid transport of the sperms. The wave-like contractions of its muscular walls, together with the action of the bulbocavernous muscle and muscular tissue of the prostate gland, produce ejaculation or the discharge of semen through the urethra. Seminal vesicles, prostate gland and bulbourethral (Cowper's) glands add their secretions. An ejaculation contains from 400 to 500 million highly active spermatozoa. Motility is maintained by presence of fructose and citric acid in the semen.

SUMMARY

The male reproductive system consists of the testes, which produce spermatozoa, a system of excretory ducts with their auxiliary glands, and the penis, the organ of copulation.

The testes are two ovoid bodies which lie in the scrotum.

Each testis is a compound tubular gland, enclosed in a firm fibrous capsule.

The seminiferous tubules of the lobules unite to form efferent ducts which enter the epididymis. Spermatogenic or germinal cells line the tubules.

The interstitial tissue of the testes which lies between the seminiferous tubules secretes a hormone, testosterone.

The epididymis is an elongated body lying along the upper and posterior parts of the testis. It is made up of a highly convoluted canal 4 to 6 meters in length.

The ductus deferens is a thick-walled tube which passes from the epididymis to the ejaculatory duct.

The ejaculatory duct arises from the union of the ductus deferens and the duct of the seminal vesicle. It pierces the prostate gland to open into the urethra.

The seminal vesicle is a tortuous pouch developed as an evagination from the ductus deferens.

The prostate gland is beneath the bladder and surrounds the first portion of the urethra. It is an aggregate of about 40 tubuloalveolar glands, whose ducts open into the urethra.

The bulbourethral glands lie on either side of the membranous urethra. Their secretion lubricates the urethra.

The penis is composed of three cylinders of cavernous tissue; two corpora cavernosa penis form the dorsal and upper part of the organ; the third, the corpus cavernosum urethrae, lies in a groove below the other two.

The spermatozoa and the secretions of the ducts and auxiliary glands added to them constitute the semen.

The spermatozoa formed in the testes pass through the epididymides, the ductus deferens and the ejaculatory ducts into the urethra, through which they are discharged.

Seminal vesicles, prostate gland and bulbourethral glands add their secretions for ejaculation.

QUESTIONS FOR DISCUSSION

1. Trace the course of the spermatozoa from the testes to the exterior. Refer to Figures 283 and 304.

2. What glands add secretions to the spermatozoa, and what is the function of each secretion?

3. What hormone interaction is responsible for proper development of the male reproductive system?

Chapter 31

Prenatal Development of the Human Body

THE ACCOUNT of development here followed is that generally held to be true of man; many conclusions, however, are based on studies of the process in animals.

Origin and Location of the Sex Cells. The development of the individual is initiated by union of two sex cells, the egg and sperm. Sex cells are set aside early in the formation of a new individual. They are there, we might say, from the beginning and eventually emerge as parts of special organs called the gonads. The female sex cells are in the *ovaries;* the male sex cells are in the *testes.* During childhood and throughout life the male sex cells increase in number by processes of mitosis, forming numerous generations of undifferentiated sex cells called *spermatogonia.* The undifferentiated cells in the female are called *oogonia.* There are two different views regarding the multiplication of these cells. The traditional view holds that the female sex cells undergo mitosis only during intra-uterine life, and that at birth the cells cease to divide. The other, more recent view asserts that no female sex cell formed before birth ever becomes functional; all degenerate and, like the male sex cells, proliferate as needed throughout the reproductive life.

Maturation. At puberty both oogonia and spermatogonia pass through changes which prepare them to take part in the reproductive process. These changes constitute gametogenesis or maturation, and the resulting matured cells are called gametes. The process involves two successive cell divisions, in one of which the chromosome number is reduced to one-half. Maturation of the male sex cells is known as spermatogenesis; maturation of the female sex cells is known as oogenesis (Fig. 308).

SPERMATOGENESIS. After a spermatogonium has divided by mitosis for the last time it increases in size and is called the *primary spermato-*

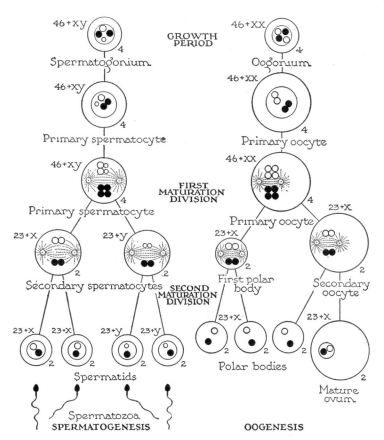

Fig. 308. Diagram showing maturation of the germ cells. Chromosome number in human sex cells is shown above and to the left of the cells. Chromosome number used in the diagram is below and to the right of the cells. The circles represent sex chromosomes. Large circles are X chromosomes, small circles are Y chromosomes.

cyte. In the primary spermatocyte the spindle appears, and chromosomes are formed from the spireme as in the usual mitotic process, but in the equatorial plane the chromosomes come together in pairs in a process known as synapsis. At the same time the chromosomes split lengthwise so that in cross section each pair presents a figure composed of four parts, called a *tetrad*. The arrangement of the chromosomes on the spindle is such that the whole chromosome lies parallel with the equator. When the cell divides, the chromosome with the split through the center moves as a whole chromosome into the new cell. As a result two new cells are formed, the *secondary spermatocytes*, each containing twenty-four whole chromosomes. This is known as the "reduction division" because the chromosome number is reduced from forty-eight to twenty-four. The second maturation division may begin without an intervening resting period. When the spindle is formed,

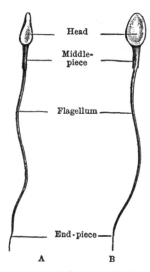

Fig. 309. Human spermatozoa. *A*, Side view; *B*, Front view. (After Retzius.)

the chromosomes, already showing two parts and now referred to as *dyads*, are arranged on the spindle so that the dyad lies at right angles to the equator. When the cell divides, the halves of the dyads separate and twenty-four new daughter chromosomes pass into each new cell. The division of the two secondary spermatocytes results in four spermatids in each of which there are twenty-four chromosomes. This is called the "equation division." The spermatids are transformed into motile cells called spermatozoa. The *spermatozoon* in man (Fig. 309) and many other animals consists of an oval head, which is composed mainly of the nucleus; a middle piece, containing the centrosome; and a thin, tapering motile organ, the tail. Four spermatozoa result from the maturation of one spermatogonium. The process is shown in Figure 308.

OOGENESIS. The female sex cells, oogonia, increase greatly in size during the growth period and become the primary oocytes, ready for the first maturation division. During the prophases the spindle is formed and the chromosomes come together in pairs, forming the tetrads, and, as described in spermatogenesis, twenty-four whole chromosomes pass into each new cell. However, the spindle forms near the periphery of the cell instead of in the center, so that, as division of the cytoplasm occurs at the equator, one large cell, the secondary oocyte, is formed and one small cell, the polar body. In the second maturation division the twenty-four chromosomes of the secondary oocyte, now known as dyads, come into position on the spindle. Each dyad, representing one chromosome already split into daughter chromosomes, takes a position at right angles to the equator, so that as the cytoplasm divides, the halves of the twenty-four dyads (or twenty-four daughter chromosomes) pass into each new cell. Again the result is one large cell and one small cell. The large cell is the ovum, and the small cell is the second polar body. While the secondary oocyte is dividing, the first polar body may divide in regular mitotic fashion into two polar bodies. The result of the two maturation divisions is one large cell, the ovum, and three small, nonfunctional cells, the polar bodies. Maturation of male and female cells is summarized in Table 18.

Fertilization.   The sex cells, spermatozoon and ovum, are now functionally mature and ready for fertilization. Fertilization involves the penetration of the ovum by the spermatozoon and the union of the nucleus of the spermatozoon with the nucleus of the ovum. The human ovum has twenty-four chromosomes, and the spermatozoon has the same number; thus, at fertilization the chromosome number, which is forty-eight, is restored. Fertilization takes place in the outer third of the uterine tube. The ovum escapes from the surface of the ovary and enters the uterine tube. Spermatozoa deposited in the vaginal tract of the female make their way through the cavity of the uterus and out into the tubes. The head, middle piece and tail of the spermatozoon enter the ovum.

The head soon undergoes development into a typical nucleus called the *male pronucleus.* It looks very much like the egg nucleus, which is now called the *female pronucleus.* As soon as the female and male pronuclei are formed, they come together and fuse to form a single nucleus called the *segmentation nucleus.* The chromatin granules of the segmentation nucleus form chromonemata, and the chromonemata separate into forty-eight chromosomes. The nuclear membrane disappears and the chromosomes lie free in the cytoplasm. While these changes are occurring in the fusion nucleus, a spindle has formed between the centrosomes, and the chromosomes of the segmentation

Table 18

Summary of Maturation

SPERMATOGENESIS

Name of Cell	No. of Cells	No. of Chromosomes Ascaris*	Human
Spermatogonium	1	4	48
Primary spermatocyte	1	4	48
Secondary spermatocyte	2	2	24
Spermatids (Metamorphosis)	4	2	24
Spermatozoa	4	2	24

OOGENESIS

Name of Cell	No. of Cells	No. of Chromosomes Ascaris*	Human
Oogonium	1	4	48
Primary oocyte	1	4	48
Secondary oocyte	1 cell; 1 Polar body	2	24
Ovum (mature)	1 cell; 3 Polar bodies	2	24

* *Ascaris megalocephala*, a roundworm of the horse, has a chromosome number of 4 which is the same as the number used in the diagram (Fig. 312).

nucleus, in all forty-eight, mingle in the equatorial plane. This brings fertilization proper to an end. The further steps are those of mitosis. The result is the division of the fertilized ovum into two cells just alike, each containing the same amount of male and female chromosome elements. This constitutes the first segmentation division of the fertilized egg.

Sex Determination. The determination of sex is currently explained on the basis of certain chromosomes observed in many animals. They differ in appearance from the rest of the chromosomes and are called sex chromosomes. The human ovum contains forty-six ordinary chromosomes and two X or sex chromosomes. In maturation the number is halved so that the ovum and polar bodies contain $23 + X$. The spermatogonia contain forty-six ordinary chromosomes and one X chromosome and a small Y chromosome. Maturation of one spermatogonium results in two spermatozoa with a chromosome number of $23 + X$ and

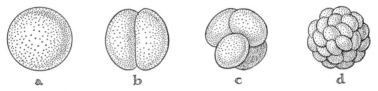

a   b   c   d

Fig. 310. Segmentation of the zygote. *a*, Ovum in pronuclear stage. *b*, Two-cell stage. *c*, Four-cell stage. *d*, Solid sphere of cells, the morula mass.

two spermatozoa with a chromosome number of $23 + Y$. When a spermatozoon with a chromosome number of $23 + X$ fertilizes an ovum with chromosome number of $23 + X$, the restored number is $46 + XX$ and the individual is a female; if, on the other hand, a spermatozoon with a chromosome number of $23 + Y$ fertilizes an ovum, $23 + X$, the number becomes $46 + XY$ and a male is the result.

Segmentation of the Zygote. Segmentation or cleavage is a term used to indicate the rapidly succeeding divisions of the fertilized ovum or zygote. The details of the first segmentation division have been given. The result is the two-celled embryo; subsequent divisions form four cells, eight cells, and so on until a solid mass of cells is formed, called the *morula* (Fig. 310).

Differentiation of the Embryo. During the development of the morula, the mass gradually moves down the tube toward the uterus. The first change appearing in the morula is its differentiation into an outer layer and an inner mass. The outer layer is the *trophoblast*, which plays an important part in the nutrition of the embryo. It enters into the formation of the chorion or outermost covering of the growing embryo. The *inner cell mass* soon separates into three portions, the ectoderm, entoderm, and primary mesoderm. In human development a primitive segmentation cavity probably never exists, for as the inner cell mass separates from the outer layer, the proliferating cells of the primary mesoderm fill in the space with a jelly-like mass. During the period of expansion of the primary mesoderm, *cavities* appear in the ectoderm and entoderm segments, converting them into hollow vesicles. These changes are shown in Figure 311. At this stage the zygote is composed of three spheres, one large and two small. The large sphere is bounded by the trophoblast; it contains the two small spheres and the jelly-like mass of primary mesoderm. The ectoderm vesicle lies near the trophoblast. It is called the amniotic cavity. The entodermal vesicle lies just below the ectodermal vesicle and is called the yolk sac. A layer of primary mesoderm fills in between the trophoblast and the ectoderm of the amniotic cavity and between the amniotic cavity and the yolk sac. The area between the amniotic cavity and the yolk sac is the portion of the zygote from which the embryo is formed. It is called the embryonic area or disc. Very soon two spaces appear in the primary or extra-embryonic mesoderm (Fig. 312, *a*) which enlarge and fuse below the yolk sac, and the single space so formed expands until the primary mesoderm is reduced to a thin layer which lines the trophoblast and covers the outer surfaces of the walls of the amniotic cavity and yolk sac. The cavity formed is called the extra-embryonic coelom.

THE EMBRYONIC DISC. The embryonic area is a flat plate which is circular in outline when first seen, but later changes to an oval form (Fig. 312, *c*) as growth continues. It is composed essentially of epithelial layers of ectoderm and entoderm. The posterior end of the oval is marked by a line, the primitive streak. The *primitive streak* is a thickened ridge of cells which grows outward from the ectoderm and projects against the entoderm. Immediately after the formation of the primitive streak a groove and two folds or ridges appear in the anterior part of the disc. These structures mark the beginnings of the nervous system and are called the *neural groove* and *neural folds,* respectively. They are formed by an infolding of the ectoderm layer; gradually the edges of the folds come together, and the loop of ectodermal cells is pinched off and comes to lie below the surface. This tube or cylinder of cells is called the *neural tube;* the anterior end develops into the brain, the posterior portion into the spinal cord.

PRIMITIVE STREAK DERIVATIVES. Two important structures which develop from the primitive streak are the notochord (Fig. 312, *d*) and the secondary mesoderm. The *notochord* develops by a proliferation

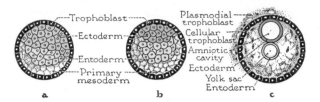

Fig. 311. Diagram of the early differentiation of the zygote. *a* and *b* show the inner cell mass separated into ectoderm, entoderm and primary mesoderm. In *c*, cavities have formed in the ectoderm and entoderm.

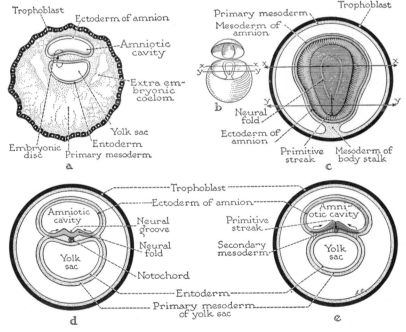

Fig. 312. Further differentiation of the zygote. *a*, Early stage in formation of the extra-embryonic coelom. *b*, Indicates how cut is made through zygote to obtain view shown in *c*. *c*, Diagram of dorsal surface of embryonic area after removal of part of the chorion and part of the amnion. *d*, Shows plan of zygote cut through *xx* in the region of the neural folds. *e*, Represents the plan of the zygote cut through *yy* in the region of the primitive streak.

of cells from the anterior end of the primitive streak. It serves as a primitive body axis about which the vertebral column is later constructed. The *secondary mesoderm* is the embryonic mesoderm, which enters into the formation of the body of the embryo and is to be distinguished completely from the primary mesoderm, which is entirely extra-embryonic. The secondary mesoderm develops by a proliferation of the cells of the primitive streak which move out between the ectoderm and entoderm layers to form a continuous sheet of cells in the embryonic disc on either side of the median plane (Fig. 312, *e*). A longitudinal constriction appears in each plate a short distance from its medial border, separating each plate into three parts: a medial bar, the paraxial mesoderm; the constricted portion, or intermediate cell mass; and the lateral portion, called the lateral plate mesoderm. The *paraxial mesoderm* lies next to the neural tube and notochord and is divided into segments called *somites*. The *lateral plate mesoderm* splits

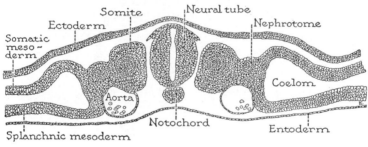

Fig. 313. Transverse section of chick embryo at forty-eight hours of incubation (semidiagrammatic).

into two layers, an outer one next to the ectoderm called *somatic* or *parietal mesoderm*, and an inner one next to the entoderm called the *splanchnic* or *visceral mesoderm*. This space between the layers is the embryonic coelom or body cavity. These structures are shown in Figures 313 and 314.

Later Development. As development proceeds, the lateral edges of the disc curve downward and inward to meet in the midline, forming a cylinder. There is also a curving of cranial and caudal portions of the disc toward each other. If we think of this cylinder as representative of the general plan of the trunk of the body, we shall begin to see how the embryonic structure is related to the fully formed human body. As the lateral edges of the disc curve downward and inward and the cranial and caudal ends incline somewhat toward each other, the cylinder is pushed upward into the amniotic cavity. With the coming together of the lateral edges of the disc, a portion of the yolk sac is pinched off and becomes the digestive tube. Comparing the embryonic cylinder in cross section (Fig. 314) with the trunk of the body, the cylinder is placed with the posterior or dorsal part uppermost and projecting into the amniotic cavity; the ventral or anterior part is below. Ectoderm forms the outer layer of the embryo, and entoderm lines the digestive tube running through it. Ectoderm and somatic mesoderm combine to form the layers of the body wall; entoderm and splanchnic mesoderm combine to form the wall of the digestive tube. The neural tube as forerunner of the brain and spinal cord is close to the dorsal surface. This account indicates the embryonic origin of a few of the structures in the body and shows that all three

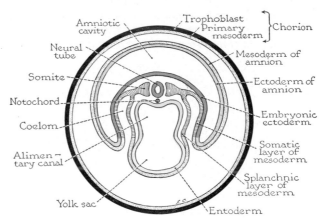

Fig. 314. Transverse section of zygote, showing differentiation of mesoderm and extension of amnion.

germ layers contribute to the formation of the fully developed body. The structures derived from each layer are listed here in some detail:

From the ectoderm: epithelium of skin and appendages, epithelium of nasal and oral passages, salivary and mucous glands of nose and mouth, the nervous system.

From the mesoderm: muscle tissue, connective tissue, tissues of vascular and lymphatic systems, lining of the pleural, pericardial and peritoneal cavities, kidneys, ureters and sex glands.

From the entoderm: epithelium of the gastrointestinal tract and glands which pour secretion into the tract, of respiratory tract, bladder and urethra.

Protection and Nourishment of the Embryo. The embryo is protected and nourished during development. It grows in a bag of watery fluid called the *amniotic fluid.* The wall of the bag is composed of two layers, an inner layer called the amnion, and an outer layer, the chorion. The *chorion* is composed of the trophoblast and primary mesoderm. The *amnion* is composed of ectoderm and primary mesoderm. Projections called chorionic *villi* develop in the outer layer of the chorion. Mesoderm spreads into some of the villi, and in the mesoderm, blood vessels develop. As the embryonic mass grows, it moves downward in the tube and at the end of eight to ten days reaches the

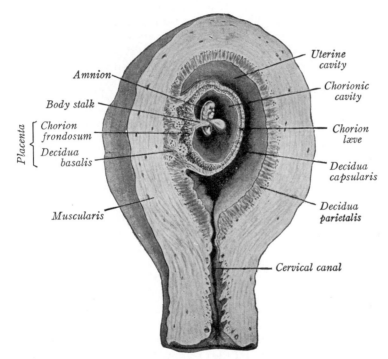

Fig. 315. Section of uterus in early pregnancy. (Arey.)

uterus. The uterine mucosa is in the premenstrual condition produced by the hormone of the corpus luteum. The trophoblast first attaches to the uterine epithelium and then through the secretion of a cytolytic enzyme proceeds to destroy it. The embryo sinks into the uterine wall and becomes embedded in the mucosa, which grows over it. This process is called *implantation*. The mucosa of the pregnant uterus is named the *decidua*. Three regions of this thickened membrane can be recognized at an early stage. They are the decidua parietalis, or general lining of the uterus, exclusive of the embryonic area; decidua basalis, the region between the chorionic sac and the muscular wall of the uterus; and decidua capsularis, a portion which covers the embedded embryo. Figure 315 shows a section of the uterus in early pregnancy.

The young embryo is connected with the inner surface of the chorion by the body stalk. The chorionic villi in this area enlarge, penetrating deeply into the uterine wall and establishing intimate connections with blood spaces. Villi on other parts of the chorion soon disappear. The structures composing the decidua basalis and the chorionic villi embedded in it constitute the *placenta* or nutritive organ of the embryo. The body stalk of the young embryo becomes narrowed down and is called the umbilical cord. In it run the blood vessels which connect the embryo with the chorionic villi. Through the walls of the villi interchanges of food and waste between mother and embryo are effected. There is no actual mingling of the blood of the embryo with the blood of the mother; all interchanges take place through the walls of the villi by means of such physicochemical processes as filtration, diffusion and osmosis. The exact nature of the *endocrine function of the placenta* has not been ascertained. It has been established, however, that the placenta produces the *chorionic gonadotropin* (CG) hormone and steroids with estrogenic and progesteronic activity. A peak secretion of CG is reached during the time after implantation of the embryo in the uterus has occurred. This is maintained for about a week and then declines to a lower, constant level for the remainder of pregnancy. Corpus luteum persists under the stimulation of CG. The placenta and corpus luteum augment the effects of one another through the synergistic action of the estrogens and progesterones which they both produce to promote the changes necessary in the reproductive structures for the protection and nutrition of the embryo.

Periods of Prenatal Life. Development continues throughout life. This story describes only that part of development which occurs before birth. It is called prenatal life. Does it begin when the germ cells are set aside as such in the parent? Does it begin with maturation, or at fertilization? In an attempt to be definite, students of developmental anatomy have usually accepted fertilization as marking the beginning of life and have divided prenatal life into three periods: the period of the ovum, the embryonic period, and the fetal period.

The *period of the ovum* extends from fertilization to implantation, about two weeks.

The *embryonic period* extends from the end of the second week to the close of the second month.

The *fetal period* extends from the beginning of the third month, when the new individual begins to resemble the human form, to birth, approximately seven months.

SUMMARY

Development of the individual is initiated by union of two sex cells, the egg and sperm.

At puberty both oogonia and spermatogonia pass through changes which prepare them to take part in the reproductive process. These changes are termed maturation.

During maturation the chromosome number is reduced to one half of that which is characteristic of the species. The human ovum has twenty-four chromosomes, the human spermatozoon twenty-four chromosomes. At fertilization, the union of the two cells restores the number to forty-eight.

Segmentation of the fertilized ovum or zygote forms a sphere of cells, the morula mass.

Differentiation of the zygote results in the development of the embryo and the membranes investing it.

The placenta forms from the chorionic layer of the zygote and the structures of the uterine wall. It establishes the nutrition of the developing embryo. The placenta carries out an endocrine function through the secretion of CG and sex hormone steroids.

Prenatal life is divided into three periods: the period of the ovum, the embryonic period, and the fetal period.

QUESTIONS FOR DISCUSSION

1. On the basis of study of the entire body, what factors do you think are most important in regulating the development of the new individual? Why?

2. Compare maturation with cellular reproduction found elsewhere in the body.

3. From what embryonic layers do the following structures arise: pancreas, epithelium of skin, connective tissue, nervous system, epithelial lining of the intestines, the muscles, the peritoneum and the salivary glands?

Reference Books

GROSS ANATOMY, TEXTBOOKS

Cunningham, D. J.: Textbook of Anatomy, edited by J. C. Brash and E. B. Jamieson. 9th ed. New York, Oxford University Press, 1951.

Grant, J. C. B.: A Method of Anatomy. 5th ed. Baltimore, The Williams and Wilkins Company, 1952.

Gray, H.: Anatomy of the Human Body, edited by C. M. Goss. 26th ed. Philadelphia, Lea & Febiger, 1954.

Morris, H.: Human Anatomy, edited by J. P. Schaeffer. 11th ed. New York, The Blakiston Company, 1953.

GROSS ANATOMY, ATLASES

Anson, B. J.: Atlas of Human Anatomy. Philadelphia, W. B. Saunders Company, 1950.

Grant, J. C. B.: An Atlas of Anatomy. 3rd ed. Baltimore, The Williams and Wilkins Company, 1951.

Jamieson, E. B.: Illustrations of Regional Anatomy. 7th ed. Baltimore, The Williams and Wilkins Company, 1947.

Sobotta, J., and McMurrich, J. P.: Atlas of Human Anatomy. 5th ed. New York, G. E. Stechert and Company, 1939.

Spalteholz, W.: Hand Atlas of Human Anatomy, edited by L. F. Barker. 7th ed. Philadelphia, J. B. Lippincott Company, 1943.

Toldt, C.: An Atlas of Human Anatomy, edited by M. E. Paul. 2d ed. New York, The Macmillan Company, 1941 (reissue 1946).

MICROSCOPIC ANATOMY

Bailey, F. R.: Textbook of Histology, revised by Philip E. Smith and Wilfred M. Copenhaver. 12th ed. Baltimore, The Williams and Wilkins Company, 1948.

Bremer, S., and Lewis, J.: A Textbook of Histology; rewritten by Harold L. Weatherford (1948). 6th ed. Philadelphia, The Blakiston Company, 1944.

Cowdry, E. V.: Textbook of Histology. 4th ed. Philadelphia, Lea & Febiger, 1950.

Greep, R. O., et al.: Histology. New York, The Blakiston Company, 1954.

Ham, A.: Histology. 2d ed. Philadelphia, J. B. Lippincott Company, 1953.

Jordan, H. E.: Textbook of Histology. 9th ed. rev. New York, D. Appleton Company, 1952.

Maximow, A., and Bloom, W.: Textbook of Histology. 6th ed. Philadelphia, W. B. Saunders Company, 1952.

Nonidez, J., and Windel, W.: Textbook of Histology. New York, The Blakiston Company, 1953.

DEVELOPMENTAL ANATOMY

Arey, L. B.: Developmental Anatomy. 6th ed. Philadelphia, W. B. Saunders Company, 1954.

Patten, B. M.: Human Embryology. 2d ed. New York, The Blakiston Company, 1953.

Potter, E. L.: Fundamentals of Human Reproduction. New York, McGraw-Hill Book Company, 1948.

ANATOMY OF THE NERVOUS SYSTEM

Buchanan, A. R.: Functional Neuro-Anatomy. 2d ed. Philadelphia, Lea & Febiger, 1951.

Kuntz, A.: Autonomic Nervous System. 3rd ed. Philadelphia, Lea & Febiger, 1945.

Ranson, S. W., and Clark, S. L.: Anatomy of the Nervous System. 9th ed. Philadelphia, W. B. Saunders Company, 1953.

Rasmussen, A. T.: The Principal Nervous Pathways. 4th ed. New York, The Macmillan Company, 1952.

White, J. C., Smithwick, R. H., and Simeone, F. A.: The Autonomic Nervous System. 3rd ed. New York, The Macmillan Company, 1952.

PHYSIOLOGY AND BIOPHYSICS

Annual Review of Physiology. Stanford University, California, Annual Reviews, Inc.

Best, C. H., and Taylor, N. B.: Physiological Basis of Medical Practice. 6th ed. Baltimore, The Williams and Wilkins Company, 1955.

Carlson, A., and Johnson, V.: The Machinery of the Body. 4th rev. ed. Chicago, University of Chicago Press, 1953.

Fulton, John F., ed.: Textbook of Physiology. 17th ed. Philadelphia, W. B. Saunders Company, 1955.

Gardner, E.: Fundamentals of Neurology. 2d ed. Philadelphia, W. B. Saunders Company, 1952.

Gerard, R. W.: Unresting Cells. New York, Harper & Brothers, 1944 (reissue 1949).

Guyton, A. C.: Textbook of Medical Physiology. Philadelphia, W. B. Saunders Co., 1956.

Harrow, B., and Mazur, A.: Textbook of Biochemistry. 6th ed. Philadelphia, W. B. Saunders Company, 1954.

Harvey, W.: Anatomical Studies on the Motion of the Heart and Blood. 3rd ed. Springfield, Illinois, and Baltimore, Charles C Thomas, 1949.

Hawk, P. B., Oser, B. L., and Summerson, W. H.: Practical Physiological Chemistry. 13th ed. New York, The Blakiston Company, 1954.

Heilbruun, L. V.: An Outline of General Physiology. 3rd ed. Philadelphia, W. B. Saunders Company, 1952.

Houssay, B., et al.: Human Physiology. 2d ed. New York, The Blakiston Company, 1955.

Luckiesh, M., and Moss, F. K.: The Science of Seeing. New York, D. Van Nostrand Company, 1948.

Mitchell, P. H.: A Textbook of General Physiology. 4th ed. New York, McGraw-Hill Book Company, Inc., 1948.

Paschkis, K., Rakoff, A., and Cantarow, A.: Clinical Endocrinology. New York, Paul B. Hoeber, 1954.

Stacy, R. W., et al.: Essentials of Biological and Medical Physics. New York, McGraw-Hill Book Company, Blakiston Division, 1955.

Starling, E. H.: Principles of Human Physiology, edited by C. Lovatt Evans. 10th ed. Philadelphia, Lea & Febiger, 1949.

Turner, C. D.: General Endocrinology. 2d ed. Philadelphia, W. B. Saunders Company, 1955.

Wiggers, C. J.: Physiology in Health and Disease. 5th ed. Philadelphia, Lea & Febiger, 1949.

BIOLOGY

Baitsell, G.: Human Biology. 2d ed. New York, McGraw-Hill Book Company, 1950.

Buchsbaum, R. M.: Animals without Backbones. 2d ed. Chicago, University of Chicago Press, 1948.

Storer, T. I.: General Zoology. 2d ed. New York, McGraw-Hill Book Company, 1953.

INDEX